Government Contracting
and Technological
Change

Government Contracting and Technological Change

CLARENCE H. DANHOF

The Brookings Institution · *Washington, D.C.*

THE BROOKINGS INSTITUTION is an independent organization devoted to non-partisan research, education, and publication in economics, government, foreign policy, and the social sciences generally. Its principal purposes are to aid in the development of sound public policies and to promote public understanding of issues of national importance.

The Institution was founded on December 8, 1927, to merge the activities of the Institute for Government Research, founded in 1916, the Institute of Economics, founded in 1922, and the Robert Brookings Graduate School of Economics and Government, founded in 1924.

The general administration of the Institution is the responsibility of a self-perpetuating Board of Trustees. The trustees are likewise charged with maintaining the independence of the staff and fostering the most favorable conditions for creative research and education. The immediate direction of the policies, program, and staff of the Institution is vested in the President, assisted by an advisory council chosen from the staff of the Institution.

In publishing a study, the Institution presents it as a competent treatment of a subject worthy of public consideration. The interpretations and conclusions in such publications are those of the author or authors and do not purport to represent the views of the other staff members, officers, or trustees of the Brookings Institution.

Foreword

An outstanding development of the past quarter-century has been the increasing commitment of the federal government to the advancement of science and technology. To accomplish this objective, the government has often utilized and depended upon private organizations operating under grants and contracts. Neither the federal interest in science and technology nor its use of private institutions is entirely new; both, however, have taken on dimensions that have required major reactions by all participants in the system. This book reports developments to June 1967. It is the result of an interest in the subject that has been active at Brookings since the late 1950's. An earlier publication expressive of this interest is Harold Orlans' *Contracting for Atoms,* published in 1967.

Clarence Danhof's study has four objectives: (1) to explain the growth of the contractual system in the scientific and technological areas; (2) to explore the government's organization and procedures for managing the contractual system; (3) to evaluate the impact of the government's system upon the participating private institutions; and (4) to examine some of the broader implications of the system. The government's ability to manage the system it has created and the ability of private institutions to serve the government's objectives while maintaining their private character and discharging adequately their other functions are viewed as central issues.

The author and the Institution are grateful for assistance in planning the work and for helpful comment on the manuscript from the members of the advisory committee: James W. Clark,

vii

Bureau of the Budget; John J. Corson, then of Princeton University; Charles V. Kidd, Federal Council for Science and Technology; Herbert Roback, House Committee on Government Operations; Irvin Stewart, University of West Virginia; Woodrow W. Storey, Martin Company. The Institution appreciates also the assistance of Philip Abelson, Editor of *Science;* Don K. Price, Dean of the John Fitzgerald Kennedy School of Government, Harvard University; Chalmers W. Sherwin, then Deputy Assistant Secretary for Science and Technology, U.S. Department of Commerce; Elmer Staats, Comptroller General of the United States; and Jerome B. Wiesner, Provost of the Massachusetts Institute of Technology.

Clarence H. Danhof was a staff member of the Governmental Studies Program of the Brookings Institution when the study was made. Other members of the Brookings staff who contributed to the study were Laurin Henry, Harold Orlans, and George W. Wright.

This study was made possible by a special grant from the Carnegie Corporation of New York. The views presented are those of the author, and do not necessarily represent the views of the advisory committee, other individuals whose opinions were solicited, or the trustees, officers, and other staff members of the Brookings Institution.

KERMIT GORDON
President

June 1968
Washington, D.C.

Author's Acknowledgments

This study owes much to the very many people, usually experts in their fields, who answered questions, provided data, and explained the whys, hows, and wherefores of policy, organization, and procedure relating to some aspect of the subject area. Though too numerous to acknowledge individually, this study would not have been possible without their help.

Members of the advisory committee and others previously mentioned in the Foreword provided numerous and valuable suggestions. Others who critically read all or part of the manuscript and who contributed generously of their time, expertise, and judgment were the following: Robert Barlow, Office of Science and Technology; Hendrik W. Bode, Bell Telephone Laboratories; Herbert L. Brewer, National Aeronautics and Space Administration (NASA); Cledo Brunetti, FMC Corporation; E. L. Dillon, Bureau of the Budget; J. B. Fisk, Bell Telephone Laboratories; J. Ronald Fox, Harvard University; L. R. Hafstad, General Motors Corporation; Rufus G. Harris, Mercer University; Edward Hincks, Aerospace Industries Association; Helge Holst, Arthur D. Little, Inc.; Harold Kube, Atlantic Research Corporation; Martin Meyerson, Martin Company; John Perry Miller, Yale University; Bernard Moritz, NASA; Frank Pace, Jr., International Executive Service Corps; William W. Parsons, Systems Development Corporation; Clarence Scheps, Tulane University; Albert F. Siepert, John F. Kennedy Space Center, NASA; Major General Leslie E. Simon, U.S. Army, Retired; Stephen Strickland, American Council on Education; Russell I. Thackrey, National Association of State Universities and Land-Grant Colleges; Robert C. Unkrich, Office of the Assistant Secretary of Defense; George J. Vecchietti, NASA; Howard P. Wile, American Council on Education; Hans K. Ziegler, U.S. Army Electronics Command; Eugene M. Zuckert, Lear, Scoutt and Rasenberger. The comments made were frequently challenging and in all cases helpful. They were carefully considered and many were incorporated in the study. Such errors of fact or of interpretation as remain are the sole responsibility of the author.

At Brookings, George A. Graham, then Director of Governmental Studies, contributed immeasurably to the planning and accomplishment of the study. Robert D. Calkins, then President of the Institution read the manuscript critically, as did James Mitchell. Three members of the Brookings staff, Laurin Henry, Harold Orlans, and George W. Wright contributed to the planning, research, and preliminary writing of the study. Frances Shattuck and Virginia Benson served for a time as research assistants. Many ideas and interpretations were first tested on Franklin L. Kilpatrick. Also helpful was the early exploratory work done by Carl Stover and Victor K. Heyman.

Special thanks must go to Janet L. Porter. Aside from undertaking a large share of the secretarial work and assuming responsibility for preparing the data for the charts, her adeptness at securing information was of great value. Mrs. Ann Crutcher gave editorial assistance and Mrs. Adele J. Garrett prepared the index.

Finally, mention must be made of my indebtedness to Ruth Ingram Danhof, my wife. Her comments on the successive drafts were valuable and her unfailing patience and good humor were a constant source of encouragement.

Permission to quote copyrighted material at some length was kindly granted by the American Management Association, Inc., the Graduate School of Business Administration, Harvard University, and the publishers of *Armed Forces Management, DATA, The Educational Review* (American Council on Education), *Financial Executive,* and *Industrial Research.* The National Security Industrial Association and Dr. John W. Gardner kindly granted permission to quote from unpublished speeches.

C. H. D.

Contents

Charts

CHAPTER I

Introduction

Among the many changes that have marked the past quarter of a century, none has been more fundamental to the nation's well-being and security than the research and development programs of the United States government—and few are more important by virtue of their variety and size, the number of people and institutions affected, or their potential impact in the future. The initiative the government has taken in accelerating the accumulation of new knowledge and promoting new technologies in selected areas, the responsibility for decision-making which it has assumed, the scale on which it has pursued certain objectives, and the close working relationships it has developed with private institutions—all these have been dynamic elements in the postwar development of American society.

The first application of nuclear energy (to the atomic bomb) was merely the most spectacular of many technological advances achieved under government auspices during World War II. Since then, there have been many others. The more dramatic include the jet airplane, supersonic flight, the nuclear-powered submarine with its inertial guidance system, high capacity computers, and sophisticated radar. Radar and computers are components of a variety of weapons systems and, like so many other defense items, are reminders that the nation's security continues to be a major spur to innovation. They demonstrate also the fact that, for good or ill, the cold war is in large measure a war of the laboratories.[1]

[1] The phrase is from Oskar Morgenstern, *The Question of National Defense* (Random House, 1959), chap. 7.

1

At the same time federally sponsored technological developments are often turned to peaceful and to civilian uses. The jet airplane, aircraft control, radar, nuclear energy, and computers in wide variety, are examples, as are earth satellites for observations and television relay. The orbiting of men in space is a direct result of government activity; so is the photographing of the moon and of Mars at close range. More such achievements are to be expected, although their exact nature is unpredictable; like the iceberg with much of its mass below the surface of the ocean, the knowledge acquired through research has hidden dimensions and unknown potentialities.

Government research and development is responsible for a dynamism in scientific and technological effort without precedent in the nation's history. We appear to have entered "a new era in which our society is being driven by sophisticated reciprocating forces of science and technology"—forces as strong as those behind the political revolution on which our society and government is founded or those which produced the industrial revolution.[2] As one scientist puts it, "It is not an exaggeration to say that the flowering of American science since the war is as spectacular an outburst of human creativity, though on a far larger scale, as the outpouring of art and literature in Florence during the days of Lorenzo the Magnificent."[3] And on the side of applied technology it has been claimed that "man is on the verge of being able to do anything he wants."[4] That claim may go too far, but the enormous increase in understanding of man's environment and in the capacity to organize research and development resources do open up entirely new possibilities of choice for man and society.[5] Whether such choices extend to the possibility of selecting from among al-

[2] Glenn T. Seaborg, "Freedom and the Scientific Society: The Third Revolution" (an address at Colonial Williamsburg, May 26, 1962).

[3] Letter to Representative Emilio Daddario, chairman of the House Science, Research, and Development Subcommittee, from Roger Revelle, in *Government and Science,* Hearings before the House Science and Astronautics Committee, 88 Cong. 1 sess. (1963), p. 430.

[4] Emmanuel G. Mesthene, "Technical Progress and Social Development," *Proceedings of the Nineteenth National Conference on the Administration of Research* (Denver Research Institute, 1966), p. 10.

[5] Such predictions may be said to be one of the characteristics of contemporary literature. For one among numerous examples, see David Sarnoff, "By the End of the Twentieth Century," *Fortune,* May 1964, pp. 116–19.

ternative futures is an intriguing but highly uncertain question.

The United States shares its commitment to accelerated technological change with the other advanced nations of the world. As a percentage of its gross national product, the American effort is the largest in the free world. However, R&D programs are growing rapidly in many countries and are known to be very substantial in the U.S.S.R. although available data do not permit accurate comparisons.[6] While the United States leads in many areas of scientific research and development, American superiority in fields which other nations select for their special attention is constantly under challenge. Other countries profit from advances made in the United States as the United States also gains from their work. It is clear, however, that the advanced position of the United States on the world's scientific and technological frontiers can be maintained only by sustained effort. Thus, external pressures as well as domestic needs suggest that large-scale government-supported R&D programs are now a permanent part of our society. It is also likely that they will continue to grow, in number and variety, though at rates below those that have marked the past two decades.[7] The impersonal market forces operating in American society over the past century have been very successful in stimulating and exploiting technological change. By increasing the capacity to utilize natural resources, new technology created new industries and new products, resulting in a marked increase in the level of living. The benefits of this process brought also such undesirable side effects as urban decay, inadequacies in transportation, water and air pollution, and a decline in the attainability of certain values which a simpler society took for granted. Problems like

---

[6] A study of the Organization for Economic Cooperation and Development estimates that in the United States there were, in 1962, 6.2 R&D personnel per 1,000 population. In the U.S.S.R. there were from 4.7 to 6.7, depending on the interpretation of occupational classifications. In the United Kingdom there were 4.0; in the Netherlands, 2.8; in Germany, 2.6; in France, 2.4; and in Belgium, 2.3. C. Freeman and A. Young, *The Research and Development Effort in Western Europe, North America, and the Soviet Union* (Organization for Economic Cooperation and Development, Paris, 1965), pp. 11–12, 72. See also James Brian Quinn, "Technological Competition: Europe vs. U.S.," *Harvard Business Review*, vol. 44 (July-August 1966), pp. 113–30.

[7] For an estimate of the possible level of expenditures for R&D in 1975, see Leonard A. Lecht, *Goals, Priorities, and Dollars: The Next Decade* (Free Press of Glencoe, 1966), chap. 11.

these are not new, nor are they now drawing attention for the first time. What is new is the range of remedial possibilities offered by the contractual system of research and development.

The system operates within an environment in which the federal government may be expected to take action if it is persuaded of the public interest in solving a problem and of the merits of proposals toward that end. Thus our society has adopted some aspects of the military approach to technological change. To the military, the emergence of a new weapon must always prompt a search for a counter—whether another weapon, a strategy, or a tactic. The contractual system provides a procedure by which society can search for and find counters for the undesirable phenomena generated by modern life wherever traditional institutions and procedures cannot deal with them. The experience of the past decade in particular has refined the techniques involved so that they are effective in accomplishing objectives of great difficulty. The systems approach, developed to deal with complex defense problems, offers promise in application to knotty social problems.

The Contractual Relationship

Over the past twenty-five years, the United States government has promoted scientific research and technological development on a scale that is unprecedented. Equally unprecedented are the methods used in pursuit of these ends. The government has relied upon private institutions, not only to carry out projects already judged necessary, but also to suggest how its objectives might best be achieved, and even what the objectives might or should be. This complex of relationships is firmly established in principle and in its broad characteristics though flexible and fluid in its details.

As the range and magnitude of the operations accepted as justifying the use of public funds have grown, the involvement of private institutions in the process has deepened. The commitment to the advancement of scientific knowledge and technology has grown concomitant with and dependent upon the use of the contract. (Throughout this study the grant used to support research in nonprofit organizations is considered a contract of a special type.[8])

---

[8] A discussion of the nature of the grant may be found in chapter VII.

The contractual relationship between public and private organizations is a fundamental factor in the growth of federal R&D programs, not only permitting but also inspiring and fostering them. The relationship operates in cooperation rather than in conflict with existing institutional arrangements. By dividing responsibilities among private and public groups, it also leads to specialization of function.

Thus the quest for new scientific knowledge and technological improvement sponsored by the government rests upon a contractual system that intricately intermingles the interests and activities of the government with those of business firms, universities, and other private organizations with special capacities. Given the nature of the R&D process, this intermingling is essential to the system. It is difficult to believe that federal activities in science and technology could have reached their present magnitude except through the involvement of private institutions.

The contractual system is, however, more than a device to get work done for a government agency. An agency's program is built upon contributions from many sources, public and private. There are numerous channels through which interested and knowledgeable groups may suggest courses of action to accomplish broadly defined objectives. A formal contract is merely a step in a process of interaction between private and public groups with an interest in a scientific or technical area. In this process the government agency assumes responsibility for preparing programs and seeing them through the normal authorization and budgeting routines. It also chooses among the proposals made to it those which it will include as contractual projects in its approved programs. In both the formulation and the execution of its program the agency is heavily, and sometimes wholly, dependent upon the initiative of outside institutions in developing the expertise necessary to prepare the proposals and do the work.

Organization of American Scientific and Technical Manpower

The government's scientific and technical goals are so wide-ranging as to call upon almost any type of specialized skill. Its needs may be met by the services of a single scientist working in a laboratory used primarily for teaching or they may require large groups of people with diverse skills, tightly organized and closely supervised. Government procedures therefore provide for both individual and team effort. Scientists and engineers engaged in research and development are employed by four types of institutions (Table 1). About three-fourths are employees of private business firms, principally in the manufacturing industries. About 11 percent are employed by the federal government, 13 percent by institutions of higher education, principally the universities, and 2 percent by nonprofit institutions other than those in education.

Federal procedures permit drawing upon the resources of these various organizations as needed to meet government objectives. These four types of institutions are characterized by considerable specialization which is, however, by no means exclusive. Business firms are primarily concerned with the development and production of devices which require the application of engineering skills. Each firm normally operates within a cluster of technologies defined as an industry. However, a striking result of government requirements has been the emergence of a few large firms which

TABLE 1

Number of Scientists and Engineers in Research and Development by Type of Employing Institution, 1954 and 1961[a]
(Full-Time Equivalents)

Type of Institution	1954		1961	
	Number	Percent	Number	Percent
Federal government	29,500	13.2	44,500	10.8
Industry[b]	164,100	73.5	306,100	74.5
Colleges and universities	25,200	11.3	52,500	12.8
Other nonprofit organizations[b]	4,400	2.0	8,000	1.9
Total[c]	223,200	100.0	411,100	100.0

Source: National Science Foundation, *Scientific and Technical Manpower Resources,* NSF 64-28 (1964), pp. 71–72.

a. Excludes social scientists and psychologists.

b. Includes professioal research personnel employed at research centers administered under contract with federal agencies.

c. Excludes scientists and engineers employed by state agencies. In 1962 an estimated 3,300 scientists and engineers were so employed.

maintain so broad a range of technical skills as to qualify for the management of extremely complex projects. To participate effectively in development programs, business firms also engage in applied research and some maintain programs in basic research relevant to their specific interests in development. Indeed, business firms have increased their interests in basic research to the degree that they now conduct a fifth of all such activity—traditionally identified with the universities.

While not contractors, the government organizations doing research are a part of the nation's research structure and also part of its administrative machinery. The work of these organizations covers the full range of R&D activities and also takes in such administrative functions as testing and evaluation. Universities claim special interests and competence in basic research—the pursuit of new knowledge for its own sake—but in fact devote a considerable part of their resources to applied research and occasionally do some development. The nonprofit institutions are primarily concerned with applied research although they also engage in pure research and some of the largest are occupied with the management of sizable development projects. Business firms, the universities, and a few nonprofit organizations also contract to furnish management services as such. Examples include the federal-contract research centers, Pan American's contract to manage the Air Force facilities at Cape Kennedy, some of the technical assistance projects of the Agency for International Development, and projects of the Peace Corps and the Office of Economic Opportunity.

Public and Private Sources of R&D Funds

The distribution of the sources of funds for research and development has changed markedly over the past few decades. Charts 1 and 2 indicate the expanding role of the federal government as a source of funds.

The contractual system has also led to shifts in the distribution of actual research and development work among institutions, as is shown in Chart 3. The nation's four principal types of institutions performing R&D have shared in the absolute growth of federal programs. However, their relative shares of federal expenditures have changed somewhat with time. Since 1940, the use of

CHART 1

National Expenditures for Research and Development by Sources of Funds

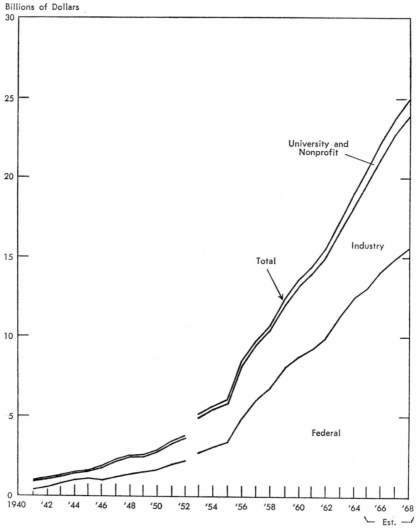

Billions of Dollars

Sources: for 1941–52, Secretary of Defense (R&D), *The Growth of Scientific Research and Development*, No. **RDB** 114/34, July 27, 1953; and for 1953–68, National Science Foundation, *National Pattern of R&D Resources, Funds, and Manpower in the United States, 1953–68*, NSF 67–7, pp. 22–23.

federal research and development funds by people employed directly by the government has grown less rapidly than has the government's aggregate program. This has happened despite the fact that government agencies have experienced a substantial increase in their functions of evaluating proposals and monitoring and testing the work of private research people. The business share of federal research and development work, on the other hand, has increased from 26.9 percent of federal expenditures in 1954 to 65.1 percent in 1964.[9] Since 1954 the portion of federal programs carried on by colleges and universities has fluctuated from 7.9 percent to 12.9 percent of federal expenditures while that of the independent nonprofit organizations has ranged from 1.3 percent to 2.6 percent.

The four types of institutions participating in federally sponsored research programs relate to the government in two distinct ways. The intramural organizations do research in a continuing administrative relationship with their sponsoring agencies. The federal research centers, although managed by private institutions under contract, have much the same continuity in their operations and maintain an intimacy with the sponsoring agency which does not differ in any significant way from that of the intramural establishments. In both cases, programs are developed within the organization, reviewed administratively, authorized by budget and program actions, and changed as events may suggest. Although advisory committees may be called in to review proposals and evaluate progress, decisions are made by administrative action. While the contractual differs from the organic relationship in a variety of ways, in the actual administration of research there seem to be few significant distinctions.

The second type of relationship views research and development groups as more or less competitive sources of the services desired. The relationship is based upon projects which have a more or less clearly defined beginning and end. Minimal formal provision is made for continuity of performance between projects. Projects are

[9] This includes the management of federal research centers by business firms. Expenditures on business-managed federal research centers amounted to 2.8 percent of federal research and development expenditures in 1964 (National Science Foundation, *Federal Funds for Research, Development, and Other Scientific Activities, Fiscal Years 1963, 1964, and 1965,* vol. 13 [1965], p. 37).

CHART 2
Percentage Distribution of National R&D Expenditures
by Sources of Funds

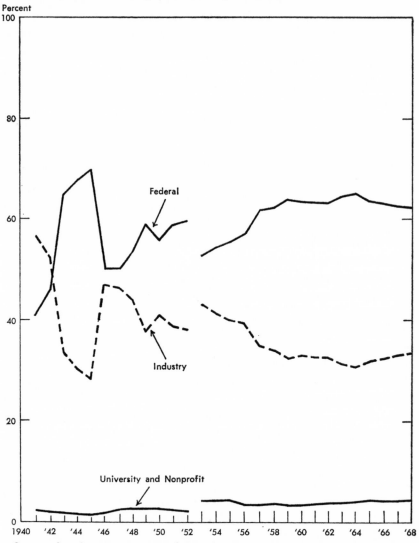

Sources: data for 1941–52 computed from Secretary of Defense (R&D), *The Growth of Scientific Research and Development*, No. RDB 114/34, July 27, 1953; and for 1953–68 from National Science Foundation, *National Pattern of R&D Reosurces, Funds, and Manpower in the United States, 1953–68*, NSF 67-7, pp. 22–23.

usually selected by the government agency from among competing proposals submitted in response to invitations. The invitations may be extended to every possible source of the desired work or may be limited to groups judged to have the special competence needed.

About 72 percent of federal R&D expenditures is for projects selected from among proposals that, in one way or another, have been submitted to the sponsoring agency by private organizations. Their competition, frequently vigorous, is not in terms of price, since choices are made on the basis of the agency's judgment of the quality and relevance of the proposed project. Costs are not unimportant but they are usually a secondary consideration.

The remaining 28 percent of federal R&D funds goes to intramural organizations and contract research centers and includes the costs of administering the R&D system as well as R&D performance. Within these organizations, the work is frequently organized as projects, but they are selected through bureaucratic rather than competitive procedures.

Together, the two approaches give federal agencies wide latitude in dealing with any and all institutions, private or public, possessing research capabilities relevant to a program. Institutions are selectively drawn into participation in the government's program by a variety of devices appropriate to the situation and the objective. While the principal procedures employed and the major institutions involved can be grouped in broad categories, the system constitutes a complex spectrum in which one type of arrangement shades off into another. It should be kept in mind that exceptions, frequently important ones, exist to almost every broad observation that may be made about the system and its components.

The Boundaries of This Study

The government contract system of research and development has been, and gives every indication of continuing to be, highly successful in accelerating the emergence of new applied technology and new knowledge. At the same time, the acceleration in the rate of change made possible by mobilization of resources through federal contracting has given new urgency to old questions. The ques-

CHART 3
R&D Expenditures by Type of Performer

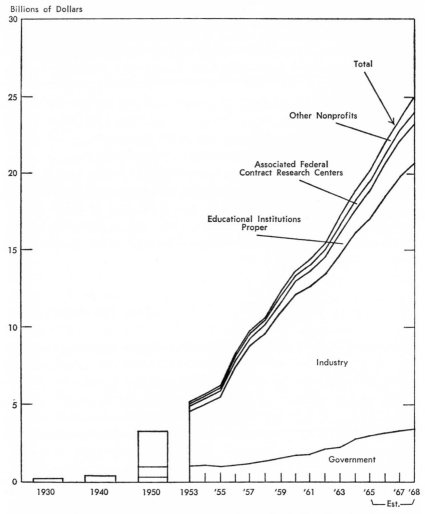

Sources: for 1930 and 1940, Vannevar Bush, *Science—the Endless Frontier* (Government Printing Office, 1945), p. 86; for 1950, Dexter M. Keezer, "The Outlook for Expenditures on Research and Development during the Next Decade," *Papers and Proceedings of the American Economic Association* (December 1959), p. 363; for 1953–68, National Science Foundation, *National Patterns of R&D Resources: Funds and Manpower in the United States, 1953–68* (NSF 67–7), pp. 22–23. The total amount of scientific research expenditures by all performers in 1930 was $166,191,000, $116,000,000 of which was expended by industry. In 1940 the total was $345,245,000, of which industry's share was $234,000,000.

tion of where science is taking man is both more pressing and more difficult. Even more immediate is the question of society's ability to control the new technology or to adapt to it in such manner as to realize its values. Important though these questions are, this study contributes to the consideration of those broad issues only in seeking a better understanding of the system for promoting change that has evolved as a function of the federal government over the past few decades.

Aside from the disturbing effects of new technology, the evolution of the government contract system has had wide-ranging and disquieting impacts upon the nation's political and economic structures, the ultimate implications of which remain, in some measure, unclear. With the evolution of the system, the government has assumed new responsibilities for decision-making and for evaluating the interests, proposals, and quality of work of private organizations by subjective criteria. These changes in its role constitute new dimensions in the political process and in the administration of public affairs. In effect, the government has reinterpreted the nature of the public interests, moving and blurring the boundaries between what is public and what is private.[10] In choosing to deal on a large scale with private rather than with governmental institutions, the system has created what has, with considerable aptness, been termed a "new federalism."[11] Some see, both in the emerging new technology and in the methods by which it is achieved "a time of trial for the democratic process."[12]

The system has encouraged private business firms to learn to work intimately with the government, selling technical services as well as the specifications needed to fabricate products. Business firms successful in contractual relationships with the government have had to achieve technical objectives of unprecedented complexity; they have had to meet standards of performance unknown

[10] Actually, the distinction between public and private has never been in practice what some held it to be in theory. See Eugene V. Rostow, *Planning for Freedom: The Public Law of American Capitalism* (Yale University Press, 1959), p. 366; but also see Carl F. Stover, "The Government Contract System as a Problem in Public Policy," *George Washington University Law Review,* vol. 32 (1964), pp. 701–18.

[11] Don K. Price, *Government and Science* (New York University Press, 1954), chap. 3, "Federalism by Contract."

[12] U.S. President's Commission on National Goals, *Goals for Americans* (Prentice-Hall, 1960), p. 64.

in normal markets. They have done so under critical scrutiny that has sought to apply standards based upon the best organization and methods to be found. The standards set by government have had significant impact upon business organization and managerial procedures.[13]

Further, the system has encouraged the rapid expansion of research in the universities as a function coequal with teaching and forced university administrators to recast their organizations to meet the requirements of their relationship with the government. It has also stimulated the growth of a variety of nonprofit organizations which seem to be claiming an ever larger role in a highly competitive milieu. Finally, the rise of the contract system has altered the nature and activities of the government's traditional intramural scientific and technical organizations.

These changes challenge accepted ideology as well as traditional forms of organization and time-honored relationships. Such changes have stimulated much criticism.[14] The purpose of this study is to show why the nation's public commitment to the support of research developed, why the contractual method of organizing that support has come to prevail, and how the government, as administrator of the system, and private institutions, as executors, have adjusted to the tasks undertaken. In the process the chief criticisms of the system are considered and continuing problems are identified.

[13] The impact on business organization and practices has been most marked, of course, in the case of contractual performers, but it is by no means limited to them. See Donald J. Smalter, "The Influence of Department of Defense Practices on Corporate Planning," *Management Technology*, vol. 4 (1964), pp. 115–38, describing the adoption of numerous DOD management techniques by a firm that is not a government contractor.

[14] A useful collection of criticisms may be found in Richard J. Barber, *The Politics of Research* (Public Affairs Press, 1966).

CHAPTER II

The Evolution of Contracting from the Prewar Period to 1950

The nation's policy toward government support of research and development programs, and the use of private institutions under contract to that end, emerged in substantially its present form as a product of the experiences of World War II. World War II was not the first war in human history that was marked by a burgeoning of technical knowledge and its application. But, to a much greater degree than had previously been the case, the technological gains of World War II had a continuing impact. Postwar appraisals of the wartime experience yielded clear conclusions. The results attained during the war followed largely from the fact that, in the years preceding, scientists, mostly in private life, had accumulated a substantial body of new knowledge and had acquired an awareness of numerous promising opportunities for application. Private industry had also accumulated wide experience with programmed research and development—enough to justify the observation that the United States had developed an industry of invention. With financing adequate to the requirements, flexible administrative arrangements, and sufficient time, the federal government had been able to direct these resources to the needs of the war with great, and probably conclusive, effectiveness.

This wartime experience was a dominating consideration as the nation plotted its course for the immediate postwar years. It was clear that the prewar institutional arrangements had been far from optimal. Two conclusions were reached by the nation's leaders with so little debate as to reflect a broad consensus. One was that henceforth greater resources should be directed to the expansion of knowledge and skills through research and development, with the results applied as rapidly as possible. The second was that this objective should be accomplished by supporting the work of qualified men wherever they might be found. In application this meant that public funds would be used to support research and development activities at private institutions.

The first conclusion represented an extension of public responsibility into what heretofore had been private functions. The second represented a change in the traditional relationships between private and public institutions, a break most obvious in the areas of research and development activities but not confined thereto. The private industry of discovery which had contributed so heavily to national growth and strength in the years before and during World War II, though retaining its basic characteristics, was now to be offered public funds to accomplish public objectives. The program that emerged was one of massive financing of pluralistic efforts administered by a large number of agencies applying a confusing variety of policies and procedures. Though work toward R&D objectives continued and expanded somewhat within the government's own laboratories, the larger part of the program involved people associated with private institutions who worked on projects which they in part had initiated. The device that permitted and facilitated these relationships was the negotiated contract.

The Prewar System and Military Technical Capabilities

The postwar research and development policies of the federal government have their roots in the nation's defense requirements, and rest upon a judgment that earlier procedures were inappropriate to the postwar situation. An understanding of the nature and operation of the prewar system is therefore useful.

The relationship of government agencies to private sources of supply in the 1930's was controlled by a body of statutes and adminsitrative regulations which had evolved from experience that stretches over the nation's history. The fundamental law which governed the procurement of supplies and nonpersonal services, excepting periods of war, until 1947 was an act of Congress passed in 1860 which provided that:

All purchases and contracts for supplies or services in any of the Departments of the Government, except for personal services, when the public exigencies do not require the immediate delivery of the article or articles, or performance of the service, shall be made by advertising a sufficient time previously for proposals respecting the same. When immediate delivery or performance is required by the public exigency, the articles or service required may be procured by open purchase or contract at the places, and in the manner in which such articles are usually bought and sold, or such services engaged between individuals. No contract or purchase shall hereafter be made, unless the same be authorized by law or be under an appropriation adequate to its fulfillment, except in the War and Navy Departments, for clothing subsistence, forage, fuel, quarters, or transportation, which, however, shall not exceed the necessities of the current year.[1]

Administration of procurement under these acts was by mandatory standard forms prepared by the Procurement Division of the Treasury Department,[2] covering the advertisement and the ensuing contract.

Briefly, the government agencies could normally procure goods and nonpersonal services only by (a) public advertising for bids

---

[1] 12 Stat. 220; Rev. Stat. 3709, 41 U.S.C. 5. An act of March 2, 1901, provided with specific reference to the Army that "hereafter, except in cases of emergency or where it is impracticable to secure competition, the purchase of all supplies for the use of the various departments, and posts of the Army and of the branches of the army service shall only be made after advertisement, and shall be purchased where the same can be purchased the cheapest, quality and cost of transportation and the interests of the Government considered; but every open-market emergency purchase made in the manner common among business men which exceeds in amount two hundred dollars shall be reported for approval to the Secretary of War under such regulations as he may prescribe" (31 Stat. 905).

[2] A source of difficulty was the "Changes" article in each of the forms which prescribed that "no change involving an estimated increase or decrease of more than $500 shall be ordered unless approved in writing by the head of the Department or his duly authorized representative," which for the Army were the chiefs of the various branches and for the Navy, the bureau chiefs.

responsive to detailed specification; (*b*) public opening of the bids at a specified time and place; and (*c*) award of the contract to the lowest responsible bidder complying with the conditions of the advertisement for bids.

The act of 1860 did permit purchase by negotiation when public exigencies necessitated immediate performance. From time to time, Congress provided specific authority for open market purchases for such items as advertising services, bunting, gauges, dies and jigs, secret apparatus, horses and mules, and medical supplies. An act of 1901 redefined the exception to the general policy of purchases by advertising to apply to "cases of emergency or where it is impracticable to secure competition." The impracticability of competition was recognized when the articles were purchased from a sole manufacturer or dealer, no suitable similar article being obtainable; when the article was patented and for sale only by the patentee or his agent at a fixed and uniform price; and when the articles or parts of apparatus already in use could be furnished by only one dealer. Open market purchases might also be made when bids had been invited and none received that complied with essential requirements and it was determined that further advertising would be useless. It was difficult to take advantage of these exceptions permitting negotiation. Approval at the secretary level was often required, and the negotiations were vulnerable to criticism.

The procurement problems of the military services involved materiel of two principal types. One included items of peculiar if not sole interest to one or both of the services. There applied to these a policy almost as old as the nation: that some active capacity to produce these items should be maintained at all times within Army or Navy establishments. Such production responsibility carried with it the implicit obligation to try to improve the product as experimental work either within the establishment or outside might suggest. The second broad class of materiel consisted of items which were available in more or less immediately useful form on the market from private suppliers. Some such items remained unchanged over long periods of time; others changed rapidly as private R&D efforts were successful. Applying the benefits of nongovernmental R&D to their needs presented problems to all government agencies, but such problems were particularly acute for the Army and Navy, since military use of products developed for civilian markets frequently required further developmental effort which was difficult to secure within the statutory and organizational framework that existed prior to World War II.

Implicit in the statutory procurement policies was a classification of technologies supporting the services, a theory of the relationship between military and other technologies, and a theory of the development of military technology. Three types of technologies were envisaged. One group consisted of those technologies that were primarily civilian in character, the products being acceptable for Army and Navy requirements with such changes as were within the capabilities of the producer. For example, under conditions of mobilization, such products as textiles, fuels, and most foodstuffs could be diverted directly from civilian to military uses. A second related type comprised purely military items without counterparts in the civilian market. The responsibility of such organizations as the Army's Ordnance and Chemical Warfare Services and the Navy's Bureaus of Ships and of Ordnance for such items was met by the government-owned and -operated laboratories and facilities with some fabricating capacity. The third category included those technologies in which both military and civilian sectors had an interest—such as motor vehicles—although there were likely to be marked differences between the civilian and military versions of the products involved. It was in relation to parts of this third large and important area that the statutory authority and institutional machinery proved inadequate.

The policy that applied to items in the second and third groups assumed that the technology of war changed in the wake of research and development activities in the civilian sphere. The usual course of events was that military applications of a new idea or device would occur only after it had been thoroughly tested and proved in civilian use.[3] Then it was necessary that the military incorporate the external innovation into its tactical or strategic doctrines. As a part of this process of absorption, the characteristics of the military version of the innovation could be developed with

[3] That military technology depended upon and lagged behind industrial technology was recognized at the time. See Waldemar Kaempffert, "War and Technology," *American Journal of Sociology,* vol. 46 (1941), pp. 431–44. See also note 50 below.

some precision. It followed that ideas or devices not accepted in the civilian sector and not included among traditional military activities could be given attention by the services only as their laboratories and arsenals broadened the scope of their interests—a difficult matter.

Products not of uniquely military character were assumed to be available on the normal civilian markets as it was also assumed that specifications describing the precise nature of military needs could be readily written by the technical personnel of the military departments. As an administrative matter, specifications as detailed as possible and going far beyond a statement of required performance characteristics were desirable for all military procurement for two reasons other than the statutory requirements. One was the need for standardization; the other, the desirability of multiple sources of supply. Standardization was important to minimize problems of training, operation, maintenance and the storage of spare parts. Multiple sources were necessary to assure the effective operation of the competitive bidding process and also to establish a broad base of potential suppliers if need for large quantities arose.

The statutory provisions governing military procurement were effective in areas where technological changes were slight, or where such changes occurred within the facilities of the Army or Navy so that precise specifications of the desired item could be developed. Difficulties existed in areas of rapid change occurring outside the military but involving devices or techniques of potential significance to military operations. It was necessary for Army or Navy personnel to appraise the usefulness of an idea, visualize its incorporation into strategy or tactics, determine precisely the performance characteristics of greatest usefulness, and identify the problems likely to arise in production. In practice, this was usually done in successive steps, with the sequence repeated as each step reacted upon the others. Machinery to accomplish these tasks was well developed in the areas of traditional arsenal responsibility— the determination of the requirement for a new type of gun automatically carried with it concern for the appropriate ammunition, projectile, gun carriage, and the other elements that constituted the weapon system. In areas outside the traditional jurisdiction of the arsenals and shipyards, both the Army and Navy sought to maintain more or less formal channels whereby information on relevant technical developments was received and appraised. Nevertheless, in many areas Army and Navy personnel could do little to project applications of new ideas and devices or to establish specifications for their use in the military context.

Each service faced difficulties in dealing with products developed for the civilian economy. Military requirements for many items called for a sturdiness and reliability beyond the characteristics of conventional products. Some items might be adapted with relatively few changes; others required extensive modification to meet service requirements. In either case the abilities of the services to establish specifications were limited. Though private firms might be interested in meeting the needs of the services few could afford or could assume the risks of undertaking the necessary development. The required investment in redesign and, perhaps, in retooling was likely to be substantial. If patentable, a small quantity of the device might be produced and submitted or possibly sold for testing in the hope that larger procurement orders would yield royalties. Frequently no patentable characteristic was involved and, once submitted to the War or Navy Department, the design became public property. Since firms that had made no investment in development had equal opportunity to bid on quantity procurement, there was no assurance whatever to a firm that its developmental costs could be recouped. In fact, the firm that refrained from incurring developmental costs but which possessed the relevant know-how had a clear advantage in bidding over the firm that did incur such costs and sought to recover them in its bid.

The system of competitive bidding was, then, a useful and effective device where precise specifications had been developed, as in the case of items that were the responsibility of the arsenals. In other areas it was a cumbersome and uncertain technique, offering some promise of effectiveness only when military procurements were sufficiently large and recurrent to maintain a private industry. Even then it was effective only if the procuring service was able to develop performance specifications that reflected a realistic awareness of the state of the specific art.

During the 1920's and 1930's the ability of the armed services to adapt technological changes to their needs was limited by public attitudes, as reflected by the "merchants of death" thesis that attracted much attention in the mid-1930's and that contributed to severely restricted defense appropriations.[4] The essentially conservative attitude toward technical change which affected military strategic and tactical concepts also contributed to low levels of R&D effort,[5] both within military facilities and in private organizations adapting new developments to military uses. Circumstances favored the Navy somewhat more than the Army in this regard since Congress was agreeable to a shipbuilding program after the expiration of the London Naval Reduction Treaty in 1936. The rebuilding of the fleet provided an opportunity to apply new technological knowledge. Major improvements in steam boilers and in turbines had been developed by private firms for the nation's electric power industry. The diesel engine had also been developed to the point where it was clearly superior to gasoline engines for use in submarines. The Navy's procurement procedures were sufficiently flexible to profit by these advances. The Navy did not usually attempt to specify in great detail what it wanted in a new vessel. Instead it prepared precise specifications only for really novel items and described the other characteristics of the vessel in general terms, leaving it to the contractor to supply as much as 95 percent of the details.[6]

[4] Two books stimulated much interest: Helmuth C. Engelbrecht and Frank C. Hanighen, *Merchants of Death: A Study of the International Armament Industry* (Dodd, 1934); and George Seldes, *Iron, Blood, and Profits: An Exposure of the World-Wide Munitions Racket* (Harper, 1934). A much publicized Senate investigation failed to confirm the charges made. See John E. Wiltz, *In Search of Peace: The Senate Munitions Inquiry, 1934–36* (Louisiana State University Press, 1963).

[5] General James M. Gavin points out that "by their very nature, military organizations must be conservative. They must prepare to win a war today with the resources at hand" (*War and Peace in the Space Age* [Harper, 1958], p. 269). Such conservatism, however, may take extreme form as Edward L. Katzenbach, Jr., points out in "The Horse Cavalry in the Twentieth Century: A Study of Public Response," *Public Policy* (Harvard University Press, 1958), vol. 8, pp. 120–50.

[6] Harold G. Bowen, *Ships, Machinery, and Mossbacks* (Princeton University Press, 1954), pp. 54–64, 127–28. On the inadequacies of naval weapon development before the war, see Buford Rowland and William B. Boyd, *U.S. Navy Bureau of Ordnance in World War II* (Government Printing Office, 1954).

The Army was in some ways less successful despite the advantage of its arsenal system.[7] It could adapt trucks of civilian type to its needs, but encountered problems over other uses of the automobile in infantry operations.[8] What became the Jeep—"our one unique contribution to land warfare . . . unmatched in military utility in any army in the world"[9]—was developed by a small private firm in the hope that the Army would find it useful. Differences between the technical services long delayed its adoption while the procurement procedures followed were such that the designing firm gained little if anything from its efforts.[10]

However, both services were able to accelerate their development efforts as the war drew near, achieving significant technological gains. Nevertheless, the low prewar level of R&D effort by both the Army and Navy left unexploited numerous scientific and technical developments that offered promise of war-related usefulness if subjected to more intensive effort. It followed that the gov-

[7] General James M. Gavin, for example, observes that despite the opportunity to learn from the war in Europe, upon American entry "much of our equipment was obsolete. . . . In land warfare, our tanks, in terms of armor, gunpower and range, were outperformed from the beginning to the end of the war. Our antitank weapons and our heavy machine guns were inferior, quantitatively and qualitatively" (*War and Peace in the Space Age,* p. 93).

One of the reputed strengths of the Army's arsenal system was in small arms and ammunition. The limitations of the Army's capabilities in the area were brought out in 1940 in hearings held in the Senate on the Army's refusal to accept the Johnson semi-automatic rifle to replace the Garand which had been accepted as standard a few years earlier. After pointing out that Garand had begun development of his rifle while an employee of the Bureau of Standards and had continued his work in a contractual relationship with the Bureau of Ordnance, an Army spokesman, Colonel Guy H. Drewry, continued: "Of all the small-arms weapons that we have in service today, not a single one of them was designed by an Ordnance officer or Ordnance employee. . . . All our automatic weapons were designed by Mr. Browning. . . . Even the Springfield rifle wasn't a development of ours. We copied it from the Mauser and we paid royalties on it" (*A Bill To Provide for the Adoption of the Johnson Semi-automatic Rifle as a Standard Arm of the Military and Naval Forces,* Hearings before the Senate Military Affairs Committee, 76 Cong. 2 sess. [1940], p. 109).

[8] R. Elberton Smith, *The Army and Economic Mobilization* (Government Printing Office, 1959), pp. 255–56.

[9] Gavin, *War and Peace in the Space Age,* p. 93.

[10] On the Jeep, see *ibid.* and also *Investigating the National Defense Programs,* Hearings before a Senate Special Committee [the Truman Committee], 77 Cong. 1 sess. (1941), pt. 7, pp. 1971–2059.

ernment was heavily dependent upon the research accomplishments of the larger society. The problem of government agencies in applying the products of technical change in the society to their objectives was not only, or perhaps even primarily, that of conducting research for intra-agency application, but in large degree that of directing research which had originated elsewhere to the needs of their programs. This was dramatically clear in the problems faced by the Air Corps of the Army and the Navy's Bureau of Aeronautics. Though frequently less clearly recognized, the same problem existed in many other areas, as, for example, in the efforts of the Post Office Department to adapt motor vehicles to its operation.

The Case of Aircraft Development

Congress has occasionally recognized the existence of situations where federal support was necessary if practical application of theoretical possibilities was to be explored in effective ways. Prior to World War II, aircraft presented such problems. Congress reached a decision in 1915 that the government would support basic research in aerodynamics and established the National Advisory Committee for Aeronautics. In the congressional view, the development of operational aircraft, including the application of the work of NACA, could be left to private industry. The work of NACA was limited to study of the characteristics and design of airframes; not until 1942 did NACA devote some attention to engines. The work of developing engines suitable for aircraft and of matching engines to airframes to produce operational aircraft was carried on largely by private industry though both the Army and Navy maintained facilities to build prototypes of engines with desired characteristics and also occasionally complete aircraft.[11] These were small-scale activities meaningful chiefly in maintaining within the services technical capabilities which could contribute to evaluation of industry efforts, although they also included some types of experimentation which industry might be reluctant to undertake. While the research contributions of the Army and

[11] A very useful critical analysis emphasizing technical issues is *Development of Aircraft Engines* [by Robert O. Schlaifer] *and Development of Aviation Fuels* [by S. D. Heron]: *Two Studies of Relations between Government and Business* (Harvard University, Graduate School of Business Administration, 1950).

Navy were significant, both services were heavily dependent upon private organizations for technological development as well as for production in quantity. In developing their own technology, the services were handicapped by the prevailing belief that they could rely on the development of planes for commercial purposes.

The problem of developing aircraft was confused by uncertainties regarding the military roles of aircraft, by the desire to encourage civilian aircraft services, and by the fact that much of the nation's technical abilities in the area was scattered among a large number of small firms that were struggling to survive in the new aircraft development and production industry. The Army's Air Corps, and to a large degree the Navy's also, followed policies of conducting their development efforts in close association with the airframe and aircraft engine industries. Effective relationships between the services and industry rested upon the willingness of the services to provide financial support for experimental and design efforts by firms in the industry. In practice, this meant that the services recognized the proprietary interest of private firms in their designs and permitted those firms to cover their development costs from production orders.[12]

The problems associated with the role of airpower and with development of aircraft were reviewed by numerous governmental boards and committees in the period from the close of World War I to 1925. A select committee of the House, chaired by Florian Lampert, found in 1924 that technical development of aircraft was proceeding at very unsatisfactory rates. The committee also found that the condition of the private aircraft industry was precarious, with numerous firms abandoning their interest in aircraft or going out of business. The committee identified as one of the principal causes of the unsatisfactory state of affairs what it termed "the destructive system of competitive bidding" and recommended that "Congress should at once pass a law permitting the procurement of aircraft engines and aeronautical equipment and accessories without requiring competitive bidding, under restrictions that will promote the best interests of the government."[13] At almost the

---

[12] Wesley Frank Craven and James Lea Cate (eds.), *The Army Air Forces in World War II* (University of Chicago Press, 1948), vol. 1, p. 56.

[13] *Inquiry into Operations of United States Air Services*, H. Rept. 1653, 68 Cong. 2 sess. (1925). The Army's experience in the prewar period is analyzed in Irving B.

same time, a board appointed by the President and chaired by Dwight W. Morrow reached similar conclusions.[14] Both groups dealt with procurement policies only as incidental to the broader question of air power policy.

In the legislative consideration of aircraft problems in 1926, the Senate agreed to consider alternatives to competitive bidding in aircraft procurement. The House Committee on Military Affairs felt otherwise. The bill that emerged from the work of a joint sub-committee on the Air Corps Act of 1926 maintained the requirement of competitive bidding, but also provided authority to negotiate for experimental planes and for quantity purchase of planes from designs submitted before the passage of the act.[15] The 1926 act required the services to advertise their interest in procuring aircraft of specified characteristics, allowing a three-month delay between the request for bids and the opening of design proposals. The bids were to include prices, graduated according to the number of aircraft that might be ordered. It was incumbent upon the services to evaluate the designs submitted in order of merit, the act requiring that the invitation for bids specifically state the weighted values assigned to the various features to be considered in the evaluation.

The respective secretaries were to award contracts to the lowest responsible bidder judged capable of doing the work required "to the best advantage of the Government." They might also reject all designs submitted if judged unsuitable. Proprietary rights in the designs submitted were recognized. Rights to utilize such designs might be purchased by the government, although patent rights against others were reserved to the firm submitting the design.

Holley, Jr., *Buying Aircraft: Materiel Procurement for the Army Air Force*, chaps. 2–6. On the Navy, see Archibald D. Turnbull and Clifford L. Lord, *History of United States Naval Aviation* (Yale University Press, 1949). See also Arnold W. Knauth, "Government Procurement of Aircraft," *Air Law Review*, vol. 12 (January 1941), pp. 34–39.

[14] *Aircraft in National Defense*, Message from the President of the United States Transmitting the Report of the President's Aircraft Board, S. Doc. 18, 69 Cong. 1 sess. (1925).

[15] Edwin H. Rutkowski, *The Politics of Military Aviation Procurement, 1926–1934: A Study in the Political Assertion of Consensual Values* (Ohio State University Press, 1966).

Procurement based on a combination of two or more partially suitable designs was also authorized.

However, one section, 10(k), authorized the purchase of designs, aircraft, aircraft parts, and accessories for experimental purposes with or without competition. The decision of the secretaries as to the awarding, interpretation, application, and administration of contracts was reviewable only by the President and the federal courts, a provision which strengthened negotiating authority.

Both the services sought to comply with the act by holding design competitions. These proved to be unsatisfactory since the operating characteristics of an aircraft could not be determined from drawings and specifications. Furthermore, the submission of a design gave no indication of the ability of the designer to translate the design into a successful airplane. Though the procuring agencies sought to limit bidding to those firms maintaining facilities and staff for designing aircraft, they were unable to do so. As a result, a designing firm frequently failed to win a competition, the procurement going instead to firms which had no design costs and which could offer lower prices. Procurements were sometimes divided among a number of bidders. The results were discouragement of firms that had invested in design efforts and the delivery of aircraft that were frequently unsatisfactory.[16] Design competition was therefore quickly abandoned.

What was needed was a procedure that would permit recognition of the rights of firms which undertook the burdens of designing new equipment. Both services sought to meet their needs by negotiating orders for experimental planes. Authority for such procedure was found in section 10(k) of the 1926 act mentioned above, as well as in the act of March 2, 1901, under which proprietary articles could be purchased without competition because for them competition was found "impracticable." Many aircraft were procured under these regulations from 1927 to 1934.

However, these procedures attracted voluminous criticism from disaffected members of the industry and from members of Congress. The critics questioned the "experimental" purposes as well as the proprietary nature of many purchases. An investigation in 1934 by the House Committee on Military Affairs resulted in se-

[16] *Ibid.,* pp. 287–88.

vere censure of the use of the negotiated contract in aircraft procurement.[17] After 1934 the use of negotiated contracts was restricted to more clearly experimental purposes—experimental being defined as the number of aircraft sufficient to equip a squadron, the smallest tactical unit of the Army Air Corps. Such procurement was normally made as a result of the informal submission of design data by several manufacturers, or after such tests as could be made upon a single airplane acquired under the same authority.

With the exception of such narrowly defined "experimental" procurement, the services relied upon "sample airplane" competitions. Under this procedure invitations to bid were issued indicating the type of aircraft desired, with each bidder required, as a condition precedent to consideration of his bid, to submit a sample airplane for examination and test, thereby assuming the heavy costs involved.[18] Evaluation of the sample airplane provided for allocation of weighted criteria relating to performance, and engineering and utility characteristics as well as price. Awards for quantity production could be made to not more than three winners of the competition and were made by negotiation at prices not exceeding the figures in the bid submitted. Approximately fifty sample aircraft competitions were held by the Army in the period 1934 to 1940. Most of the aircraft that saw extensive service during World War II emerged from this process, including the B-17, 24, 25, 26, and 29, the A-20 and 24, and the P-38, 39, 40, and 47.[19]

In 1939 these procedures were abandoned as too time-consuming for emergency procurement. The requirement for a sample airplane was eliminated, and a new type of "design competition" was inaugurated, the participants limited to firms qualified to manufacture aircraft in quantity. In these competitions it was incumbent upon the manufacturer to guarantee the attainment by the airplane of the performance promised in his bid. Either the invitation to bid or the manufacturer's proposal specified the partic-

[17] *War Department Investigation,* H. Repts. 1506 and 2060, 73 Cong. 2 sess. (1934), and H. Rept. 4, 74 Cong. 1 sess. (1935).

[18] U.S.C. 312. As administered, the sample method of procuring new aircraft was not specifically provided for in the Air Corps Act of 1926. An act of April 3, 1939, gave implicit approval.

[19] Craven and Cate, *The Army Air Forces in World War II,* vol. 1, p. 109.

ular type and model of engine to be furnished by the government as a condition of the specified performance. It followed that with the award of a contract for aircraft the particular engine to be obtained was determined and the engine manufacturer became a sole source. This procedure was attacked in numerous instances but was successfully defended as within the discretion of the Secretary of War. Ten such competitions were held, and the contracts resulting included options for additional procurement without further competition so that the services were in a position to procure for emergency purposes.

Another significant deviation from standard methods of procurement involved what were termed "policy" items. These included such aircraft accessories as fuel pumps and other articles where considerations of safety required that procurement in quantity be made only from bidders whose product had been tested. With regard to such items, a policy statement including approved specifications was distributed to all known manufacturers of related equipment, inviting the submission of sample articles without payment therefor. If the product was found to meet the standards established, a number were purchased under section 10(k) and subjected to detailed field tests. If his work passed the tests, the manufacturer was placed on the approved list and was eligible to bid on a competitive price basis for quantity production.

Limitations of Prewar Procedures

The slow and laborious evolution of the government's policies in the development of aircraft reflected the uncertainties and conflicts of an emerging situation in which the government had assumed the initiative to secure development objectives but relied upon private institutions to perform many of the essential functions. Prior to World War II the procedures applied to aircraft development remained unique.

In other areas, the principle that military technology should follow upon the civilian continued to be applied. Because of statutory restrictions, organizational restraints, and, most important, the very limited funds made available, the transfer of civilian technical developments to military applications was very slow, as was also the exploration of new ideas arising from but not applied by the civilian society. The Army's chief of ordnance observed that "between 1919 and 1939 it had been practically impossible to call on the vast store of engineering talent and scientific knowledge of industry except in an advisory capacity and without compensation." The result was that "the development and production of artillery, weapons, and fire-control instruments had not kept pace with scientific and technological knowledge in other fields."[20] Though the situation was somewhat better in other areas (in naval craft and in electronics, for example), the experience of ordnance was paralleled in many other fields. The transfer of well-developed civilian technology to military uses was generally a time-consuming and cumbersome procedure. Of perhaps greater importance was the fact that the government's interest in areas of possible technical change which were not being exploited in the interest of civilian objectives was hard to deal with and frequently remained unidentified. One very important exception must be noted however. The Army in 1938 established the Ballistic Research Laboratory to provide means to perform the very numerous computations needed to provide ballistic tables for artillery use. The BRL promised, by making use of the privately developed Bush Differential Analyzer, a vast improvement over mechanical desk calculators. It was the Army's experience with the advantages and limitations of the Differential Analyzer that led the BRL during World War II to undertake the support of projects which led to the electronic computer.[21]

World War II Procurement

In the late 1930's, as the war in Europe came to hold ominous implications for the United States, it became clear that the nation's

[20] Levin H. Campbell, Jr., *The Industry-Ordnance Team* (Whittlesey House, 1946), p. 207.

[21] The Army's activities in electronic computation began in 1942 when it accepted a proposal from the Moore School of Electrical Engineering of the University of Pennsylvania. The original contract provided $61,700 for six months of work on an electronic numerical integrator and computer (ENIAC). Nine supplementary contracts for a total of $486,804 produced a working pilot model in 1946 which weighed over 30 tons and contained 19,000 vacuum tubes and hundreds of thousands of resistors, capacitors, and inductors. General Chester W. Clark, "Interrelations of Army R&D Expenditures and Industry Planning," in National Security Industries Association, *The Impact of Government Research and Development Expenditures on Industrial Growth* (Government Printing Office, 1963), pp. 39–40.

interests required that the military services be given greater flexibility in drawing upon private sources for their needs. In the National Defense Expediting Act of July 2, 1940, Congress took a major step in providing such flexibility.[22] By that act the services were granted the authority to buy through negotiated contracts involving either a fixed price or cost-plus-fixed-fee. This sweeping break with procurement tradition also authorized other procedures intended to facilitate the defense effort. Among these may be mentioned the making of advance payments during the performance of contracts in amounts not exceeding 30 percent of the contract price; the authority to furnish government-owned facilities to privately owned plants; and the suspension of statutory limitations on construction.[23]

The first War Powers Act of 1941 in its Title II provided even more sweeping authorizations. The act empowered the President to permit any department of the government having wartime functions to enter into contracts and to amend or modify them "without regard to the provisions of law relating to the performance, amendment, or modification of these contracts whenever he deems such action would facilitate the prosecution of the war." The President granted this authority to the War and Navy Departments by executive order.[24] The services were now freed of most legal restraints and restrictions in the way of speedy procurement; the sole consideration was whether the action proposed would facilitate the prosecution of the war. Long-established procedures were not, however, quickly set aside even under the pressure of very large-scale purchases. Procurement officers reacted slowly, and purchasing by advertised bids continued as standard practice until a directive of the War Production Board in 1942 required a shift to negotiation.[25]

The negotiated contract of the cost-plus-fixed-fee type was of great significance during World War II in those numerous situa-

---

[22] P.L. 703, July 2, 1940.

[23] Other legislation authorized the waiver of performance and payment bonds on cost-plus-fixed-fee contracts: P.L. 800 (Oct. 8, 1940) and P.L. 43 (April 29, 1941).

[24] Act of Dec. 18, 1941, 55 Stat. 83, implemented by Exec. Order 9001 (Dec. 27, 1941).

[25] War Production Board Directive No. 2, March 3, 1942 (*Federal Register*, vol. 7, p. 1732).

tions where important elements of uncertainty existed which could not be permitted to interfere with immediate production. Such uncertainties might relate to the production of an item for which precise specifications were available but with which a manufacturer lacked experience. Another kind of uncertainty existed when efforts were made to direct the capabilities of research staffs or of manufacturers to the production of items which required considerable development before they could be standardized and hence ready for the preparation of firm and detailed specifications. Where development effort of this sort was required, the staffs of the Navy's bureaus and the Army's technical services frequently worked closely with the employees of the private contractors. In such cases, costs could not be known or even reasonably estimated in advance and some form of contract providing for reimbursement of contractor costs protected both parties while permitting progress toward the objective without delay for legal reasons.

Both the War and Navy Departments pursued policies of replacing negotiated cost-plus-fixed-fee contracts with fixed price agreements as rapidly as manufacturers acquired sufficient experience to accumulate the necessary cost data. When such information had been acquired, fixed-price contracts were more desirable since they made possible the use of incentives toward increasing efficiency. In the case of the Army, 42 percent of all contracts over $10 million were of the cost-plus-fixed-fee type in 1940–41. That percentage declined to 32 percent in the last six months of 1944. In areas where development efforts were continuously involved and in all contracts involving research, the departments accepted throughout the war the necessity of employing negotiated cost-plus-fixed-fee contracts.

Wartime Research and Development Activities

Besides their obvious concern with immediately needed equipment, the military services had an interest in knowledge and skills that had developed in industry, scientific laboratories, and the universities, but which had been seldom applied during the 1920's and 1930's and remained unused or unperfected. The very low level of R&D effort by the Army and Navy had left unexploited numerous scientific and technological developments that promised to be useful for military purposes if further developed.

During World War I, the Army and Navy had sought to apply scientific knowledge to some of their problems by offering scientists commissions and assignments in military laboratories. The same procedure was followed during World War II and the military laboratories secured the services of a substantial number of well qualified scientists and engineers. Scientists entering government service during the war as civilians or as commissioned officers contributed to the development of such organizations as the Army's Ballistic Laboratory and a number of the test centers. Inventors were also encouraged to submit their ideas to a National Inventors Council, established by the Secretary of Commerce in 1940. More than 200,000 inventions and ideas were submitted to the Council, but only a few proved to be of value.[26]

Mobilization of the nation's technical resources to its defense needs was sought on a much larger scale in World War II than in World War I, and touched numerous areas of knowledge not dealt with adequately or at all in military establishments. Governmental facilities were inadequate to any large expansion, and building new, or even expanding existing, organizations was a slow process. It was necessary to use whatever organizations and facilities were available with such additions as a specific project might require. More important was the fact that in some areas the services needed the assistance of all the nation's scientists. The need was not confined to areas where problems could be well defined by the services but was almost equally pressing in areas where part of the research contribution would be the identification of application possibilities by the scientists.

Machinery whereby specific research needs of the government could be made the responsibility of civilian scientists had existed since 1863 in the form of the National Academy of Sciences (NAS) and its operating subsidiary organization, the National Research Council (NRC) organized in 1918. An effort to enlarge the government's role in science in the mid-thirties through a Science Advisory Board proved abortive.[27] As the need to draw more heav-

[26] National Inventors Council, "Administrative History of the National Inventors Council" (processed; Department of Commerce, n.d.).

[27] Although the Science Advisory Board was short-lived and of little effectiveness, its establishment in the mid-thirties did provide some experience in developing closer contacts between the scientific community and the federal government. See

ily upon the nation's scientific resources became more apparent and funds became more readily available, the services opened negotiations with the academy, looking toward the establishment of research projects employing academic scientists under academy sponsorship. Meanwhile, new appraisals of the existing machinery led to the conclusion that some more effective procedure was required. The NAS and its research council were viewed by its officers, some of its members, and others as unable to work as swiftly and effectively as necessary because the magnitude of the desirable effort required the direct disbursement of government funds rather than the indirect procedures of the academy. In the minds of some scientists the fact that the academy played a passive role, acting only upon requests made of it, seemed a serious limitation.[28] Circumstances called for an organization that would take the initiative, an organization with its own funds, and one that could assume administrative responsibility for establishing research programs and for evaluating progress. The NAS-NRC was in fact to be heavily involved in the future of government-related R&D, its need for working capital being supplied by grants from philanthropic foundations.[29]

An organization designed to overcome the limitations of NAS-NRC was established on June 27, 1940, when the President appointed the National Defense Research Committee (NDRC) as a part of the Council of National Defense. The committee consisted of four government officials and five civilians. One of the civilians, Vannevar Bush, was chairman. The committee's responsibilities were to "correlate and support scientific research on the mechanisms of warfare, except those relating to problems of flight included in the field of activities of the National Advisory Committee for Aeronautics." It was further to "aid and supplement the

---

Lewis E. Auerbach, "Scientists in the New Deal: A Prewar Episode in the Relations between Science and Government in the United States," *Minerva,* vol. 3 (Summer 1965), pp. 457–82.

[28] For the judgment of NAS President Frank B. Jewett, see *Technological Mobilization,* Hearings before the Senate Military Affairs Committee, 77 Cong. 2 sess. (1942), pt. 2, pp. 310–11. For an example of contemporary evaluation of the limitations of the National Academy of Sciences, see *Journal of Applied Physics,* vol. 14 (August 1943), pp. 374–75.

[29] National Academy of Sciences–National Research Council, *Annual Reports Fiscal Year 1946–47* (Government Printing Office, 1948), pp. 1–3.

experimental and research activities of the War and Navy Departments"; and it might "conduct research for the creation and improvement of instrumentalities, methods and materials of warfare."[30]

At its first meeting the NDRC decided to operate primarily through contracts and at no time did it attempt to acquire its own laboratories or research staff.[31] Both the Army and Navy promptly submitted some of their problems to this new organization. In October 1940 some eighteen ordnance research projects were accepted by the NDRC and many others followed.

The National Defense Research Committee was absorbed within a year by a new organization with broader authorities and centralized administration. An executive order in January 1941 created the Office of Scientific Research and Development (OSRD) within the Office for Emergency Management. The director of the new office was made responsible to the President on all aspects of defense-related research, and had the authority to initiate and support research in all areas relating to the national defense, including medicine. The OSRD was financed through allocations of funds by the President and by direct appropriations. Though organized with the intention of utilizing the facilities of existing government research organizations, the office followed the policy laid down by its predecessor organization and operated principally through contracts with private institutions having or able to attract qualified staffs and facilities. As part of the OSRD effort, large government-owned laboratories were established to be administered and staffed by university employees. It did not operate in areas where strong capabilities already existed, as in aviation, or in areas where other agencies were active as for example the Army, Navy, or the War Production Board's Office of Product Research Development which was concerned with substitute materials.

The Office of Scientific Research and Development generally undertook work upon request for aid from the Army or Navy although some of its more dramatic efforts were undertaken on its

[30] Irwin Stewart, *Organizing Scientific Research for War* (Little, Brown & Co., 1948).

[31] "At its first meeting the committee decided to operate primarily through contracts. This decision was never modified . . ." (*ibid.*, p. 12).

own initiative and occasionally in the face of service indifference, if not opposition. The principal function of the OSRD was to determine the feasibility of a project and then to identify the private facility or individual scientist best able to handle it. Having reached an agreement with a scientist, OSRD entered into a simple contract with the scientist's institution. Over the war years OSRD entered into some 2,200 contracts with over 440 institutions, contracts involving expenditures of about $500 million.[32] Included are OSRD expenditures during the initial stages of the Manhattan Project. That project, like some others, was turned over to one of the services when it entered the developmental stage. About half of the money spent was used in the universities.

The OSRD worked closely with both the military services in Washington and the numerous military organizations elsewhere which engaged in or were affected by R&D activities. Most important of the military organizations was the Joint Committee on New Weapons and Equipment. Established in 1942 and composed of both civilian and military members, the committee reported to the Joint Chiefs of Staff on proposals for new equipment but was responsible also for coordinating the R&D efforts of civilian and military agencies.

The research activities stimulated and financed by the Office of Scientific Research and Development were massive, but the R&D efforts of other agencies were also on a very large scale (Table 2). The Army's development program involved a wartime expenditure more than twice that of OSRD and the Navy's was also slightly larger, both exclusive of the development effort that was implicit in many production contracts. Army expenditures for R&D within its own facilities during the war were at an annual rate six times greater than in the mid-thirties and Navy expenditures increased by three times. However, the in-house efforts in both Army and Navy were less than a third of their total R&D expenditures. More than two-thirds of the expenditures by the two services for R&D involved contracts with industrial firms.

In addition to the War and Navy Departments and OSRD, some wartime emergency agencies found themselves charged with responsibilities that required R&D efforts. Since such agencies had

---

[32] James P. Baxter, *Scientists against Time* (Little, Brown & Co., 1946), pp. 456–57.

TABLE 2

Research and Development Expenditures by Sponsoring Agency and Type of Performer, Fiscal Years 1940–44

Sponsoring Agency	Total[a] (In Millions of Dollars)	Type of Performer (Percent of Total)			
		Government	Industry	Educational Institutions and Foundations	Others
Military and emergency agencies:					
War	$754.8	30.1	69.4	0.5	—
Navy	348.6	28.1	71.4	0.5	—
Office of Scientific Research and Development	336.8	1.8	32.7	65.6	—
Reconstruction Finance Corporation	24.4	—	97.2	2.8	—
War Production Board	5.7	—	46.2	48.4	5.4
Others	8.4	2.1	81.7	14.5	1.6
Other agencies:					
Agriculture	148.4	76.7	—	—	23.3[b]
Commerce	34.7	97.7	1.4	0.9	—
Interior	88.4	100.0	—	—	—
Public Health Service	16.0	95.4	1.2	2.9	0.5
National Advisory Committee for Aeronautics	94.4	98.9	0.1	1.0	—
Tennessee Valley Authority	12.9	77.7	—	22.2	0.1
Others	4.9	32.3	59.3	7.5	0.9
Semigovernmental agencies:					
National Academy of Sciences and National Research Council	6.0[c]	18.1	n.a.	n.a.	n.a.
Total	$1,884.4	36.6	48.6	12.7	1.9

Sources: *The Government's Wartime Research and Development, 1940–44*, Subcommittee on War Mobilization of the Senate Military Affairs Committee, Rept. No. 5, 79 Cong. 1 sess. (1945), pt. 1, pp. 277–326; *Legislative Proposals for the Promotion of Science: The Texts of Five Bills and Excerpts from Reports*, Subcommittee on War Mobilization of the Senate Military Affairs Committee, S. Doc. 92, 79 Cong. 1 sess. (1945), p. 22. "n.a." = not available.

a. Omits interagency transfers.

b. Consists primarily of grants by Department of Agriculture for state experimental stations.

c. Total includes $4.9 million of National Academy of Sciences and National Research Council expenditures for which no breakdown into facilities used is available.

no research personnel or facilities, they secured the needed services by transfer of funds to other federal agencies possessing appropriate facilities or by contracting with private insititutions. The War Production Board was the most important source of demand.[33] That agency's Office of Production Research and Development placed some projects with other federal agencies but relied most heavily on contracts with industry and the universities. The Defense Plant Corporation of the Reconstruction Finance Corporation, at the request of the War Production Board, provided plant and/or equipment for some projects which were conducted entirely by contract. The Rubber Reserve Corporation, also of the RFC, charged with responsibility for the nation's rubber supply, was deeply involved in organizing the nation's technical competence and facilities to increase the supply of synthetic rubber. While this task involved primarily the pooling of knowledge, including arrangements for the cross-licensing of patents, in the process substantial gaps were found which called for further developmental efforts. These gaps were bridged by research programs conducted entirely by contract.

Among the permanent agencies, contracts were used during the war to supplement existing facilities or to undertake projects which could be best or most promptly handled by private organizations. The Bureau of Public Roads entered into a few R&D contracts with universities in 1940 and conducted about 15 percent of its wartime R&D program by contracts. The Tennessee Valley Authority undertook R&D for other agencies and increased its utilization of contracts to about 20 percent of its total R&D expenditures. The Maritime Commission, which had conducted no R&D prior to 1940, carried out some small programs during the war, partially by agreements with other agencies and partly by contract.

The National Bureau of Standards and the National Advisory Committee for Aeronautics were two permanent nonmilitary agencies of the government with capabilities in areas closely re-

---

[33] On the War Production Board's R&D activities, see *National War Agencies Appropriations Bill,* Hearings before the House Appropriations Committee, 78 Cong. 2 sess. (1944), pp. 703–41, and Senate Committee on Military Affairs, *The Government's Wartime Research and Development, 1940–44,* pt. I: *Survey of Government Agencies,* 79 Cong. 1 sess. (1945), pp. 227–30.

lated to war problems. Wartime expenditures of the National Bureau of Standards increased some eleven times above 1939 levels, about two-thirds being work requested and financed by funds from other agencies. NACA's expenditures increased ten times, financed entirely by direct appropriations. Both organizations relied upon expansion of their staffs and facilities to conduct their work. NACA employed contracts for about one percent of its wartime expenditures; NBS placed only a single, small contract.

For the government as a whole, expenditures within agency laboratories during the war period were at an annual rate about twice the 1937–38 levels. These expenditures were, however, only a third of the total. About half of wartime R&D expenditures were made with private industrial firms and about one-sixth were with educational and nonprofit institutions.

The Development of Policy, 1944–50

The many new devices contributed by scientific and engineering efforts to the nation's military power during World War II, the new materials developed, and the higher standards of medical treatment made possible by research—all these were dramatic achievements, recognized as of critical importance long before the full story was available to the public. Within the government, both in the Congress and in the executive agencies, there was widespread conviction that after the war the nation's R&D efforts should be continued at high levels.

In November 1944, President Roosevelt requested Vannevar Bush to prepare a statement as to how the lessons learned in the Office of Scientific Research and Development experience might be profitably employed in peacetime. In *Science—the Endless Frontier,* published in 1945, Bush, supported by the members of a number of committees formed for the purpose, urged a broad commitment by the federal government to scientific activities.

While the Bush report provided a general survey of the government's scientific activities and the nation's needs, it was directed most specifically to the problems of supporting basic scientific research and to increasing the capacity of the nation's manpower to engage in scientific endeavor in all fields, including those of primary military interest. The precise suggestions made as to the amount of the support, the areas to be covered and the organizations to be established were to be debated for some years.

In his message to the Congress in September 1945 calling for legislation to facilitate the conversion to a peacetime economy, President Truman pointed out that "progress in scientific research and development is an indispensable condition to the future welfare and security of the nation. The events of the past few years are both proof and prophecy of what science can do. . . . No nation," he said, "can maintain a position of leadership in the world of today unless it develops to the full its scientific and technological resources." The President recommended the establishment of a single federal agency which would administer a program of scientific research, observing that "no government adequately meets its responsibilities unless it generously and intelligently supports and encourages the work of science in university, industry, and in its own laboratories." The President pointed out that "during the war we have learned much about the methods of organizing science, and about the ways of encouraging and supporting its activities. The development of atomic energy is a clear-cut indication of what can be accomplished by our universities, industry and Government working together. Vast scientific fields remain to be conquered in the same way."[34]

The President's observations reflected a broad consensus. Few questioned the need for a greater federal role in achieving such higher levels of activity. There was also widespread agreement that the wartime procedure of involving private institutions and individuals in the attainment of government objectives had been very effective and should be continued.

In Congress, the war experience stimulated a widespread interest in scientific and technical research. The question was how the programs that had come into existence during the war could be continued. The major issues related to the organization of postwar R&D programs in atomic energy, military technology, and medicine, and the extent of the need for the federal government to promote research in the basic sciences. Each of these required action

[34] *Public Papers of Presidents of the United States: Harry S Truman, 1945* (Government Printing Office, 1961), pp. 293–94.

in the immediate postwar period. President Truman's message in effect suggested that the time had come to take action on all of them.

Concern with the peacetime relationships of the government to scientific research and development programs had been active and widespread, well before the end of the war. Public discussion looking toward the establishment of a broad policy may be said to have begun with Senator Harley M. Kilgore's proposal for more effective mobilization of scientists in 1943.[35] When hearings before a Subcommittee of the Committee on Military Affairs generated little support for and considerable opposition to the proposal, Senator Kilgore turned to postwar problems. For the next seven years, problems of the government's relationship to research were continually on the subcommittee's agenda. Senatorial participation broadened when the Committee on Naval Affairs held hearings on a research and development bill and the Committee on Labor and Public Welfare held hearings on a National Science Foundation bill. In the House, a Select Committee on Post-war Military Policy, under the chairmanship of Representative Clifton A. Woodrum, undertook in 1944 to develop an answer to the question: "What shall we do to assure our armed services in time of peace as well as in time of war, the active and organized support of scientific research and development?"[36] Over the next several years the House committees on Military Affairs and on Interstate and Foreign Commerce also turned their attention to the problems.[37]

In the hearings on the Army's 1946 appropriation bills held early in 1945, some congressmen had expressed the fear that the lifting of war pressures would be followed by a relaxation of efforts and urged that R&D programs be maintained after victory

[35] *Scientific and Technical Mobilization,* Hearings before the [Harley M. Kilgore] Subcommittee of the Senate Military Affairs Committee, 78 Cong. 1 sess. (1943). It should be noted that there had been some exploration in 1942 by congressmen during departmental appropriations hearings of the possibility of extending the OSRD-type activity. See Richard H. Heindel, "The Discussion of Federal Research Problems in Congress and the 1943 Appropriations" (mimeographed).

[36] *Surplus Material—Research and Development,* Hearings before the House Select Committee on Post-war Military Policy, pursuant to H. Res. 465, 78 Cong. 2 sess. (1944).

[37] *National Science Foundation Act,* Hearings before a Subcommittee of the House Interstate and Foreign Commerce Committee on H. R. 6448, 70 Cong. 2 sess. (May 1946).

over Japan.[38] When Congress started hearings on the budget for fiscal 1946–47, the war had been won on both fronts. Large sums included in the 1945–46 budget had been rescinded by Congress or withheld by the administration. Some reductions had been made in R&D funds but they represented what the agencies involved felt to be sums that could not be used effectively. There was a consensus to the effect that the R&D effort should be maintained at levels desired by the procuring agencies, which was to say, levels determined by their ability to program and by availability of the necessary scientific and technical personnel.

In the years immediately following the war, the problems of the government's postwar policies with regard to R&D were dealt with more or less simultaneously by numerous congressional committees. In the hearings, reports, and statutes resulting from these considerations, general approval was expressed of close relationships between government agencies and scientific and technical institutions supported through grants and contracts. The possibility of expanding such activities within the government arose occasionally but aroused little interest.

In the transition from war to peacetime conditions, federal agencies engaged in reappraisals of their research and development programs and submitted proposals and budgets to the Congress. In these areas, the development of policies and programs followed the standard pattern of congressional reaction to recommendations from the executive branch. Agencies interested in R&D frequently found the Bush report useful in justifying their proposals and their requests for funds. Those agencies that were engaged in contractual or grant research programs found Congress particularly receptive to that method of carrying out their projects. However, requests for expansion of government-owned and -operated facilities and enterprises were almost always successful though sometimes requiring more detailed justification and involving greater delays. The positions taken by the executive agencies and by the Congress in the first few years after the war were almost universally in support of some increase in R&D programs. The actions taken on immediate problems typically followed closely the wartime pattern and, in the aggregate, constituted the foundation

---

[38] *Military Establishment Appropriations Bill, 1946,* Hearings before the House Appropriations Committee, 79 Cong. 1 sess. (1945), pp. 663, 670.

upon which were built today's long-range R&D policies and programs.

Some of the war-generated programs and proposals for some new programs were less easily and expeditiously dealt with. Atomic energy presented special problems. While there was no disagreement regarding the war-established procedures for conducting the R&D program in atomic energy through privately managed, government-owned laboratories, the choice between military and civilian control generated vigorous and prolonged debate. The debate over the government's program in support of basic research was even more prolonged as wide differences were exposed regarding the form of organization and the extent of jurisdiction of the proposed program.

Other issues that impinged upon R&D activities included the organization of the armed forces, the nature of procurement authority to be granted, and such matters as the salary structure for career employees in federal laboratories. The actions that were taken were heavily influenced by the administrative experience accumulated during the war, and by the wide variety of scientific and technical frontiers that had been exposed. The magnitude of the effort reflected the recurring appraisals of the shifting nature of the nation's international position.

Military R&D Programs, 1946–50

Although still preoccupied with the administration of the war effort, groups in both the War and Navy Departments had begun in January 1944 to consider the problem of maintaining military scientific research after the war. Assistant Secretary for War Robert P. Patterson established their mood when in 1944 he said in testimony before the House Select Committee on Post-war Military Policy that "we cannot have a sound military policy for the future unless we set it down that the inventive and technical resources of the Nation will be made available to the armed forces, in peace as well as in war." The military services would not have the best available weapons "unless there is steady teamwork between the military services and the most capable minds in scientific research and development."[39] Secretary Patterson's statement was perhaps a truism but it suggested that the prewar system had

[39] *Surplus Material—Research and Development,* Hearings, p. 126.

failed in maintaining such a relationship and that there were lessons in the war experience that should be applied in the postwar period.

There was no disagreement in the Congress with the judgments expressed about the need to make the nation's resources of scientific and technical capabilities available to the armed services. Congressman W. Sterling Cole responded to Secretary Patterson's remarks quoted above, saying that "we are all agreed that scientific research and development must be undertaken into the indefinite future." Congressmen did take some pains to absolve themselves of responsibility for the inadequate levels of prewar R&D, as a colloquy between Representative Cole and Secretary Patterson illustrates:

MR. COLE. Perhaps you have told us, but if you did I missed it, to what extent the Army engaged in scientific development during peacetimes?

MR. PATTERSON. Very little. They had no funds.

MR. COLE. Was that the sole reason?

MR. PATTERSON. That was the principal reason. Some of the services did a good deal. The amount carried on, I believe, varied according to the interest of the chief of the service. I know now that some of the technical services of the Army were far ahead of others; but they were all limited by being starved for funds.

MR. COLE. I have no recollection of any great demand having been made by either of the services for funds for purely scientific development by the services themselves. Perhaps it occurred, but not within my recollection.

MR. PATTERSON. I will go along with you on the thought that we are far more alive to the need of it now, having been taught some lessons during the war.[40]

Secretary Patterson's conciliatory reply reflected the mood.[41] There

---

[40] *Ibid.*, p. 130.

[41] There were, of course, other efforts to place responsibility for the nation's unpreparedness. The Special Committee to Investigate the National Defense Program (the Mead committee) made some critical comments regarding the complacency of the prewar Army. For the Army's reaction, see Skinner Watson, *The War Department Chief of Staff; Prewar Plans and Preparations* (1950), pp. 18–34. Congressional attitudes and Army policies are analyzed in Elias Huzar's *The Purse and the Sword: Control of the Army by Congress through Military Appropriations, 1933–1950* (Cornell University Press, 1950), pp. 300–303. The appraisal of the war experience was, however, essentially positive, looking toward application of the lessons learned rather than seeking to identify specific shortcomings of prewar participants.

was nothing to be gained by mutual recriminations while such appraisals might divert attention from the important task of profiting from the lessons learned.

The services were meanwhile exploring the ways and means by which more effective R&D programs might be pursued. By joint action of the Secretaries of War and Navy, a Committee on Postwar Research was established under the chairmanship of Charles E. Wilson, then executive vice chairman of the War Production Board. The committee reported in September 1944, urging the establishment of a substantial postwar research and development effort by the services and suggesting appropriate methods.

Though the specific procedural recommendations of the Wilson committee were not adopted, the report merits attention since its basic position not only reflected the attitudes of the day but also has characterized the postwar research program. The committee reported that

[it] has taken for granted that the Army and Navy must continue to carry the major responsibility for such work, especially in times of peace. Experience with the Office of Scientific Research and Development during the past four years, however, has demonstrated that scientists in civilian life, when given the opportunity, are capable of making outstanding contributions to the invention, development, and operation of all manner of instrumentalities of war. Obviously, the Government cannot, after the war, continue to employ on military research all of the scientists who were mobilized under the Office of Scientific Research and Development for such work during the war. Furthermore, the great majority of these men would not be willing, after the war, to devote all of their time to such work. Nevertheless, a way should be found for keeping the country's outstanding scientists interested in military research after the war, so as to give the Army and the Navy the continued benefit of their thinking and of their assistance.[42]

The committee further stated its belief that

the best device for carrying out the above objective is the prosecution of scientific research by contracts under a board composed of civilians of distinction in science, engineering, and industry, and of officers of the Army and of the Navy who have important responsibilities in connection with research and development work.

The committee recommended that a permanent research board

[42] *Surplus Material—Research and Development*, Hearings, p. 135.

for national security be established by Congress. The immediate issue before it was the problem of providing arrangements whereby the existing relationships between the government and scientific institutions could be maintained. Two problems were involved. One was that of establishing institutional relationships that would be acceptable to the type of scientists that the services would wish to attract. The second was that of making funds available.

The suggested solution to these problems made use of the National Academy of Sciences as the agency representing the scientific community and hence capable of enlisting the interest of scientists. In the area of finance, the problem was that in both the House and Senate, R&D funds for the services were appropriated by separate subcommittees for the Army and Navy. Further, such funds were appropriated to the various services and bureaus in the Army and Navy. One solution to the problems so presented was to arrange that each bureau or service make funds available to the Army or Navy, such funds then being transferred to the proposed Research Board for National Security and hence by contract to the National Academy of Sciences. This involved the danger that some of the services and bureaus would divert funds to objectives that appeared to them to be more immediately pressing. It was thought possible to seek funds from the Congress earmarked by the appropriate committee for contract research through the NAS. However, this procedure involved the possibility of quite different reactions to the programs presented by the various committees. It involved also the possibility that, in the absence of legislation authorizing such earmarking, the action of the Appropriations Committee would be subject to challenge on the floor of the House. In view of these problems the committee recommended that funds be appropriated directly to the NAS by the Congress in amounts to be recommended by the two services. These arrangements were proposed as an interim action, pending congressional consideration of the problems both of policy toward science and of defense organization. Though the reaction to the committee report was favorable, Congress failed to act.

Although no specific guidance by the Congress was forthcoming, the general environment was highly favorable to continuing support of research and development programs. An immediate problem was the imminent liquidation of the Office of Scientific Research and Development. President Truman in his message of 1945 had requested that the board continue its operations. However the OSRD operated on the assumption that it could not hope to maintain its program for long after the end of hostilities. The universities faced the task of meeting the educational needs of the very large numbers of young men and women whose education had been postponed by military service. Though many of the scientists working on OSRD projects retained an interest in continuing their research, most felt a major commitment to their teaching functions. The passage of the G.I. Bill of Rights effectively established the immediate postwar priority of education over a continuance of the wartime structure of research by university faculty.

Planning for the demobilization of OSRD had begun in September 1944. Though the Battle of the Bulge forced temporary shelving of those plans, OSRD operations after that date were restricted to projects which held some prospect of application to a war now nearing its end.[43] It was also clear that many OSRD projects would be incomplete at the end of the war. Although the objectives of such projects required reassessment, many would remain highly desirable and much effort would be lost if abrupt cancellations of contracts should occur.

To meet the immediate problems created by the dissolution of OSRD, the secretaries of War and of the Navy drew upon the precedent of the Joint Chiefs of Staff Committee on New Weapons and Equipment and in June 1946 established a Joint Research and Development Board. The board was composed of two representatives from each department, with Vannevar Bush as chairman. In its procedure the board continued the OSRD system of relying for guidance upon committees composed of qualified consultants. The board represented a temporary arrangement for evaluating selected OSRD projects of continuing interest. It was also a means for reaching agreement between the two departments on common

[43] Stewart, *Organizing Scientific Research for War*, pp. 300–303, 311.

policies, for allocating responsibilities for projects in which both were interested, and for arranging for joint use of facilities and of R&D results.

In large degree, however, the initiative remained with the military services. As OSRD was moving toward dissolution, the Navy sought to provide an organization that would enable it more effectively to assert its interests in research. As a result of action taken as early as 1914, there was a Naval Research Laboratory serving Navy-wide interests. Expanding that capability had long been the objective of a group within the Navy.[44] The goal was achieved when in 1946 the Navy secured from Congress approval for the establishment of an Office of Naval Research. The new ONR included the Naval Research Laboratory and similar facilities but also had authority to administer programs of contract research with the universities in areas relevant to the Navy's mission. With an initial appropriation of $21 million, the ONR was in a position to assume some OSRD projects and also to seek out and offer research contracts to scientists who had returned to their universities. Within a short time ONR had established "the greatest peacetime cooperative undertaking in history between the academic world and the government."[45] Contracts had been entered into with some 220 universities for about 1,200 projects involving 3,000 scientists and 2,500 graduate students.

There is every evidence that elements in the Army were equally determined to maintain a strong R&D capability.[46] The Army, however, returned to its prewar organization and procedure under which responsibility for research was a procurement function of the technical services, delegated to the arsenals and other development and production units. Because of this decentralized responsibility, and because Army contracts were of the conventional procurement types, the Army's participation in continuing OSRD

[44] "The Evolution of the Office of Naval Research," by the Bird Dogs, *Physics Today*, vol. 14 (1961), pp. 30–35.

[45] Office of Naval Research, *Annual Report, 1949*, pp. 1–3; U. S. Department of Defense, *First Report of the Secretary of Defense* (Government Printing Office, 1948), p. 134.

[46] General Leslie Simon's report on *German Research in World War II* (John Wiley & Sons, 1947) was influential. The report in its longer, classified form stimulated the formation of the Office of Technical Services in the Department of Commerce with the responsibility of disseminating information on technical developments within Germany and other countries during the war.

projects is difficult to evaluate. Its aggregate spending on university research contracts was substantial, particularly in applied research.[47] OSRD's Radiation Laboratory at MIT, for example, closed in 1946 but reopened as the Research Laboratory of Electronics under tri-service sponsorship and on Army contract. The Army continued to support among other projects the Jet Propulsion Laboratory at the California Institute of Technology and the development of electronic computing machines at the University of Pennsylvania.[48] The Army and Navy agreed that the two groups that had developed the VT fuze during the war were too valuable to permit them to dissolve. Accordingly the Army agreed to finance the group at the National Bureau of Standards. Eventually this was transferred to Army administration as the Harry Diamond Ordnance Fuze Laboratory. The Navy for its part undertook responsibility for the Applied Physics Laboratory administered under contract by the Johns Hopkins University. The Air Force also supported a variety of basic and applied research programs. Until 1949 it followed the Army's administrative pattern but in that year the Office of Air Research was established following the ONR precedent.[49]

These arrangements operated effectively to permit an orderly and selective transfer of OSRD contract projects to the Office of Naval Research, Air Force or Army technical services having cognizance of the subject matter. The assumption of sponsorship of OSRD projects in effect abolished the wartime division of responsibilities under which the Army and Navy had limited themselves to developmental problems which lay in their traditional areas, or which could be dealt with in contracts with industry. As a result these agencies not only became much more heavily involved in R&D than had been the case before the war, but with a new range of research interests bounded by no limits other than that of relevance to military problems.[50]

[47] A brief account of developments over this period is made by Admiral Frederick R. Furth in *Proceedings of the Ninth Annual Conference on the Administration of Research* (New York University, 1955), pp. 15 ff.

[48] Peregrine White, "Ordnance Basic Research, 1944–45" (mimeographed; Army Research Office, 1956).

[49] U. S. Department of Defense, *Second Report of the Secretary of Defense* (Government Printing Office, 1949), p. 51.

[50] Morris Janowitz writes: ". . . By 1945 the classical view of the military professional standing in opposition to technological innovation was no longer applicable.

Postwar Procurement Authority

A critical test of Congress' position occurred with consideration of the peacetime procurement authorities to be granted the armed services. As has been mentioned, procurement during the war was carried on under the First War Powers Act which suspended the requirements for sealed-bid procurement "when such action would facilitate the prosecution of the war." To the Army and Navy, a continuation of authority to negotiate contracts, at least in areas involving research and development, was essential to effective operation. The war experience had demonstrated the advantages of such flexibility. The problems of the Army and Navy in attempting to work with industry before the war, as illustrated in the case of aircraft development, emphasized the fact that rigidly prescribed procurement authority was inconsistent with ready access to the sources of technological growth. As early as November 1945, the War Production Board had urged that government agencies seek permanent legislation to replace the temporary wartime arrangements.[51] In January 1947, the War and Navy Departments jointly prepared and submitted to the Congress a draft of a bill to facilitate peacetime procurement.

The bill passed with little change, to become the Armed Services Procurement Act of 1947.[52] The statute continued the long-established principle that all purchases and contracts for supplies and services be made by advertising for bids. However, the statute provided exceptions to the formal advertising requirement and authorized agency heads to negotiate a purchase or a contract in seventeen classes of cases. Those most relevant to this subject matter include purchase of or contracts for

any service by a university, college, or other educational institution;

And the present cycle of the arms race in nuclear and guided weapons has converted the armed forces into centers of continuous support and concern for innovation. . . . The realistic assessment of needs and prospects has become as widely routinized and automatic as it is in civilian industry . . . extensive organizations are created whose vested interests press for continuous innovation" (*The Professional Soldier* [Free Press of Glencoe, 1960], p. 27). A similar observation is made by Warner R. Schilling, "Scientists, Foreign Policy, and Politics," *American Political Science Review*, vol. 56 (1962), p. 288.

[51] *Armed Services Procurement Act of 1947*, S. Rept. 571, 80 Cong. 1 sess. (1947).

[52] P.L. 413, 80 Cong. (62 Stat. 21), repealed by P.L. 1028, August 1956, which codified its provisions into U.S.C. secs. 2301–14.

. . . for property or services for which it is impracticable to obtain competition; for property or services that [are] determined to be for experimental developmental, or research work, or for making or furnishing property for experiment, test, development, or research; . . . [for] technical equipment whose standardization and the interchangeability of whose parts are necessary in the public interest and whose procurement by negotiation is necessary to assure that standardization and interchangeability; [for] . . . technical or special property . . . [which] requires a substantial initial investment or an extended period of preparation for manufacture, and for which . . . formal advertising and competitive bidding might require duplication of investment or preparation already made or would unduly delay the procurement of that property; [and if] the interest of industrial mobilization or of national defense in maintaining active engineering, research and development would otherwise be subserved.

Among other exceptions to competitive bidding were those related to personal or professional services, the need for secrecy, and unsatisfactory bids received after advertising.

The ASPA included certain limitations on contracts which were viewed by some as obstacles to efficient arrangements for procuring R&D services. These difficulties were met by the passage in 1948 of a bill entitled "To Facilitate the Performance of Research and Development Work."[53] The statute authorized long-term R&D contracts (up to five years), the furnishing of research or test equipment and facilities to contractors, indemnification of contractors against losses arising out of certain types of R&D work, simplified vouchering and payment procedures, and authorization for the establishment of R&D advisory groups, as well as some minor matters.

The postwar role of the R&D programs in the civilian agencies evolved as the Congress acted upon specific proposals and provided specific authorizations. The Congress also provided general authority. With the passage of the Federal Property and Administrative Services Act of 1949 the civilian agencies acquired through delegation from the General Services Administration authority to contract that was essentially similar to provisions of the Armed Services Procurement Act.[54] Included among the exceptions to the

[53] P.L. 557, 82 Cong., codified into U.S.C., Title 10. A useful review of this procurement legislation is in Edwin P. Bledsoe and Harry I. Ravitz, "The Evolution of Research and Development as a Procurement Function of the Federal Government," *Federal Bar Journal,* vol. 17 (1957), pp. 189–215.

[54] P.L. 152, June 20, 1949.

general requirement for advertisement was the authority to negotiate contracts for "experimental, developmental or research work," as well as for personal services.

Mention should also be made of an earlier statute which has served as legal authority for contracting in some areas. In 1946, by Public Law 600, the Congress provided for the employment of experts or consultants, as individuals or organizations, on an intermittent basis and outside the regular civil service. Public Law 600 specifically requires that the agency seek authorization for such employment in an appropriation or other act and the agencies have customarily sought and obtained such implementing authority.[55] While the law is utilized for its primary purpose to secure the short-term and intermittent services of experts and consultants, it has also been used to justify the employment, under contract, of experts for considerable periods.

The Intramural Laboratories

The postwar arrangements of the military agencies evolved as pragmatic responses to problems that required prompt solutions. The arrangements made reflected conflict between the values and procedures of the prewar system and those developed during the war, modified by much uncertainty as to postwar needs. There was virtually no disposition on the part of those in a position to influence policy to return to the prewar pattern of relationships or to force into the prewar mold the enlarged and more intimate relationships between the private and public sectors of technical development that were desired. Bearing on such attitudes was the fact that their role during the war had left the government laboratories with narrower and more specialized functions. While some of these laboratories had developed high levels of capabilities on some specialized technical frontier, there were many highly important technologies emerging from the war in which they had played secondary roles or none at all.

The judgment that the prewar system of providing scientific R&D support for the military services had been inadequate was

---

[55] Carl S. Mallow, Jr., "Experts and Consultants in Government," *Federal Bar Journal*, vol. 14 (1954), pp. 357–87.

implicit in the establishment of the Office of Scientific Research and Development and had been confirmed by its record. The theory that private industry could be relied upon to apply what the Army's technical services and the Navy's bureaus could specify had worked well in those areas in which those organizations held specialized competency, given the long period of time for preparation which the nation had fortunately enjoyed.[56] There proved to be numerous areas which had been covered inadequately or not at all by prewar organizations, and the limitations of the system had been impressively demonstrated by the success of the Office of Scientific Research and Development in contributing to the military strength of the nation.

The prewar system and the role of the military laboratories in it was further on the defensive since there was some reason to suspect that the system which had produced the inadequate prewar levels of preparedness might again fail to impress Congress with R&D needs or might again divert funds intended for research and development to other uses. Congressional interest centered then upon the broad problems of responsibility for research, of agency organization for that purpose, and of control and coordination. While congressmen listened with some sympathy to accounts of the achievements of the government-owned laboratories they left their position in the postwar organization to be determined administratively. Congress established no broad positive policy that would guide the agencies in making distinctions between intramural and contract R&D.

On their part, the agencies with substantial intramural operations sought to maintain their staffs, partly because such personnel were highly specialized in important areas, partly because they were needed to administer whatever contractual programs might develop, and partly because they might help to preserve their freedom to choose between the intramural and contractual approaches.

[56] The Army's wartime Chief of Ordnance, for example, while emphasizing the need for well-rounded R&D programs also insisted that "the record of the Second World War demonstrated conclusively that if Ordnance has the drawings, specifications, and pilot models of first-class equipment, industry can be relied upon to mass-produce this equipment, given a reasonable make-ready or conversion period" (Levin H. Campbell, Jr., *The Industry-Ordnance Team* [Whittlesey House, 1946], p. 449).

The problem of the relationship of external to internal R&D arose immediately after the war. Scientists directly employed by the federal government had increased in number from 17,000 in 1939–40 to 35,000 in 1945–46; in terms of Ph.D.'s the numbers were 2,000 and 3,000 respectively. Virtually all this wartime increase had occurred in the military laboratories or in civilian agency laboratories working on military projects.[57] Some of these scientists and engineers had played key roles in the establishment of new facilities such as the Naval Ordnance Test Station at Inyokern or in developing new capabilities such as the computer facilities at the Army's Ballistic Missile Laboratories.

With the end of the war, the government, and particularly the Army and Navy, experienced heavy losses in staff as their employees returned to private employment.[58] The universities were preparing for swollen enrollments and private research organizations were planning large expansions of their activities. When personnel left government there were few replacements available since the universities had produced few newly trained scientists and engineers during the war years. To protect the capabilities of its laboratories, the administration sought to secure upward wage and salary adjustments for the civil service.

Increases in civil service salaries were granted in 1946 and in the following year Congress provided new, well-paid positions for scientists in the War and Navy Departments.[59] Such adjustments were made in view of testimony such as that of the Army which asserted that "continued loss of key personnel in the fields of research and management will emasculate its total program."[60] As a

[57] U. S. President's Scientific Research Board, *Science and Public Policy* (Government Printing Office, 1947), vol. 4, p. 31. The National Resources Committee estimated that there were 11,800 research workers employed by the federal government in 1938 (*Research—a National Resource*, vol. 1: *Relation of the Federal Government to Research* [Washington, 1938], p. 171).

[58] On the problems of retaining professional scientists and engineers in the Ordnance Department, see Constance McLaughlin Green, Harry C. Thomson, and Peter C. Roots, *The Ordnance Department: Planning for War* (Government Printing Office, 1955).

[59] "Federal Employees Pay Act of 1946," 60 Stat. 216; P.L. 313, 80 Cong.

[60] *Salary and Wage Administration in the Federal Service,* Hearings before the House Post Office and Civil Service Committee, 79 Cong. 2 sess. (1946), p. 60. On the Navy, see p. 83.

part of the demobilization process, the 15 percent decline in the number of government scientists between 1945–46 and 1946–47 was small. However, that decline was concentrated in military establishments and involved many of the leading men. The difficulties of keeping personnel were accentuated by the environment created by the McCarthy hearings, sufficiently so to prompt a discussion of the problem by President Truman.[61]

The discussions over the civil service salary problem and over the proposed Research Board for National Security included a brief skirmish between the advocates of broader federal activities in R&D by direct hire and those who preferred contracting. Edward U. Condon, director of the National Bureau of Standards, looked upon the contract as an evasion of civil service legislation and urged basic reforms in civil service salary scales and administrative regulations as a foundation for expanding intramural R&D programs.[62] Condon found few allies. The existing laboratories were defended but there was little support for the view that the expanding federal program should be carried on by federal employees within federal organizations.[63] Vannevar Bush argued that every case should be viewed on its merits but emphasized the very great scarcity of capable research administrators.[64]

The position taken by the Army and Navy was that civil service salaries should be high enough so that the men who were holding key laboratory positions could be retained. In both services, general policies were established looking toward intimate relationships with private institutions through contracting. While specific guidelines were not immediately drawn, efforts to expand intramural operations were few and limited.

With considerable freedom to choose, each of the military agen-

[61] *Public Papers of Presidents of the United States: Harry S Truman, 1948* (Government Printing Office, 1964), pp. 484–85.

[62] *Salary and Wage Administration . . .* , Hearings, p. 242.

[63] Assistant Secretary of the Interior Abe Fortas, for example, appeared before the committee to suggest amendments which were intended to protect existing government laboratories and particularly those of the Bureau of Mines (*Establishing a Research Board for National Security,* Hearings before the Senate Naval Affairs Committee, 79 Cong. 1 sess. [1945], p. 9). See also *Legislative Proposals for the Promotion of Science,* Senate Military Affairs Committee, S. Doc. 92, 79 Cong. 1 sess. (1945), pp. 84–86.

[64] *Establishing a Research Board for National Security,* Hearings, p. 257.

cies elected to continue the relationships developed during the war and those inherited from the Office of Scientific Research and Development. Within the framework of traditional organization and procedure, such policies developed independently and not without considerable internal conflict within the Army and Navy. The newly established Air Force, however, found entirely congenial a policy of close relationships with contractual sources that was similar to but much more flexible than the prewar system with which the Army Air Corps and the Navy's Bureau of Aeronautics had operated. The Secretary of Defense formalized the postwar practices of the services by announcing in 1949 that "it is a matter of policy to assign to government-owned laboratories only those projects that cannot be contracted for with academic or industrial facilities because the facility costs are prohibitive, and those which, because of the purely military nature of the problem, are unsuitable for private enterprise to undertake."[65]

War-created Programs

Virtually all R&D programs initiated during the war were continued in some form thereafter. Largest in terms of expenditures and most important in terms of its implications was the atomic energy program, which posed knotty problems in establishing national objectives and determining the appropriate form of organization and control. The program had been initiated by the Office of Scientific Research and Development and was carried out through contractual arrangements. As research on nuclear energy progressed from the laboratory to the prototype plant and production stages, the problems involved became those of very large-scale, if still experimental, development. The OSRD had consequently transferred operational responsibilities for the project to the Army, which administered it as the Manhattan Engineering Project. The requirements of the project for very large-scale engineering efforts had led the Army to contract the building and operation of the plants to private industrial firms. The closely integrated laboratory research program continued to be administered by universities under contract.

[65] U. S. Department of Defense, *Annual Report of the Secretary of Defense* (Government Printing Office, 1949), p. 52.

The establishment of postwar objectives and organization for the nation's atomic energy program was one of the major items on the congressional agenda immediately after the war. It was resolved by the passage of the Atomic Energy Act of 1946. Here it is sufficient to point out that the contractual arrangements with private industry and the universities utilized by the Office of Scientific Research and Development and the Army's Manhattan Project were continued and expanded by the Atomic Energy Commission.[66]

Among the smaller agency projects, the rubber program merits mention. The Rubber Reserve Corporation had sought to assure the nation a supply of rubber by assisting in the establishment of a synthetic rubber industry. When that agency was abolished July 1, 1945, important difficulties remained to be overcome if the war-created industry was to be maintained under the competitive circumstances of peacetime, and if the nation's $700 million expenditure in the area was to prove a remunerative investment. To give the industry a technological foundation that would assure its existence in the postwar world, Congress provided for a research program in synthetic rubber administered by the Office of Rubber Reserve.[67] The program was carried out entirely by contract with industrial firms except for a laboratory operated by a university to carry out pilot and testing functions. A competitive synthetic rubber industry was established. With the sale of the government synthetic rubber plants the program was terminated except for the university managed laboratory which operated under sponsorship of the National Science Foundation until 1957 when it, too, was sold.[68]

Medical Research

Research in medicine grew rapidly in the United States in the interwar years, made possible primarily through increased private and state financial support of medical schools and the expansion of

[66] For the early period, a definitive historical account is Richard G. Hewlett and Oscar E. Anderson, Jr., *The New World, 1939–46: A History of the United States Atomic Energy Commission* (Pennsylvania State University Press, 1962), vol. 1.

[67] The Crawford act, P.L. 24, 80 Cong.

[68] A critical review of the program is given by Robert A. Solo, *Synthetic Rubber: A Case Study in Technology Development under Government Direction,* Study No. 18, Subcommittee on Patents, Trademarks, and Copyrights of the Senate Judiciary Committee, 85 Cong. 2 sess. (1958).

related activities in private industry. Although slowly increasing, the federal government's activities were minor at the outbreak of the war.

The urgency of wartime medical needs and the possibility that intensified efforts in research and particularly in development could help to meet them, led OSRD, at the request of the Army and Navy, to establish a major program that greatly increased support for medical research. The OSRD Committee on Medicine spent only 5 percent of the agency's funds during the four war years but the $27.7 million so committed was spread over some 600 contracts with private institutions, thereby involving a very large proportion of the nation's facilities for medical research. In addition, during the war, the War and Navy Departments undertook organized R&D in medicine for the first time. The introduction of penicillin and atabrine were only two of the more dramatic results achieved.

Congress took action on medical research in 1944. What was done was significant not only because it reflected an interest in increasing support for medical R&D but also because of the choice of methods by which such support was to be provided. Before 1944 a small-scale federally supported program of research in specified areas of medicine had come into existence, originating in 1901 with the establishment of the Hygienic Laboratory to deal with the health problem of immigrants. A marked expansion followed the statutory establishment of the National Institutes of Health in 1930 as a part of the Public Health Service.

The 1930 act broke new ground when it provided for the establishment of a system of fellowships supported by the institute and permitting participation in its research program. The principle of grants-in-aid to responsible public and private institutions for medical research equipment was established in the National Cancer Institute Act of 1937 along with a high degree of freedom in the use of allotted funds. In this, as in the 1930 act, provision was made for the establishment of advisory councils made up partly of representatives of other government agencies but principally of professionally qualified private citizens. The important functions of the council were to review research problems and applications for research grants and to certify to the Surgeon General those which it approved.

Influenced in large part by the opportunities in medical research demonstrated by the work of the Office of Scientific Research and Development, the Congress in 1944 reconsidered the whole range of the federal government's activities in the field. In the Public Health Service Act of 1944 the 78th Congress reviewed and consolidated the many statutes related to the Public Health Service, approved the policies which had been established, and broadened the authorizing language. On the recommendation of the Surgeon General, the Public Health Service was "to conduct and encourage, cooperate with, and render assistance to other appropriate public authorities, scientific institutions and scientists in the conduct of research, investigations, experiments, demonstrations and studies" relating to the physical and mental diseases of man and to such related problems as water purification, sewage treatment, and pollution of water. Also included was the authority to "make grants-in-aid to universities, hospitals, laboratories, and other public or private institutions, and to individuals for such research projects as are recommended by the National Advisory Health Council, or with respect to cancer, recommended by the National Advisory Cancer Council."[69] Statutory limitations on appropriations, averaging \$3 million per year from 1935 to 1945, were removed. Further broadening occurred in 1946 when the Congress in the National Mental Health Act established a third council and provided for grants to universities for training specialized personnel connected with mental health. In each area it was required that grants were to be made upon the recommendation of the advisory council in the particular field. In less than a year—by the end of 1946—the three councils were supporting 264 research projects in 77 universities representing obligations of \$3.9 million.[70]

The rapid development of the National Institutes of Health as the central federal agency for medical research was not anticipated in the Bush report. That report recommended instead that basic medical research be supported in medical schools and universities

---

[69] A brief account of the growth of the National Institutes of Health is given by Donald C. Swain, "The Rise of a Research Empire: NIH, 1930 to 1950," *Science*, vol. 138 (1962), pp. 1233–37.

[70] See C. J. Van Slyke, "New Horizons in Medical Research," *Science*, vol. 104 (Dec. 13, 1946), pp. 559–64.

through a program of grants and fellowships to be administered by the Division of Medical Research of the proposed National Research Foundation. The Medical Advisory Committee organized by Bush to advise him had recommended a somewhat different program that included granting universities unrestricted general research funds to be administered by a new and independent organization called the National Foundation for Medical Research. During the prolonged debate over the National Science Foundation, the National Institutes of Health assumed and developed the full range of proposed functions which it had full statutory authority to do.

In December 1945, all outstanding contractual projects of the Office of Scientific Research and Development involving medical research were transferred, some to war-created programs of the War and Navy Departments, but the larger number to the Public Health Service. Budget proposals for 1946–47 by the three agencies calling for a continuation of many of these projects were favorably received. Congress appropriated $12.5 million to the Public Health Service and $12 million to the Army and Navy for medical research.

These agencies expanded grant and contract support for medical research conducted by private institutions. The 40 percent of the 1947 appropriations of $28 million that was allocated to grants and contracts represented a substantial expansion over wartime levels of federal support for medical research. In addition the Congress at the same time appropriated $2.5 million for the newly inaugurated medical research program of the Veterans Administration which was aimed to make use of the extensive clinical research opportunities available in the agency's hospitals.

Supporting Basic Research

Although the Bush report was influential in encouraging federal R&D programs of all types, the problem to which the report was specifically addressed was that of the postwar status of basic research, in terms of the nation's needs, and the adequacy of the efforts that were likely to be made in that area. The war period had witnessed the application of many concepts drawn from earlier contributions to knowledge. Much of the underlying research had been done by Europeans, a source not likely to be productive in the immediate postwar years. Basic research had been seriously neglected in the United States during the war period and the postwar educational burden on American universities suggested that research activities in the universities would be far below optimal levels for some time. It followed that if basic research was to receive the attention that was desirable, the federal government would have to assume responsibility for its support. This new function of the government, Bush felt, should be assigned to a new agency which would support research conducted outside the government, which should coordinate to whatever degree possible research programs of importance to the national welfare, and should in other ways stimulate and further scientific activities. Such an agency would not conduct research and would not operate scientific laboratories. Active programs in applied research should be continued wherever they might be located.

This agency, Bush suggested, should be a National Research Foundation controlled by a board composed of qualified individuals not otherwise connected with the government. The agency's chief administrative officer would be appointed by the board. Bush suggested an organization with five divisions: medical, natural sciences, national defense, scientific personnel and education, and publication and scientific collaboration. Under the guidance of the foundation, these divisions, working with advisory committees, would make contracts and grants to educational and nonprofit organizations, in order to initiate and finance research projects, as well as making necessary facilities available.

Although these objectives and procedures were widely endorsed and Congress was eager to establish a program satisfactory to the scientists, five years of debate were to ensue before the basic recommendations were accepted. Two bills were before the Congress. One, introduced by Senator Warren G. Magnuson, incorporated Bush's recommendations. The other, introduced by Senator Kilgore, visualized a broad program including applied research to be directed by a Presidential appointee. There were three principal issues. One concerned the organization of the foundation. Many scientists, fearing that "political" considerations would hamper their work, wanted an organization which would represent scientific interests with minimal subordination to the executive branch of the federal government. A second issue related to the inclusion of the social sciences in the new program; most, although not all, physical scientists were opposed to such inclusion. A third controversy concerned the nature of the patent provisions to be applied to research grants. In addition there was a variety of other more manageable issues. Some preferred no federal organization at all but wanted the government to support basic science indirectly by stimulating private expenditures through changes in federal income tax statutes. Some argued for statutory provisions that would require research grants to be distributed in whole or in part along geographic lines.[71] The suggestion that the foundation coordinate federal activity in research aroused fears that the coordinating agency would seek to control all the nation's research. Although all existing government research agencies supported the proposed foundation, many of them opposed giving it any control over federal agencies and they sought assurances that it would not infringe upon their independence.

These and other problems were discussed at length as the Congress sought to create a structure which would accomplish the government's objectives and which would satisfy the scientific community. The result was the National Science Foundation Act of 1947 which provided for the type of organization desired by many scientists—a board with twenty-four part-time, unpaid members appointed by the President. The Board would elect an executive committee that would in turn appoint the agency's chief executive officer. President Truman, in a letter to the Senate, had earlier expressed his opposition to such an arrangement which he held to be unsound since administration of the agency would be insufficiently responsible to the executive. The President vetoed the bill on the

---

[71] The Association of Land-Grant Colleges and Universities urged that a percentage of the proposed foundation's funds be distributed to the land-grant institutions and the bill passed by the Senate in 1946 made such provisions. The suggestion was in conflict with both the Bush and the Kilgore proposals, and was opposed by the Bureau of the Budget. The idea was dropped in the Senate-House conference which produced the 1947 act and thereafter received little attention, although the Association has on numerous subsequent occasions urged the land-grant university model as particularly appropriate for federal programs in support of research. The result of the 1946–47 congressional action was significant in firmly establishing the principle of selecting proposals in a quality competition. *Hearings on Science Legislation,* Senate Military Affairs Committee, 79 Cong. 1 sess. (1945), pp. 96, 794.

grounds that it represented "a marked departure from sound principles for the administration of public affairs. . . . It would, in effect, vest the determination of vital national policies, the expenditure of large public funds, and the administration of important governmental functions in a group of individuals who would be essentially private citizens."[72]

Meanwhile, dissatisfaction with the views expressed in the Bush report together with the changing circumstances generated by the rapid establishment of postwar R&D programs suggested to members of the administration that the state of the nation's R&D endeavors, both public and private, should be appraised in a broader perspective. To gather necessary data and to make recommendations which would form the basis for policy suggestions by the Executive to the Congress, President Truman in October 1946 established the interagency President's Scientific Research Board, with John R. Steelman as chairman. The Steelman report, published the following year as *Science and Public Policy*, provided the most comprehensive survey of the relationship of the government to scientific activity that had been made up to that time.[73] The report ranged more widely than the Bush report, placing the need for university-based science in a broader perspective, particularly in its recommendations for programs of assistance to university students. The report also emphasized the need for federal control by recommending the creation within the Bureau of the Budget of a unit to review federal scientific research and development programs. In urging the designation of an assistant to the President on scientific matters it anticipated future developments by a decade or more.

The Steelman report also directed its attention to the question of the desirable magnitude of the nation's research effort and to the identification of existing obstacles to the attainment of that level. It was suggested that the federal government would be obliged to provide for at least half of the nation's research and development expenditures but the report pointed out that it did not follow that half should be performed in government-owned labo-

[72] *Congressional Record,* vol. 93, pt. 8 (1947), p. 10568.
[73] In five volumes (Government Printing Office, August-October 1947).

ratories. It was estimated that 68 percent of all federal R&D expenditures in 1947 had gone to private industrial firms and universities—the percentage was 80 for military research and development. The report observed that

the development of contractual devices, one of the outstanding contributions of the war to Government-sponsored R&D, probably will be extended. There is greater insistence on reduction of Government employment than upon other elements of expenditure. Further, the success of war contract research will continue to exert a powerful stimulus.[74]

The report continued, "There is no reason to recommend any substantial change in this general pattern for the future. Each of the three segments of the research triangle is especially adapted to the performance of a particular type of research and each can make a unique contribution to our total research and development effort."

Congressional discussion of a National Science Foundation continued over the next three years, principally in the House. The expansion of R&D programs in other agencies made it clearer that the proposed NSF should concentrate on basic research. The problem of patent ownership was then judged to be less critical and that issue lost some of its significance for the time being. At the same time, the diffusion of research activities among federal agencies suggested that a coordinating function was necessary and that responsibility, too, was assigned to the NSF. When in 1950 both houses passed a bill providing for a director and a board appointed by the President, the bill was signed and the NSF came into being. With an appropriation authorization of only $15 million, and an initial appropriation of only $1 million, the agency assumed a place in the government's organization for R&D far from that envisaged by its original promoters. Nor was the NSF the government's sole agency supporting basic research. As has been pointed out, during the years of debate, each of the military services and particularly the Office of Naval Research had established programs in the area. The programs of the National Institutes of Health were also increasingly involved with the basic sciences.

[74] U.S. President's Scientific Research Board, *Science and Public Policy,* vol. 3, p. 183.

R&D Programs of Other Agencies

In the civilian agencies, as in the military, government research programs which antedated the war continued thereafter as intramural operations although sometimes supplemented by contracts. In these agencies research programs established during the war tended to be continued under wartime institutional arrangements, the larger part being conducted by contract. Agencies which assumed R&D functions during the war continued such programs in some revised form after the war and frequently relied for their execution upon contracts with private institutions.

The programs of the Department of Agriculture, much the largest of federal R&D activities prior to 1940, grew slowly after 1945 along conventional lines. There was a concentration on the expansion of the activities of the regional laboratories controlled by the department rather than on grants-in-aid to the state agricultural experiment stations. An exception to the otherwise uniform reliance upon intramural performance was provided in the Production and Marketing Act of 1946. By that act the Department of Agriculture for the first time received authority to contract for research and there followed a relatively small program of contract research chiefly with universities in the area of the social sciences.

The National Bureau of Standards, largest research agency of the Department of Commerce, had supplemented its facilities by a small contract research program during the war. Among its important activities shortly after the war was its work on a large-scale digital computing machine for the Bureau of the Census. The Bureau of Standards was to remain primarily an intramural operation though it has continued small contract research programs.

Other agencies of the Department of Commerce relied more heavily on contract research. The Civil Aeronautics Administration supplemented the work of its own research staff with contract studies, which accounted for about a fifth of its research expenditures. External research by the Civil Aeronautics Administration was arranged through a contractual relationship with the National Research Council of the National Academy of Sciences. The Weather Bureau pursued a modest program of expanding basic knowledge in its area of responsibility by contracts with educational institutions.

Of some special interest was the effort of the Department of Commerce to provide technical research and information services to the public. In early 1946 the department formed the Office of Technical Services from a number of wartime agencies including the Office of Research and Development of the War Production Board. One function of the OTS was to collect and make available to the public the scientific and technical information which had been accumulated in Germany and other conquered countries during the war as well as to facilitate the declassification and release of information developed within the United States. The OTS's Division of Industrial Research and Development also undertook a program in support of research intended to increase technological productivity in selected industries. The cost of research projects which might create new or improved products was shared with business firms which contributed either funds or personnel time. The research required on accepted projects was conducted through contracts with universities or private industrial research laboratories. An appropriation of $5 million supported this program in fiscal 1947.

This experimental effort did not survive long enough to permit any judgment of its merits. The department sought statutory authority from the Congress for a new Bureau of Scientific Research which was to continue and expand the 1946–47 program of the Division of Industrial Research. The proposal encountered opposition from private organizations which viewed it as infringing upon their activities. By failing to act, Congress terminated the program.[75]

In the Department of the Interior the principal research agencies were the long-established Geological Survey, the Bureau of Mines, the Fish and Wildlife Service, and the Bureau of Reclamation. All conducted their programs with their own staffs and facilities although Fish and Wildlife administered a program of grants-in-aid to the states for wildlife restoration purposes. Among small research programs elsewhere in the department only the Bonneville Power Administration made use of contracts with private institutions.

[75] The bill, S. 1248, was reported back favorably by the Senate Commerce Committee; see *Congressional Record,* vol. 92, pt. 2 (March 1, 1946), pp. 1818–19.

The Public Roads Administration, then a part of the Federal Works Agency, also conducted research programs directly related to its responsibilities in administering federal aid to the states. A small program of cooperative research was maintained, involving joint financing of projects carried on by universities and grants to research projects administered by quasi-public groups such as the National Academy of Sciences.

There were other small-scale programs involving contractual R&D. The Council of Economic Advisers, which by statute was required to utilize the services and facilities of other government agencies as well as of private research agencies, in 1947 entered into a contract with a private institution for a regional study.[76] The Munitions Board, established by the National Security Act to centralize common procurements of the military services, sought the assistance of contractual research to cope with some of its problems.[77] The National Security Resources Board similarly relied heavily upon contractual research as the most flexible method whereby it could acquire the skills necessary to its mission. And the plans of the Office of Civil Defense for protection of the civilian population were developed very largely by private contractors.[78]

[76] The Employment Act of 1946 (P.L. 304, 79 Cong.) provided that "in exercising its powers, functions and duties under this act . . . the Council shall, to the fullest extent possible, utilize the services, facilities, and information (including statistical information) of other Government agencies as well as of private research agencies, in order that duplication of effort and expense may be avoided."

The second annual report of the Council commented favorably on the possibilities of contractual assistance from private sources. The first contract entered into was with the National Planning Association's Committee on the South. The Committee report was transmitted to the Joint Committee on the Economic Report in 1949. It was printed as a report of the Joint Committee, *Impact of Federal Policies on the Economy of the South* (81 Cong. 1 sess. [1949]).

The Council has since made only modest use of its contractual authority. A recent example was its sponsorship, jointly with the Treasury Department, of a contractual study by the Brookings Institution, published as *The United States Balance of Payments in 1968*, by Walter S. Salant and others (Government Printing Office, 1963).

[77] House Committee on Government Operations, *Military Supply Management Program*, 83 Cong. 1 sess. (1953), pp. 16, 57; Joint Economic Committee, *Background Material on Economic Aspects of Military Procurement and Supply* (Government Printing Office, 1960).

[78] Joint Committee on U. S. Defense Production, *Tenth Annual Report, 1959–60*, pp. 98, 187.

Other Applications of Contracting

To both Congress and the agencies involved, the principal purpose of the service contract was to promote R&D objectives. The
Congress occasionally specifically authorized the use of the contract for other objectives while other wartime practices were continued within the authority provided by the 1947 legislation. The
Office of the Coordinator of Inter-American Affairs had made pioneering use of private institutions under contract in carrying out
its wartime program in Latin America. Such activities were continued after the war while the Economic Cooperation Administration
employed private institutions under contract to carry out much of
its program of technical assistance in Europe and elsewhere. The
Surplus Property Administration utilized private firms under contract to inventory and appraise the stocks turned over to it for dis-
posal, as well as to conduct its public auctions. Both the Army and
Navy had long contracted with universities to provide facilities for
training reserve officers. The traditional ROTC programs served
as precedents for the much larger wartime programs which utilized university facilities and staffs in officer training. In addition
the air branches of both the services utilized the facilities of private aircraft flying schools for the flight training of aviators. Both
services made use of firms providing management, accounting and
similar services to meet their heavy postwar workloads.

Such uses of the contract were, however, on a small scale. In
1950, their significance was unclear.

Summary

By the end of 1947, the foundations had been laid for a new permanent policy toward scientific and technical activity and a new
pattern of relationships had developed by which that policy was to
be applied. The new policy was the assumption by the federal government of responsibility for stimulating the expansion of scientific knowledge and for the accelerated application of such knowledge through research and development in areas identified by the
government, particularly defense and health. This policy was positive and aggressive. Although the new system relies upon private

institutions to carry out most of the nation's R&D effort those pre-war federal R&D programs that relied upon government-owned and -operated laboratories to do the work have continued and have expanded substantially. However, in those numerous areas in which the government has enlarged its commitments, or made new ones, most of the R&D effort has been executed by private institutions, financed from public funds, and guided and directed to objectives that constitute a set of national programs administered by agencies of the government. The effectiveness of very large federal funds made available to the nation's scientific and research institutions in increasing the magnitude of that effort is clear. In the process, a large part of the nation's R&D resources was drawn into activities programmed by federal agencies. Given the close and necessary intimacy between representatives of the government and representatives of private institutions, the nature of control over the total R&D effort is not so easily measured.

The key statutes which established this policy were those relating to medical research, atomic energy, the procurement authority of the armed services, the Office of Naval Research, and the National Science Foundation. In these and many other actions, the Congress concerned itself largely with establishing the policy of increased federal responsibility for R&D by providing authority and organizational structure. The policy was also expressed in the positions the Congress took on appropriation requests from the executive agencies. Subsequent developments have broadened the range of national commitments to R&D activities and have vastly increased the funds applied to them. Essentially, however, the basic policies established in the legislation of the 1944–47 period have remained unchanged.

CHAPTER III

Changes in R&D
Contracting Policy
since 1950

The United States approached the decade of the 1950's with a strong faith in scientific research and development. Three major subject areas—medicine, atomic energy, and basic scientific research—had been added to the principal prewar areas of federal interest—military aeronautics, agriculture, and standards. Civilian federal agencies charged with responsibilities for the new programs shared with the military agencies authority which permitted them to invoke any potential source of R&D performance to work toward agency objectives. Though modestly employed in 1950, such authority was clearly a most potent device to arouse participant interest in the government's programs and to accelerate efforts in desired directions.

The discussions which established the immediate postwar policy proceeded expeditiously—except in the matter of support for basic science—but they did so with no great sense of urgency. The United States had emerged from World War II with a technology that appeared to be without peer in either its civilian or its military aspects. The only problem was to maintain its eminence. In view of the postwar problems of the European nations, any challenge to American leadership seemed remote. In the military area, strenuous efforts to maintain secrecy were relied upon to protect that leadership. With the exception of the medical research programs of the National Institutes of Health, which began to increase rapidly in 1948, determinations of the expenditures on R&D by the federal government in the years 1946–50 were made largely in terms of maintaining ongoing programs with some small additions as needs and opportunity suggested. The environment was such that President Truman in 1947 impounded funds appropriated to support the War Department's contracts for the development of an intercontinental ballistic missile without serious protest from the Congress.

The nation's sense of freedom to determine the size of its R&D effort was severely shaken on September 9, 1949, when President Truman announced that the U.S.S.R. had achieved a nuclear capability. Thereafter the reality of the cold war was a dominant consideration. A reluctance to accept the implication that Russia might also be engaged in other broad-ranging R&D efforts found expression in an intense concern with the operation of the security mechanism. The assumption that a technological lead could be maintained by secrecy collapsed in August 1952 when the Russians exploded a thermonuclear bomb, less than a year after the United States had successfully tested such a device on the island of Bikini.

The more positive approach was to increase the nation's R&D efforts. The Korean War prompted a sharp rise in military expenditures for R&D. Although support for numerous R&D programs in the unconventional area of rockets and missiles had grown rapidly, the demonstration by the U.S.S.R. of its capability in this area by the Sputnik I launching in 1957 came as a severe shock.[1] That event shattered whatever remained of the view that the United States held a monopoly of the frontiers of scientific and technological capabilities, a monopoly that could be protected by secrecy. There was no longer any question that much more strenuous ef-

[1] Department of Defense obligations for missile systems (including R&D and procurement costs involved in bringing missiles to operational status) in 1957 were $4,470 million compared with $2,270 million in 1956. From prior to 1946 through 1957, DOD obligations for missile systems totaled $12.7 billion. *The United States Guided Missile Program*, Report Prepared by Charles H. Donnelly, Legislative Reference Service, for the Senate Armed Services Committee, 86 Cong. 1 sess. (1959), p. 99.

forts were required if the nation was to maintain its technological equality in all areas and, hopefully, its superiority in some. The American response to the cold war was the adoption of a "logistic strategy"—the production of new weapons to render obsolete those of the opponent.[2] The fact that the U.S.S.R. was known to be, or could be suspected of being, engaged in R&D in an area became a strong argument supporting comparable programs in the United States. The Russian influence upon the American space program is obvious,[3] but references to Russian accomplishment or interest have also been used to support such diverse projects as desalination,[4] drilling to the earth's mantle,[5] and education in the sciences.[6] More recently the nation has responded to pressures from other sources. The question of supporting the development of a supersonic commercial airplane, for example, has been strongly influenced by plans for the development of such an aircraft by Western European countries though the possibility also exists that the U.S.S.R. will undertake such an effort.

If international considerations have been a very strong influence on many programs, the rapid increase in the expenditures followed in part from the research process, in part from the acceptance of new nonmilitary areas for R&D expenditures. Research effort provides new knowledge but also identifies areas of ignorance which suggest new and promising areas of research effort and therefore stimulates a demand for more research funds. Another influence upon expenditures is the fact that research from time to

[2] The phrase is from André Beaufré, *An Introduction to Strategy: With Particular Reference to Problems of Defense, Politics, Economics, and Diplomacy in the Nuclear Age* (Frederick A. Praeger, 1965), p. 77.

[3] Vernon Van Dyke, *Pride and Power: The Rationale of the Space Program* (University of Illinois Press, 1964). See also Gabriel A. Almond, "Public Opinion and the Development of Space Technology: 1957–60," in Joseph M. Goldsen (ed.), *Outer Space in World Politics* (Frederick A. Praeger, 1963), pp. 71–96.

[4] "Russians Make Headway in Desalination, Udall Says," *Washington Post*, Dec. 10, 1964.

[5] That is, NSF's Project Mohole. See Daniel S. Greenberg, "How Science and Government Work Together in Washington," *Research Management*, vol. 8 (March 1965), p. 81.

[6] Nicholas DeWitt's *Soviet Professional Manpower: Its Education, Training, and Supply* (National Science Foundation, 1955) was, for example, of great influence upon the thinking that led to the National Defense Education Act of 1958. The study was prepared "under the auspices of the National Academy of Sciences–National Research Council, with encouragement and financial support from the National Science Foundation."

time yields information which suggests the desirability of its application to some end use. The decisions made regarding the development of such applications typically involve large expenditures. It was possible, for example, for the United States to react vigorously to the disclosure that Russia had developed the atomic bomb because research had suggested the possibility of developing a much more powerful fusion bomb. The reluctance to make the effort required gave way to a sense of urgency that it be developed as quickly as possible. In the case of missiles, interest was at low levels until 1953–54 when the reduction in the size and weight of the nuclear bomb suggested its use as the warhead of a missile. Thereafter development efforts increased rapidly. Similarly, research in possible applications of nuclear energy to power production proceeded slowly until the knowledge accumulated could be interpreted as sufficient to make its application to submarine propulsion feasible. The possibility of arming the nuclear powered submarine with missiles similarly stimulated intensive efforts to apply the knowledge derived from research on solid fuels to the development of a weapon suitable for shipboard use. It is inherent in the process that new knowledge emerging from research, usually at relatively modest cost, invites, if it does not force, decisions to undertake much more expensive efforts toward development and application.

The Growth of Federal R&D Expenditures

The record of federal expenditures on R&D as shown in Chart 4 reflects the nation's reactions to the factors mentioned above. The postwar low came in 1948 when R&D expenditures fell to $855 million, about half the wartime peak though representing an effort substantially less than half, since allowance must be made for increases in wage and price levels. It should be noted that after the war R&D expenditures by the Army and Navy did not decline but instead showed a slight upward trend, partially as a result of the transfer of some OSRD projects, but primarily because many wartime projects—those involving rockets, for example—were continued. On the other hand, expenditures for atomic energy fell sharply from the wartime levels, this decline being principally responsible for the drop in the total.

CHART 4
Federal R&D Expenditures (including R&D Plant) by Selected Agency for Fiscal Years 1940–66[a]

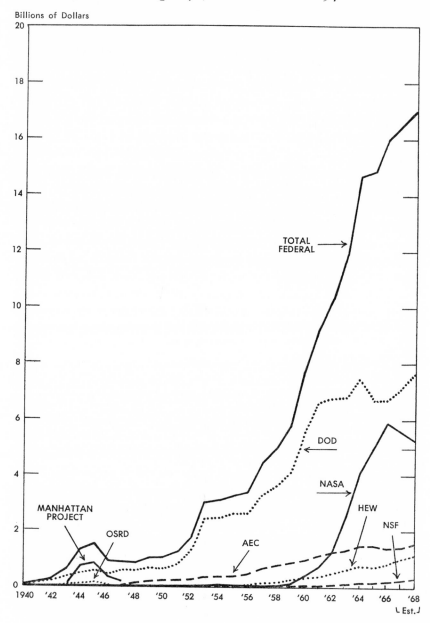

Billions of Dollars

In 1949 and 1950, R&D spending increased to slightly more than $1 billion. A slight upward tendency was sharply accelerated by military programs prompted by the Korean War. Military and space programs interrupted the short pause that followed. Obligations in 1957 doubled the 1956 figures, and from 1958 to 1964, federal R&D obligations increased by an average of 17 percent annually. The relative increases in 1965 and 1966 were small, but the dollar amounts involved were sufficient to send estimated obligations for 1968 to $17.1 billion. That figure represents a dramatic commitment of the federal government to R&D. In 1966, 15.0 percent of federal expenditures were for R&D as contrasted with 1.5 percent in 1946 and 2.7 percent in 1950. Federally financed R&D grew from about 0.5 percent of the GNP in 1946 to 2.2 percent in 1966.[7] The costs of conducting R&D have increased rapidly, and the increase in the real effort applied to federal R&D over the 1950–65 period has lagged substantially behind expenditures.[8]

[7] National Science Foundation, *Federal Funds for Research, Development, and Other Scientific Activities: Fiscal Years 1964, 1965, and 1966,* vol. 14 (1965), pp. 143–44; and U. S. Bureau of the Budget, *The Budget of the United States Government: Fiscal Year Ending June 30, 1967* (1966), p. 432.

[8] "It should be recognized that costs of R&D have increased rapidly—an estimated 7 percent per year since 1950. As a result, the increase in the real effort applied to federal R&D over the 1950–65 period was not fifteen times but about seven or eight times." Ellis A. Johnson and Helen S. Milton, "A Proposed Cost-of-Research Index" (multilithed; Operations Research Office, Johns Hopkins University, 1961).

Another source estimates that the annual amount of total R&D per scientist-engineer has increased from $10,000 in 1940 to $36,000 in 1962 in current dollars

---

SOURCES FOR CHART 4: for 1940–65. NSF, *Federal Funds for Research, Development, and Other Scientific Activities,* vol. 15 (1966), pp. 149–52; for 1966–68, U. S. Bureau of the Budget, *Special Analyses: Budget of the United States Fiscal Year 1968* (1967), p. 143.

a. The data in Chart 3 are from reports of government agencies, while the data in Chart 4 are derived from reports from research performers. The two sources yield different results. For 1967 industrial performers reported $9.7 billion of R&D sponsored by the government, while government agencies reported their obligations with industry as $8.9 billion. The discrepancy can be explained at least in part by differences in accounting practices, the lag between obligations and expenditures, and incomplete survey coverage. These considerations do not explain discrepancies such as those in the period 1957–61, which were much larger than in 1967. In 1959, industry reported $4.8 billion in government R&D while the agencies reported $2.6 billion.

The National Science Foundation, the source of the data used in all charts in the volume, points out that "the development of economic data on the Nation's scientific effort is still in a relatively early stage of evolution, compared with many other established national statistical indicators . . . . Only with more and better data can we hope to try to develop more sophisticated methods for dealing with such difficult matters as: the utilization of resources, particularly scientific and engineering manpower, criteria of scientific productivity, and indicators of innovation" (NSF, *National Patterns of R&D Resources: Funds and Manpower in the United States, 1953–68* [NSF 67–7], p. iii).

While the growth of total federal expenditures has followed an exponential line, the programs of the principal agencies have grown erratically. Expenditures by the military agencies have dominated in absolute terms. Until 1962, Defense Department expenditures accounted for at least half of the annual increases in federal expenditures in every year, with the exception of 1956 when its increase was very small. In relative terms, DOD expenditures have grown since 1946 at an annual rate of 19 percent, somewhat below the annual rate of increase of total federal expenditures. In dollars, DOD expenditures for R&D rose slowly from the postwar low of $418 million in 1946 to $652 million in 1950 (60.2 percent of the federal total) and to $7,672 million in 1964 (51.2 percent of the federal total).

The very large expenditures on nuclear energy by the Manhattan project declined markedly after the war. In 1948 the newly established AEC expended $107.5 million, one-eighth of the peak annual expenditure of the predecessor Manhattan project. Thereafter AEC expenditures increased steadily at an average annual rate of 29 percent to the current level of slightly over $1.5 billion, about 10 percent of the federal government's R&D effort.[9]

Programs of the type conducted by HEW and NSF are less responsive to forces external to American society than defense-oriented programs. In the broad sense that the national strength is enhanced by better health and by vigorous programs of basic scientific investigation they are, of course, equally important, but their urgency is less likely to sway public opinion. The Congress has therefore been freer to deal with both programs in terms of the intrinsic merits of their objectives and in the light of the needs, opportunities and resources available.

---

and from $18,000 to $28,000 in constant dollars (1950 = 100). John H. Rubel, "Trends and Challenge in Research and Development," in *The Role and Effect of Technology in the Nation's Economy,* Hearings before Senate Select Committee on Small Business, 88 Cong. 1 sess. (1963), pt. 1, pp. 40–41. On a more recent effort to develop an index of price changes for R&D resources, sponsored by NSF, see Kathryn S. Arnow, "Indicators of Price and Cost Change in Research and Development Inputs," and Allan D. Searle, "Measuring Price Change in Research and Development," in American Statistical Association, *Proceedings of the Business and Economics Section* (1966), pp. 18–27.

[9] National Science Foundation, *Federal Funds . . . ,* vol. 14 (1965), pp. 145–46.

If the considerations that have applied have been different, the results have been similar. In both areas interest has been of such a character as to push the expenditures on medical and general basic research rapidly to high levels. In absolute terms, NIH's growth was relatively slow until 1957: expenditures rose over the preceding ten years from $10 million to $86 million. The rise to $144 million in 1957 resulted from a broad appraisal of the nation's needs, and the opportunities and capacity for research. Large annual increments followed resulting in obligations in 1967 of $857 million.

The agencies identified in Chart 4 accounted in 1950 for 89 percent and in 1964 for about 96 percent of federal funds expended on R&D programs. R&D expenditures of the 20 or more agencies not identified in the chart have increased since 1950 from $116 million to more than $900 million in 1967, accounting for about 5.5 percent of federal funds.

Change in Prewar Programs

For the most part, the R&D programs of the executive agencies that were well established before 1950 have since experienced modest increases in the level of effort provided by appropriated funds. These programs before World War II had been exclusively intramural operations. Most agencies have since acquired authority to use private sources of R&D through contracts. Such authority has been used, usually on a modest scale. In some cases, Congress has denied requests for contractual authority.[10]

The government's largest prewar research agency, the Department of Agriculture, received authority to contract for R&D in 1946. The major R&D organization of the Department is the Agricultural Research Service with expenditures for R&D of $139 million in fiscal 1965. About 18 percent of those expenditures were applied to contractual performance of research, including foreign programs. For a time the Department made significant use of private sources of R&D, particularly with regard to economic

---

[10] A useful compilation of agency R&D programs including the applicable statutory authorities and the distribution of their operations between intramural and contractual arrangements is *Federal Research and Development Programs*, Hearings before the House Select Committee on Government Research, 88 Cong. (1963–64).

problems such as in agricultural marketing, but the Economic Research Service has built up its own staff in that area. The most marked trend in the organization of agricultural research has been not in the use of the contract but in the growth of the Department's national and regional experimental centers. In contrast, the federal government's grant-in-aid support for state agricultural experiment stations through its Cooperative State Research Service has grown relatively slowly.[11]

The National Bureau of Standards continues to be a principal research activity of the Department of Commerce, its interest centered upon its original responsibility for methods and standards of measurements. The NBS has in recent years, with the help of the National Academy of Sciences, sought to strengthen its position in the government's scientific effort. It has acquired an extensive new plant and has, over a decade, doubled its appropriations for scientific and technical services, almost all of the additional money going for intramural operations. In addition to its large responsibility for basic standards, NBS's work in materials research has been strengthened and applied technology programs have been emphasized. The information storage and retrieval functions of the Department of Commerce, the Office of Technical Services, became a part of NBS in 1964.

The Department of Commerce has made a number of efforts to establish a Civilian Industrial Technology Program intended to make the facilities of the nation's land-grant colleges and universities available for research in selected areas. However, the Congress has not reacted enthusiastically to these proposals,[12] and the relatively modest applied technology program in NBS and the state technical services programs are the principal efforts in this area.

The establishment of the Environmental Science Services Administration (ESSA) in 1965 consolidated the hitherto separate Weather Bureau, Coast and Geodetic Survey, and the Central Radio Propagation Laboratory. The ESSA organization includes

[11] National Science Foundation, *Federal Funds . . .* , vol. 14 (1965), p. 22.

[12] *Departments of State, Justice, and Commerce, the Judiciary, and Related Agencies Appropriations, 1964,* Hearings before the Senate Appropriations Committee, 88 Cong. 1 sess. (1963), pp. 1593 ff., and *Departments of State . . . , 1965,* 88 Cong. 2 sess. (1964), p. 1227.

the Environmental Data Service, National Environmental Satellite Center, and the Institutes for Environmental Research (composed of the Institute for Telecommunication Services and Aeronomy, Institute for Atmospheric Sciences, the Institute for Oceanography, and the Institute for Earth Sciences). In recent years, about one-third of the Weather Bureau's steadily increasing research had been conducted by contractual performers, amounting to about $5.4 million annually.[13] The Coast and Geodetic Survey is primarily an intramural operation with relatively few research contracts.

Research activities of the Bureau of Public Roads, administered by its Office of Research and Development, have increased slowly, reaching a total of about $8 million in 1966.[14] Areas of interest include urban transportation and reductions in costs of highway construction and maintenance and highway safety, the latter of augmented importance by the Highway Safety Act of 1966. More than half the Bureau's research programs are pursued by contract. The office also has the task of providing some coordination for the research conducted by the states under the federal aid highway trust fund. The 1966 legislation mentioned prohibits the Secretary of Commerce from approving any state highway program that fails to give adequate attention to R&D directed to safe driving.

The Department of Commerce has also long conducted statistical and analytical studies such as those of the Bureau of the Census and the Office of Business Economics. These are primarily staff operations although the Bureau of the Census frequently seeks contractual assistance in conducting its major censuses.

The Treasury Department conducts relatively little research and relies principally on staff for its needs. The Coast Guard's expenditure of about $3.5 million annually is the largest program within the Treasury Department and it is primarily intramural in character. A few of the Department's agencies make occasional use of contractors. An example is the Internal Revenue Service's contractual project to assess the operation of its 1962 regulations on business depreciation allowances for income tax purposes.[15]

---

[13] *Department of Commerce Appropriations, 1966,* Hearings before the House Appropriations Committee, 89 Cong. 1 sess. (1965), pp. 627–30, supplies a list of contractual projects.

[14] *Ibid.*, pp. 840–50.

[15] *Evening Star* (Washington), Sept. 12, 1964.

In the Department of the Interior, R&D is directed to such areas as electric power generation, mineral discovery and technology, water conservation and water desalination, and fisheries. Interior expenditures for R&D doubled between 1960 and 1966. With two major exceptions this department's operations are principally intramural. Increases have been modest for such old-line agencies as the Bureau of Mines, the Bureau of Reclamation and the Geological Survey. Not until 1966 was the Bureau of Mines given authority to use contracts for R&D.

New Programs

Since 1950 the Congress has authorized a wide variety of new R&D activities. Many of them represent the assumption by the government of responsibilities that are new or very much enlarged. In many cases new organizations and procedures were established to carry them out. The more important are briefly described below. With the few exceptions noted, all these programs rely in whole or in large part on contractual performers.

One of these new programs was the somewhat anticlimactic establishment of the National Science Foundation to provide support for basic research as well as to administer programs designed to increase the nation's trained manpower in scientific areas. Organized in 1951 and with an initial appropriation of only $1 million, NSF doubled its expenditure in each of the next five years. Since then increases have been at a somewhat slower rate, expenditures for research reaching $248 million in 1967.

Among the programs undertaken since 1950, the largest by far and best known are the variety of efforts directed to the development of techniques for exploring space, culminating in the Apollo program, the massive effort for a manned landing on the moon.

The National Aeronautics and Space Administration was born in 1958 as a response to Sputnik I, to mobilize the technological capabilities that emerged from the work with missiles of the NACA, Army, Navy, and Air Force. The possibilities of exploring space forced consideration of the objectives to be pursued and the arrangements by which those goals were to be accomplished. Some space booster programs of the Army and Air Force were transferred to the new NASA of which NACA and the Navy Research Laboratory's Vanguard International Geophysical Year satellite team[16] also became a part. The NASA budget the first year was $145 million, thereafter nearly doubling each year to $4,990 million in 1965. No peacetime technological program in the American experience has grown so fast over such a short period.

Transportation

Problems associated with civilian air traffic have stimulated R&D efforts that have increased from a level of $2.9 million in 1953 to about $40 million in 1966.[17] About 1950, the Civil Aeronautics Administration assumed responsibility for navigation and landing facilities for civilian aircraft as well as for compatible airborne electronic devices. The rapid growth of the civilian aviation industry and its adoption of new and faster equipment outstripped the capabilities of available air traffic control and air navigation systems. Meanwhile economy drives reduced CAA's efforts to meet these problems through R&D down to very low levels.

Following a number of evaluations of the needs of the industry, the Federal Aviation Agency was created in 1959, succeeding the CAA. While accelerating efforts to develop a variety of navigation control techniques, FAA also sought to adapt automatic data processing machines to air traffic control problems.[18] In pursuing its objectives, FAA has sought to apply technologies developed for other purposes to its needs and to do so by inducing private industry to undertake the needed development effort.[19] The FAA is not necessarily the purchaser of the developed item. Many are intended to be employed on privately owned aircraft. However, FAA strongly influences the adoption of improved equipment through its regulatory authority. It stimulates development of equipment by entering into contractual feasibility studies followed by development contracts offered competitively and of a fixed-

[16] National Aeronautics and Space Administration, *Administrative History of NASA, 1958–63* (1966).

[17] See *Federal Research and Development Programs*, Hearings, pp. 128, 145–49.

[18] Gary Fromm, *Economic Criteria for Federal Aviation Agency Expenditures* (Federal Aviation Agency, 1962).

[19] Robert J. Shank, "Transference of Government Sponsored R&D to Commercial Application," in National Security Industrial Association, *The Impact of Government Research and Development Expenditures on Industrial Growth*, Proceedings of an R&D Symposium (NSIA, 1963), pp. 93–98.

price type normally involving cost-sharing on the part of the developer. Some FAA contracts also include a clause providing that the developer may purchase full rights to the developed item by reimbursing FAA for its contributions to development costs.[20]

The FAA maintains intramural facilities which in 1966 absorbed about half its R&D expenditures. The National Aviation Facilities Experimental Center devoted to testing and evaluation activities is its principal intramural operation. There are also two small aero-medical laboratories.

Expenditures cited above do not include FAA's program to develop new civilian aircraft. Except for some efforts to stimulate the development of lower cost short-haul aircraft, the FAA had not until 1961 assumed such responsibilities.[21] In 1961, however, the President with the assent of Congress assigned to FAA the responsibility for working with the aircraft industry in the development of a civilian supersonic transport plane (SST) based on military experience. The agency has pursued the SST objective by entering into study and feasibility contracts with private firms during 1962–63 and then into initial design-phase contracts with three airframe and three engine manufacturers. Second-phase design work was continued in 1964 with four companies participating and a 1966 target date.[22] Each stage was followed by presidential and congressional review. Meanwhile studies of the sonic boom problem were undertaken under the guidance of the National Academy of Sciences.

Aside from collecting statistical data, the R&D interests of the Maritime Administration (Department of Commerce) have grown spasmodically. During the 1950's that interest was represented principally by the development of two experimental vessels. One was the USS Savannah, the first nuclear powered merchant vessel developed as a joint project with the AEC. The other was the first oceangoing hydrofoil vessel, the Denison, developed

[20] The "recovery of development costs" clause was applied for the first time in November 1965 in the case of a general aviation transponder intended for use by small aircraft for air traffic control identification purposes (*New York Times*, Nov. 2, 1965).

[21] *Independent Offices Appropriations, 1966*, Hearings before the Senate Appropriations Committee, 89 Cong. 1 sess. (1965), pp. 1334–37.

[22] *Ibid.*, pp. 302–3; Federal Aviation Agency, *Annual Report, 1965*, pp. 72–76.

through cost-sharing arrangements with private industry. The operating costs of the two vessels account for about three-fourths of the Maritime Administration's 1966 R&D budget of approximately $11 million.

Broader interests were identified in 1960 with the establishment of an Office of Research and Development. The office was given responsibility for R&D directed to increasing the competitiveness of United States flag shipping in international trade. This wide-ranging assignment has been pursued almost entirely through contracts with private institutions.[23]

Another new program in the Department of Commerce was established in 1963 in response to congressional interests in appraising the need for and improving the technology utilized for ground transportation. In 1965 major emphasis was placed upon developing means for providing high-speed rail transportation in the Washington-Boston corridor, the objective being sought entirely through contracts including some which are cost-sharing with the business firms involved.[24] The program was transferred in 1966 to the new Department of Transportation.

Also in the transportation area is the program of the Department of Housing and Urban Development in implementation of the Urban Mass Transportation Act. The program, inaugurated in 1962 and considerably expanded in 1966, is primarily directed to providing cost-sharing grants-in-aid to state and local governments to assist in meeting urban transport problems. The 1966 Demonstration Cities and Metropolitan Development Act authorizes contractual and intramural research and demonstration for research programs to advance the technology of housing and urban development.

Resources

Also oriented to the improvement of civilian technology are three organizations established since 1950 within the Department of the Interior. In 1952 the Congress authorized a Saline Water Con-

---

[23] Samuel A. Lawrence, *United States Merchant Shipping Policies and Politics* (Brookings Institution, 1966), pp. 278–79.

[24] A list of contracts as of early 1965 is in *Department of Commerce Appropriations, 1966*, Hearings, p. 903.

version Program contemplating the immediate construction of a large demonstration plant. Instead it was determined that further research should be conducted on each of the principal known desalination methods.[25] Provision for plants demonstrating the four processes that seemed best was made by joint congressional resolution in 1958.[26] A fifth was undertaken in 1965 in a contractual agreement between OSW and the Oak Ridge Institute for Nuclear Studies.[27] The program, which in 1966 had obligational authority of $23.2 million, has been conducted entirely by contract.

The Office of Coal Research was established in 1960 reflecting dissatisfaction with the progress being made by the Bureau of Mines in its long-standing research on coal and following a congressional decision that a new and separate agency was preferable to an enlarged program in the Bureau, even if it were given contractual authority. The Department therefore has two programs dealing with coal utilization: the predominantly intramural program of the Bureau of Mines and the contractual program of the Office of Coal Research.[28] Both operations have expenditures of about $6 million annually.

The third new program is the Office of Water Resources Research, established in 1964. This office operates principally through support given regional centers in water research, centers which are located for the most part at the nation's land-grant colleges and universities. In 1966, the Federal Water Pollution Control Administration was transferred from the Public Health Service to the Interior Department considerably enhancing its R&D in the area.

Mention should also be made of the Bureau of Commercial Fisheries together with the Bureau of Sport Fisheries and Wildlife which were formed in 1956 out of the former Fish and Wildlife Service. The Bureau of Commercial Fisheries is financed by an

[25] David S. Jenkins, "Saline Water Conversion Program," in Department of the Interior, *Annual Report of 1954*, pp. 124–25.

[26] *Department of the Interior Appropriations, 1966*, Hearings before the House Appropriations Committee, 89 Cong. 1 sess. (1965), pp. 1398–1401.

[27] *AEC Authorizing Legislation, Fiscal Year 1967*, Hearings before the Joint Committee on Atomic Energy, 89 Cong. 2 sess. (1966), pp. 616–19.

[28] The Bureau of Mines has the authority to make research grants of up to $25,000 and in 1966 received authority to enter into research contracts up to the same limit.

amount equal to 30 percent of the custom duties collected on imported fishery products. Its R&D activities increased from $9.4 million in 1957 to $29.3 million in 1965, a little over 10 percent being contractual. One of its largest R&D programs has been concerned with the development of a fish protein concentrate,[29] an activity which has received considerable publicity, both favorable and adverse.

Health

Research in health is dominated by the National Institutes of Health but there are also a number of activities of an applied nature. The Public Health Service, parent organization of NIH, administers some fourteen programs that have supporting research components as well as a variety of demonstration activities. These are administered by the PHS Bureau of State Services with appropriations for R&D amounting in 1964 to $74 million. Among the more important subject areas were communicable diseases, chronic diseases, radiological health, air pollution, and water supply and pollution control. Somewhat more than half of these programs were conducted through contracts.[30]

Of special interest is another medical research program, that of the Veterans Administration. This program is unique among federal research programs in that it began as a contract program and in time became almost entirely an intramural operation.

After World War II, the Veterans Administration established research programs on the medical problems associated with the patients in its hospitals. Such research was conducted under contractual arrangements by the faculty of medical schools associated with VA hospitals. In 1949 there were some 76 projects under contract with 32 institutions. The agency by that time was well embarked on its program of building VA hospitals in close physical proximity to established medical schools. As new facilities were brought into use, the VA recruited physicians and surgeons and other qualified staff with the expectation that they would undertake research programs particularly related to its large patient population. As the agency's professional staff was built up the contract

---

[29] *Department of the Interior and Related Agencies Appropriations, 1966,* Hearings before the Senate Appropriations Committee, 89 Cong. 1 sess. (1965), pp. 320–22.
[30] *Federal Research and Development Programs,* Hearings, pp. 702–13.

program was reduced. By 1955 the contract program had been reduced to the role of small-scale supplementation.[31] Expenditures on the VA research program have increased from $5.4 million in 1956 to about $40 million in fiscal 1966.

One of the results of the increase in medical research has been a sharp rise in the work load of the Food and Drug Administration. In the early 1950's, FDA conducted relatively little research in support of its primary responsibility of testing. From a level of about $1 million annually in the years 1953–57, FDA has increased its expenditures for research to about $12 million. Its research programs continue to be conducted primarily by agency staff but the capabilities of various private institutions are being used increasingly to develop new techniques and also as participants in FDA's work with drug toxicity and efficacy.[32] In 1966, FDA faced the task of reevaluating a large number of drugs approved before 1962. FDA sought the assistance of private sources and entered into contract with the National Academy of Sciences to that end.

Education and Training

Not until 1954 did the federal government support research in education other than a statistical program of the Office of Education. In 1954 a cooperative research program was established providing for research by private institutions under grants and contracts and also jointly with state education agencies. Others have followed, particularly in grant programs relating to vocational education in modern language teaching, new educational media, and educational improvements for the handicapped. These and a number of smaller efforts accounted for increases in expenditures from less than $1 million in 1954 to approximately $78 million in 1966.

The limitations of project research led the Office of Education in 1964 to adopt a policy of supporting large contractual research centers or regional laboratories modeled upon the agricultural experiment stations and extension service centers. By late 1966, twelve Research and Development Centers specialized by broad

[31] See Veterans Administration, *Annual Report: 1950*, p. 39; *1952*, pp. 43–44; *1954*, pp. 34–35.

[32] *Departments of Labor and Health, Education and Welfare Appropriations for 1966*, Hearings before the House Appropriations Committee, 89 Cong. 1 sess. (1965), pt. 1, pp. 231–32.

subject areas were in operation. Each center is in substantial degree self-directed in planning and executing its research activities within its assigned area of interest. In addition, twenty regional research laboratories had or were being established, most of them managed by consortia of colleges and universities.[33]

While these programs sought to apply research to improve the nation's educational effort other legislation sought to meet problems created by inadequacies in the existing educational and training process. In the Manpower Development and Training Act of 1962, Congress authorized training programs to be executed by the Secretary of Labor and the Secretary of Health, Education and Welfare. On-the-job training programs were assigned to the Department of Labor. The Department requested and was given authority to contract with "whatever group can provide a good system of training, whether it be a union or a trade association, an employer, a private or public agency, an educational institution, or a community group."[34] Responsibility was given to HEW for providing programs of vocational training and retraining to persons selected by the Secretary of Labor. The Department was to enter into agreements with state vocational education agencies to provide the needed training. However, "when a state does not enter into an agreement, or when the state agency does not provide the training required," HEW was authorized to provide the training needed "by agreement or contract with public or private educational or training institutions.[35]

In application, the Department of Labor implemented its on-the-job training program through contractual arrangements with employers, trade associations, and labor unions and with community organizations for their locales. Contracts with national organizations provided for subcontracts with local organizations.

Many of these programs were of an experimental and demonstration nature. The act also provided for research into manpower problems, a provision given added emphasis as experience with the

[33] See U.S. Office of Education, *Support for Research and Related Activities* (n.d. [*ca.* 1967]), pp. 18–21.

[34] Secretary Arthur Goldberg, in *Unemployment and the Impact of Automation*, Hearings before the House Education and Labor Committee, 87 Cong. 1 sess. (1961), p. 13.

[35] *Ibid.*, pp. 108–9.

act accumulated. A judgment that research resources in the subject area were inadequate led the Secretary of Labor to adopt the policy of encouraging the development of manpower research centers. Such centers were to be at or closely affiliated with academic institutions, and were to be concerned with research of a "basic" as well as of an operational nature.[36]

Of a related nature is the Job Corps program of the Office of Economic Opportunity. Whereas most of the OEO programs are pursued through grants to local organizations (such as the Community Action Program), the Job Corps program is contractual. To achieve its objective of reducing the educational deficiencies of urban youth, the program maintains a number of training camps operated by private institutions, mostly business firms. Business firms appear to have undertaken such activities in the belief that their experience with training programs is relevant. They seem also attracted by the opportunity to experiment with new educational devices and methods.[37] The OEO also supports extensive research programs, the conductors including universities, independent nonprofit organizations, and business firms.[38]

Of a different nature is the Economic Development Administration formed in 1965 as successor to the Area Redevelopment Administration established in 1961. The Area Redevelopment Administration was primarily concerned with providing financial assistance to areas it designated for redevelopment. However, it was also authorized to make grants and contracts for research in support of a long-range program "to develop and expand knowledge of the causes of unemployment and under-employment and to resolve questions concerning the nature of area economic distress."[39] The ARA obligated about $1 million annually for this type of research. The nature of the implementation of the broader mission of the Economic Development Administration is not yet clear.

[36] *Amending the Manpower Development and Training Act of 1962,* Hearings before the Senate Labor and Public Welfare Committee, 89 Cong. 1 sess. (1965), p. 21.

[37] *Examination of the War on Poverty Program,* Hearings before the House Committee on Education and Labor, 89 Cong. 1 sess. (1965), pp. 102–14, 187.

[38] *Examination of the War on Poverty Program,* Hearings before the House Education and Labor Committee, 89 Cong. 1 sess. (1965), pp. 69, 102–14, 187; and *Supplemental Appropriations, 1966,* Hearings before the House Appropriations Committee, 89 Cong. 2 sess. (1966), pp. 293–95, 650–52.

[39] *Annual Report of the Secretary of Commerce, 1964,* p. 15.

The agency has sponsored a variety of research studies to assist it in carrying out its responsibilities.[40]

Welfare

In the welfare area, intramural research on a small scale dates back to about 1912 but included little more than the compilation and analysis of statistical data. The agencies now under the Department of Health, Education and Welfare (the Social Security Board, Vocational Rehabilitation and Welfare Administration) inaugurated research and demonstration programs in the mid-1950's, utilizing contracts for research and grants for research and demonstration projects. The principal welfare areas include juvenile delinquency and youth development and child health and welfare. Appropriations for these purposes in 1966 approximated $14 million. Research and demonstration programs of the Vocational Rehabilitation Administration in the same year approximated $25 million.[41] Direct-hire employees carry out most of the operating programs of these agencies, but occasionally private institutions are used through contracts as was the case with the Cuban Refugee Program, which utilized the capabilities of a number of voluntary agencies.

Overseas Technical Assistance

Since its beginning in 1950, the federal policy of providing technical assistance to less developed countries has involved the extensive use of private institutions under contract. The pattern of contractual performance of its projects was established by the Technical Cooperation Administration in 1950, special emphasis being given to university cooperation. Utilization of university personnel was given increased emphasis under the successor Foreign Operations Administration about 1955 and has since been continued under AID. In 1965 some 67 universities held 110 contracts, most of them for operations in foreign countries.

While university contractual projects have received much pub-

[40] U.S. Department of Commerce, Economic Development Administration and Office of Regional Economic Development, *Building Communities with New Jobs,* First Annual Report (1966).

[41] These programs are described in Senate Committee on Government Operations, *National Foundation for Social Sciences,* Hearings before a Subcommittee on Government Research, 90 Cong. 1 sess. (1967), pt. 1, pp. 161–212.

licity, the technical assistance agencies have relied also upon business firms to execute many of their projects. The use of business firms has covered a very wide spectrum of activities ranging from mapping and similar activities relating to planning to the construction of buildings and roads. In 1962, AID inaugurated a program of research on the problems of economic development, relying on contractual sources.[42]

From its beginnings the Peace Corps has made extensive use of private institutions in support of its operations. With the exception of a new experimental training center in Puerto Rico operated directly by the Peace Corps, all volunteers receive their training on college and university campuses operating under contract. Overseas the volunteers work with support arrangements that vary. Originally the Peace Corps sought the assistance of educational and other nonprofit institutions to provide such administrative support. A number of noneducational organizations undertook such activities as did also a few universities. The reluctance of universities to involve themselves in activities for which they had uncertain qualifications and little experience led the Peace Corps to devise other arrangements. Since 1965 the Corps has supplemented its own staff support of volunteers by arranging for Contractor's Overseas Representatives who provide specialized professional and technical assistance. The Peace Corps also maintains programs of research and evaluation relating to its operations. All such projects are carried out by contract.[43]

Other R&D Areas

There are a variety of other programs established since 1950 that are directed principally to increasing the effectiveness with which an agency seeks to achieve its objectives. There follows an incomplete list, selected to suggest the variety of ways in which the federal government has come to seek the solution of problems through R&D.

Since about 1950 the Post Office Department has sought to

[42] *Agency for International Development Contract Operations,* Hearings and Report of the House Committee on Government Operations, 87 Cong. 2 sess. (1962).

[43] *Peace Corps Appropriations, 1967,* Hearings before the House Appropriations Committee, 89 Cong. 2 sess. (1966), pp. 496–97.

apply new technological possibilities to its operations. In the later part of that decade the Department pursued through contracted projects a substantial program intended to develop an automated post office for handling the mail. There followed a few years of reduced R&D expenditures but in 1964 the Department through its Office of Research and Engineering resumed its efforts to develop a variety of devices to identify and sort mail and to mechanize its operations. These efforts have been carried on through contracts with business firms supplemented by contracts for engineering services. Expenditures in 1965 and 1966 were at an annual rate of $12 million.[44]

The Law Enforcement Assistance Act of 1965 established a program administered by the Department of Justice to improve state and local law enforcement capabilities and techniques in the prevention and control of crime and the correction of offenders.[45] These objectives were to be sought through training and demonstration, and through research grants to public and private nonprofit organizations as well as through the collection and dissemination of information. Such grants are made as proposals of public and private organizations are received and approved. The program in fiscal year 1966 had appropriated funds of slightly less than $10 million.

The United States Arms Control and Disarmament Agency under its authorizing act is directed to acquire a fund of theoretical and practical knowledge concerning disarmament and to act towards that objective by making arrangements with private and public institutions for relevant research and studies. The ACDA has elected to administer its programs principally under grants.

The Federal Reserve Board has long maintained a research staff which conducts most of the statistical and research functions undertaken on its behalf. However, in 1946 the board conducted a national survey of consumer finances by arrangement with the Program Survey staff of the Department of Agriculture.[46] Such consumer finance surveys have been conducted annually since

[44] *Post Office Department Appropriations, 1967,* Hearings before the House Appropriations Committee, 89 Cong. 2 sess. (1966), pp. 318, 323–26, 354.

[45] *Supplemental Appropriations Bill, 1966,* Hearings, pp. 368–71.

[46] Federal Reserve Board, *Annual Report of Board of Governors, 1946,* p. 65.

1947 but they have been performed by a university contractor. The board has also on occasion entered into research contracts for other purposes, most recently a study of its open market operations.

The Federal Home Loan Bank Board has conducted little research and, until 1965, none by contract. In that year, however, the board requested congressional authorization to use funds derived from member assessments to conduct a small contractual research program.

Similarly the Securities and Exchange Commission utilizes its own personnel for most of its research needs, sometimes assembling a special staff as in the case of its major study of security markets. However, the Commission also on occasion secures special studies by contract as in the case of a study of open-end mutual investment companies.[47]

In its work relating to mobilization readiness the Office of Emergency Planning relies principally on its own staff and the resources of other government agencies. It has, however, used contractual sources in developing its capabilities as in the development of the National Resource Evaluation Center computer.[48]

The State Department's Bureau of Intelligence and Research maintains a small contractual research program, as do a few other units of the Department. The United States Information Agency utilizes private sources to supplement its own research efforts relating to attitudes, opinion trends and similar topics. The agency has also occasionally commissioned the preparation of material for use in its overseas libraries.[49]

With the strong trend toward the assumption of increased responsibility for R&D and related demonstration projects on the part of the government, few programs of this kind have been terminated. The few that have gone out of existence include the programs of the Small Business Administration, one established in 1958 for research in the management problems of small business, and the other set up in 1961 for economic research. About $2 mil-

---

[47] Securities and Exchange Commission, *Annual Report, 1962*, pp. 1–3.

[48] *Appropriations for the Office of Emergency Planning, 1967*, Hearings before the House Appropriations Committee, 89 Cong. 2 sess. (1966), pp. 787–88.

[49] *Appropriations for the United States Information Agency, 1966*, Hearings before the House Appropriations Committee, 89 Cong. 1 sess. (1965), pp. 505–8.

lion was appropriated in fiscal 1959 and 1960 for research in management problems. The authorizing statute required that the studies be made through grants to colleges and universities, with no more than $40,000 allocated to a single state during a single year. Over the active period of the program, some 105 grants for over 240 studies were made covering every state, the District of Columbia, Puerto Rico, and the Virgin Islands. Economic research studies were financed on a much smaller scale—about $300,000 over a three-year period—and were not subjected to geographic restrictions. Although SBA has requested contract research funds annually, nothing has been appropriated for management studies since fiscal 1960 and nothing for economic studies since 1964.

The Shift to Contractual Research and Development

The rapid growth of federal expenditures on R&D programs has been paralleled by an increasing reliance upon private contractors (Table 3). In 1940 virtually all federal R&D programs were conducted within the government's own organization or as grants to state institutions; to a large degree the government relied upon developments in the private sector of the economy. In 1945, half of the federal government's expenditures were made within government organizations, the other half through private institutions. Since that time expenditures for intramural performance have increased but at rates far below the government's overall expenditures. The result has been that in 1955, 54 percent of expenditures for R&D went to private institutions; in 1958, 74 percent; and since 1960, about 79 percent.

The fact that most of the growth of federal R&D programs has involved contractors has followed from an extension and hardening of policies which were well formulated before 1950. With few important exceptions, the programs that originated during World War II were continued with heavy reliance upon contractual performance. Agencies which had long-established policies relying upon intramural facilities have since World War II sought authority to contract for R&D to supplement those facilities or to carry out new programs. Most of them received such authority and some of them in time came to rely heavily upon contracting. In the years after 1950 some of the agencies pursued policies of restrict-

TABLE 3

Federal R&D Obligations by Type of Performing Institution, 1955–67

Type of Institution	1955	1956	1957	1958	1959	1960	1961	1962	1963	1964	1965	1966[a]	1967[a]
	Percent of Total												
Federal government	46.5	45.1	47.0	26.1	24.9	24.2	21.0	21.6	19.3	20.0	21.2	20.4	21.1
Profit organizations (proper)	31.1	30.8	27.3	57.0	57.3	56.1	60.1	57.4	61.1	60.6	59.4	60.0	58.4
Profit organizations (research centers)	6.6	8.8	8.6	6.3	6.1	6.3	5.0	4.1	3.4	3.5	2.8	2.5	2.5
Educational institutions (proper)	6.8	7.1	8.0	5.1	5.1	6.0	6.0	7.8	6.9	7.5	8.1	8.6	9.3
Educational institutions (research centers)	6.6	5.7	5.8	3.5	3.8	4.4	4.6	5.4	5.2	3.8	3.8	3.5	3.6
Independent nonprofits (proper)	1.3	1.3	1.8	1.1	1.2	1.5	1.5	1.6	1.8	2.1	2.4	2.6	2.5
Independent nonprofits (research centers)	0.9	0.9	1.0	0.6	0.6	0.6	0.9	1.5	1.6	1.6	1.6	1.5	1.6
Other extramural (U.S. and foreign)	0.2	0.3	0.5	0.3	1.0	0.9	0.9	0.6	0.7	0.9	0.7	0.9	1.0
	Total Expenditures in Millions of Dollars												
All institutions	2.5	2.4	2.7	5.5	6.9	7.6	9.1	10.3	12.5	14.1	14.6	16.0	15.9

Source: National Science Foundation, *Federal Funds for Research, Development, and Other Scientific Activities*, vols. 5–15.
a. Estimated.

ing contracting to the role of supporting inhouse programs. In other operations, particularly the larger ones, contracting became the dominant and characteristic method of pursuing agency objectives. By 1952 the Defense Department was interpreting the actions of Congress as clearly indicating approval of its efforts "to contract for services whenever it is found to be practicable to do so" and each of the three services had issued staff directives to that effect.

In a few instances, Congress has specifically required that an agency's R&D programs be carried out by contract (or grant)—as in the case of the National Science Foundation or in the desalination program. In some other areas, such as atomic energy and aircraft, the Congress expressed itself as strongly in favor of policies that would strengthen private free enterprise.[50] The general shift to heavier reliance upon contracting, however, was the result not so much of explicit congressional direction as of agency decisions, in which Congress acquiesced, to seek the important advantages believed to be gained from close contacts with the capabilities of the private sector in R&D. The direct influence of Congress upon the expansion of contracting was in its generally favorable attitudes towards agency proposals involving the participation of private institutions and its occasional reluctance to expand intramural capabilities.[51]

[50] In the case of atomic energy by statute, as in the Atomic Energy Act, which declares in sec. 1(*b*) the "policy of the United States" to be that "the development, use and control of Atomic Energy shall be directed so as to . . . strengthen free competition in private enterprise." In the case of aircraft by statements of formal policy, as in Senate approval of the position taken by the Aviation Policy Board in 1948 that "application of research results in the design and development of improved aircraft and equipment . . . is the function of the industry" while only "evaluation" of this equipment and the "exploration of possible military applications of research results are considered to be the function of the Army and Navy." *National Aviation Policy*, S. Rept. 949, 80 Cong. 2 sess. (1948).

[51] For example, a subcommittee reported to the House Science and Astronautics Committee the observation that the committee "has been very mindful of the fact that a vast in-house capability leads to bureaucracy after a length of time. That is why in our subcommittee we reduced the budget request in the area of construction and facilities more than 35 percent. . . . We were somewhat fearful that a good deal of the requests that were made were not really necessary and could be done by other agencies of the Government or could better be done by private industry where private industry had the capability." *Research Programs*, Hearings before the House Rules Committee, 88 Cong. 1 sess. (1963), p. 18.

The agencies, however, have not always had the freedom to choose between the direct-hire and contractual methods of conducting R&D programs. The range of agency discretion has been severely restricted by congressional attitudes towards the size of the civil service, the composition of the civil service as that is determined by salary schedules, and by forces affecting the prestige of the civil service, such as the events of the McCarthy period.[52] Such factors undoubtedly served to increase agency reliance upon private R&D and may have led to the use of contractors when an agency's purposes or predilections favored direct employment. Expanding R&D programs necessarily required some increases in administrative staffs to manage the programs. Such increases in R&D management personnel in many cases absorbed an agency's ability to increase its staff, leaving no choice but to secure the performance of the work through contracts with private institutions.

Personnel Ceilings

While Congress has always taken a keen interest in controlling the employment of personnel by the agencies, congressional action asserting such controls by setting personnel ceilings independently of appropriations originated with the Federal Employees Pay Act of 1945.[53] That statute instructed the director of the Bureau of the Budget to determine quarterly the number of full-time civilian employees (or equivalents) required by the executive branch for the proper and efficient performance of authorized functions. The Bureau of the Budget was to make this determination on the basis of reports by the agencies and was in turn to report to the Congress. This act exempted the Army, the Navy, the War Shipping Administration, and the Maritime Service for the duration of hostilities.

The following year, by amendment to the act cited, actual ceilings were set for the larger agencies and the director of the Bureau of the Budget was instructed to determine the ceiling for each

[52] Paul P. Van Riper, *History of the United States Civil Service* (Row, Peterson & Co., 1958), pp. 502–4.

[53] P.L. 390. An earlier effort to control numbers of personnel was made in the First Wartime Pay Act of 1942, which required the agencies to report and justify certain types of personnel to the Bureau of the Budget for approval.

agency not specified in the act.[54] There were some agency protests at the restrictions so applied. Secretary of the Army Royall, for example, in 1949 pointed out that "failure to waive this law [P.L. 390] would force the Army to place contracts for personal services at greater cost than if we used our own civilian personnel in our own facilities," citing the matériel rehabilitation program as an example.[55] Other administration officials have occasionally protested the effect of personnel ceilings as established by salary appropriations. Such protests have cautioned Congress on the consequences of its actions, but have not constituted vigorous defenses of direct-hire performance of agency programs, including R&D. With time, the justification of inhouse R&D staffs has changed from the view that they engage in activities that are of interest only to the government to the view that it is to the government's interest that the agencies possess the capabilities necessary to furnish objective technical advice to agency administrators.

The statutes setting agency employment ceilings were repealed in September 1950. The interest of Congress in reducing or, in any case, limiting the growth of the civil service has remained strong and has been a fundamental consideration throughout this period.[56] Close controls over numbers of personnel were applied

[54] P.L. 106 gave the Army a maximum of 176,000 employees as of July 1, 1947, and the Navy 100,000, each exclusive of wage board employees. For the rest of the federal government, exclusive of the Post Office Field Service and the Veterans Administration, a ceiling was set of 447,363 full-time civilian employees (with equivalents in man-months of part-time employees).

[55] *Military Functions Appropriations Bill for 1949*, Hearings before the Senate Appropriations Committee on H.R. 6771, 80 Cong. 2 sess. (1948), pt. 1, p. 5.

[56] That concern has been expressed in various ways from time to time. The House Post Office and Civil Service Committee in 1958 expressed the view that "unremitting vigilance is required to resist and contain pressures toward an ever-larger number of Federal jobholders and an ever-higher level of Federal salaries. The history of governments demonstrates a strong disposition, on the part of those administering public programs, to enlarge their numbers, their spheres of activity, and their compensation, coupled with resistance to any diminution or limitation thereof.

"(A) 'Parkinson's Law'

"This condition has been reduced to an economic formula known as 'Parkinson's law' in a treatise by Cyril Northcote Parkinson [*Parkinson's Law and Other Studies in Administration* (Houghton, Mifflin, 1957)]. Although the studies from which 'Parkinson's law' was developed were conducted on the British civil service, all evidence points to the fact that it is a law of universal application. This committee,

by establishing employment ceilings as a part of the appropriation process. Congressional committees have closely scrutinized appropriations for salaries. The number of positions suggested and the changes proposed, their grades, and functions, are normally reviewed in detail in the annual hearings on each agency's appropriation. Requests for an increase in the number of civil service positions are usually singled out for special consideration and detailed justification by agency representatives is frequently required. By P.L. 801, passed in 1956, agencies requesting funds for new and expanded programs are required to indicate the number of new employees involved.[57] Heavy emphasis has also been placed upon efficiency of manpower utilization.

The strong and persistent desire of the Congress to restrict the size of the civil service and to hold its growth to rates below that of federal expenditures has been reflected in the policies of the executive branch. Under President Eisenhower, the Bureau of the Budget established personnel ceilings for each agency. President Kennedy sought through manpower utilization surveys to increase efficiency so that the agencies, while reaching their other objectives, might also meet the provisions of the Federal Employees Salary Act of 1962 requiring that the cost of the salary increases be absorbed by each agency to the fullest extent possible. One of the

---

on the basis of its studies and investigations, has found that 'Parkinson's law' is operative in our Government. We have found no abatement—rather, there is and has been strong acceleration—in the pressures toward mushrooming public payrolls and in the resistance to legislative controls. But, though existing, this 'law' is not necessarily immutable. Its effect can be counteracted by proper legislative controls and vigorous legislative review of executive activities. This presents one of the gravest problems facing the Congress.

"The post-World War II period has provided an apt demonstration of the workings of 'Parkinson's law.' It has developed a hard core of self-generating Federal jobholders, with built-in resistance to legislative efforts to hold payrolls within reason. Increased employment and higher salaries brought about by past emergencies have left in their wake new plateaus for public employment and have been used as points of departure, or springboards, for more and more jobs and higher and higher salaries at public expense. This condition is aggravated each time there is a national emergency. The tremendous 'starting load' of gearing to space-age defense needs could provide the impetus for another upward surge in Government jobs and payrolls" (*Legislative Control of Federal Positions and Salaries*, H. Rept. 2706, 85 Cong. 2 sess. [1958], p. 7).

[57] *Personnel Requirements and Cost of New Functions*, S. Rept. 2534 to accompany H.R. 10368, 84 Cong. 2 sess. (1956).

early actions of President Johnson was to promise to hold agency employment at or below the personnel targets established in response to President Kennedy's policies.[58]

Civil Service Policies

Congressional policies in two other areas have also served to increase the role of contracting in the expanding federal R&D programs. These policies relate to the salary structure of the civil service and attitudes toward the construction of new facilities for intramural operation.

Since 1945 civil service salary schedules have been revised frequently by the Congress. There exists general agreement that the salaries so established have been generally competitive with private employment opportunities at the lower and middle levels although the salaries of the upper grades have lagged behind. At the same time the Congress has sought to control the distribution of grades within the civil service. Concern with "grade inflation" led to the adoption in 1950 of the Whitten amendment,[59] which sought to prevent what the Congress considered the "too-rapid promotion of personnel." This legislation required an annual report to the Congress on the results of reviews of all positions which had been increased in grade, and of the adjustments that were made including the number of positions abolished as a result of such review. In effect, overall manpower ceilings were translated into ceilings for each grade and the review requirement operated to freeze the grade distribution within the agencies from time to time, reducing the ability of the agencies to act upon their personnel requirements. The review requirement did not stop the upward movements in the grade distribution of the civil service or in salaries—which had their source in the upward movement of wage and salaries in the private economy. It did reduce the ability of the civil service to make adjustments to changing conditions in the labor market. With the burgeoning demand for scientists and engineers which followed from the expansion of federal programs,

[58] The actions of Presidents Kennedy and Johnson are reviewed in *Manpower Utilization Symposium,* Print of the House Post Office and Civil Service Committee, 88 Cong. 2 sess. (1964).

[59] Sec. 1302, P.L. 1052, 81 Cong., reinforced by further legislation in 1951 under sec. 1310, P.L. 253, 82 Cong.

the agencies faced difficulties in recruiting R&D men with the desired qualifications. Aside from the general increases in salary, some adjustments in grade requirements have been made.

The more important and persistent problems have related to the ability of the government to attract and to hold men of experience and proven ability, particularly those with scientific and technical training. With the very rapid growth of federal programs, competition for personnel has been keen and the problems of filling the higher positions in federal R&D organizations has been identified as a critical one on innumerable occasions. The problem has been twofold: securing R&D technicians and securing qualified R&D managers. Since most R&D projects can be conducted by contractors, of the two problems, the latter is much the more important. However, the tasks of managing programs require that the government have an adequate number of men who are technically competent to supply objective and informed advice as administrators. The difficulties of securing and retaining such men have increased greatly with the growth of federal expenditures.

To meet their immediate postwar problems the Army and Navy requested, and the Congress in P.L. 313 in 1946 authorized, the establishment of 45 positions in the professional and scientific services "to effectuate those research and development functions relating to the national defense and military and naval medicine." The compensation for these P.L. 313 positions was to be fixed by the secretaries at not less than $10,000 and not more than $15,000 per annum—pay rates significantly above the salary schedules of the classified services at that time.

In the years since, the numbers of P.L. 313 appointments allowed the Defense Department have steadily increased as have also the salaries provided. Specified numbers of appointments similar to P.L. 313 also have been provided in the statutory authorizations for the Public Health Service, NASA and other agencies.

The ability of the agencies to compete in the labor market was somewhat further strengthened by the Classification Act of 1949. That act added the new grades of 16, 17, and 18 to the existing general schedule. The Civil Service Commission was instructed to allocate the 400 positions authorized in these grades among the agencies. The number grew year by year and agency by agency so that by 1962 the number of supergrades authorized had increased to 1,989. That growth was, however, a defensive one. Most of the supergrade positions have been used by the agencies to retain their personnel and a relatively small percentage are filled by recruitment.

The rate of growth of funds supporting federal R&D programs since about 1955 has exceeded by some substantial figure the growth of the nation's supply of the highly trained manpower required to execute federal programs. The supply of qualified manpower available to government programs has been expandable within fairly narrow limits. It could be enlarged by attracting personnel from nongovernmental activities in private industry or from university faculties, by upgrading personnel, and by increasing the numbers of students receiving university training in the areas of interest. Programs to increase the numbers of men with relevant training have been undertaken under the National Defense Education Act and the more narrowly focused programs of the Defense Department, NASA, and the National Science Foundation. The fact remains that the requirements of government-sponsored programs could be met only by effective competition with alternative sources of employment. Such competition generates substantial and persistent increases in the salaries offered in the skill areas involved. It is a competition in which the private contractors—business firms, the universities and the nonprofit institutions—enjoy a freedom of action not paralleled within the federal civil service.

In the R&D area numerous surveys have been made showing that the salaries paid by private business firms and nonprofit contractors tend to be somewhat higher on the average and very much higher for key personnel than the salaries provided by civil service schedules. Although in testimony before Congress agency officials have tended to vacillate in evaluating the significance of the competition for personnel by contractors upon agency operations, it is clear that the government as a whole has been strongly affected by the pay scales of private institutions. In establishing salary schedules, the government has normally followed the practices of private institutions, though frequently with some significant lag. That procedure is reasonably satisfactory when the government employs some small fraction of the supply of a given skill or when the skill involved is unique to government programs and salaries can be established to attract the necessary numbers. In the R&D area, however, a very large proportion of the nation's scientific and technical personnel are employed on government programs, many of them urgent. Most such personnel are employed by contractors rather than directly by the government.

The inflexibility of government salaries therefore presents a particularly acute problem in the retention of the staffs of government-operated laboratories and the more critical task of retaining or attracting those highly qualified men essential to the effective management of agency programs. The need for retaining and increasing the numbers of highly qualified personnel employed by the government, particularly in scientific and technical areas, has been recognized as a critical problem since 1945. It has also been emphasized in the reports of the Hoover Commission, the Cordiner committee, and the Bell task force, among others.

The fact that the government must react to salary problems generated by private employers expending government funds is, at the very least, a source of frustration. Suggestions have been made that the government impose controls upon salaries payable by contractors, controls that would be much more rigid than the current review for "reasonableness."[60] Since the government's problems are

[60] As a result of his investigations into NIH grant operations, L. H. Fountain was led to recommend that "the President establish a uniform policy with respect to acceptable salary practices in the use of Federal research funds applicable to all Federal agencies making grants to educational and other research institutions." The report continued:

"The Committee . . . supports the principle of compensating the participants in Government-supported research in accordance with the regular salary schedules of their institutions, and . . . is concerned by reports that some institutions are using Federal funds to pay higher than regular salaries. Since this is a matter of concern to many Federal agencies, the Committee felt it should be dealt with on a Government-wide basis . . ." (*Administration of Grants by the National Institutes of Health; Reexamination of Management Deficiencies*, H. Rept. 1958, 87 Cong. 2 sess. [1962], pp. 5, 21–22).

The recommendation was viewed as a warning by the American Council on Education, which after a survey of university practices by its Committee on Sponsored Research issued "Recommendations on Faculty Salaries Charged to Government Contracts" (April 1963).

The possibility that there existed a need for more rigid controls over salaries was touched upon in the Bell report. Thought in the Bureau of the Budget ap-

not confined to scientific or technical personnel but include a number of other categories, any effort to establish more rigid controls over salaries would have very wide implications. The difficulties involved in imposing such controls appear to be great enough to discourage any development of the concept. The policy applied has been to follow the practices of private institutions in establishing salary levels. In the broader view, the federal government's problem is to hold its R&D expenditures in any given area to levels reflecting the availability of personnel and the costs of attracting them into the programs established.

Aside from the problem of competition for personnel, there has been the possibility that contractor freedom to establish salary schedules might result in abuses. Though congressional committees have frequently called for data on contractor salaries they appear to have been satisfied by the publicity so generated and by administrative regulations which require review of all salaries above an established level, usually $25,000. The agencies have, in fact, exercised some control over salaries by occasionally disallowing as reimbursable costs portions of salaries judged to be unreasonable.

---

parently was in the direction of formalizing and strengthening the existing requirement that salaries be "reasonable." Elmer B. Staats, Deputy Director of the Bureau of the Budget, expressed the view that "where the research and development contracting system does not provide built-in controls (for example, through adequate competitive bidding), contractors should be reimbursed only for reasonable compensation costs. The basic standard for reimbursement of salaries and related benefits should be one of comparability with the compensation of persons doing similar work in the private economy.

"Thus I foresee the development, through special compensation surveys to be undertaken, of an average compensation curve or curves for that part of the private sector engaged in research and development work whether for the Government or private sponsors. Those averages would then become the measure of reasonableness against which the compensation systems of cost-type and certain other contractors would be measured" (Press release of address before the Design Engineering Conference, American Society of Mechanical Engineers [May 1, 1962], Chicago, Ill.).

More recently, John Macy, chairman of the Civil Service Commission, has advocated controls over contractor compensation practices: "Now that we are setting Federal rates based on comparability, why should we be paying a contractor above that comparability?" (Federal Council for Science and Technology, *Current Problems in the Management of Scientific Personnel,* Proceedings of the First Symposium, Oct. 17–18, 1963, p. 102).

The Problems of Facilities

Mention must also be made of the problems which arise when new facilities are required for research and development projects. New construction requires both authorization and appropriation actions by Congress. The Congress has rarely raised serious objections to proposals for new facilities, particularly when it could be demonstrated that the facility was a necessary adjunct to the effective management and application of R&D programs carried out in large part by contract. Nevertheless, there have been difficulties in securing funds for the construction of new facilities which tended to encourage reliance upon contracting. In the case of the military services, new R&D facilities have been considered in the general construction budgets. Within each service, as well as at the Secretary of Defense level, such proposals have competed with all other construction proposals and have frequently suffered in competition with what appeared to be urgent operational requirements. Since there are few or no alternatives available for much of the construction required for operational purposes, and contracting is an alternative for R&D and some other types of services, the budgetary process has placed a premium on the contract method.

Of significance also were the delays experienced in many though not all construction projects related to R&D. It required four years from the time the Quartermaster Corps secured acceptance of its plan to build an R&D laboratory before it secured congressional approval of the site. More recently, controversy over site selection has delayed action on NIH's choice of site for its Environmental Health Center[61] and also on the Food and Drug Administration's research center.

Securing necessary facilities is a much simpler process if the contract is used. If the contractor has the facility or an existing government-owned facility can be adapted to contractor use, problems are minimized. If a new facility is necessary, provision covering the cost of leasing a facility or amortizing the cost of a capital expenditure can be made as a part of a contract with few of the diffi-

[61] See "Environmental Health Center; PHS Project Stalled on Several Counts; Site and Scope Are Still in Dispute," *Science,* vol. 1414 (Aug. 23, 1963), pp. 703-4.

culties or delays that are characteristic of projects requiring a new government-owned and government-operated facility.

The Hoover Commission and Executive Policy

While the concern of the Congress with the size and operations of the executive agencies led to the actions discussed in the preceding pages, Congress also sought a more effective appraisal of the activities of the executive branch than its own machinery provided. That objective was sought through the Commission on Organization of the Executive Branch of the Government established by statute in 1947. The interests of the first Hoover Commission were principally with the effectiveness of top-level organization of federal agencies. In its 1949 report the commission gave little attention to contracting except that it pointed out with regard to medical research that "to build up within the Federal Government a research potential of sufficient size to meet the full research needs of [the proposed National Bureau of Health] would be at the expense of well-established non-Federal centers of investigation, and would have far-reaching, damaging consequences for the medical economy of the Nation."[62] The commission went on to recommend that emphasis be shifted from project research to a "more sustaining type of support," based upon broad research programs formulated with the participation of nongovernmental advisers. With regard to the military programs the commission concerned itself largely with the need for an integrated plan of research and development related to strategic needs. The commission supported the establishment of a national science foundation and recommended that the basic research programs of the military agencies be transferred to such an agency.[63]

The second Hoover Commission, established in 1953, directed its attention to the functional organization of the executive branch as well as to the relationships between government agencies and private organizations. It strongly urged that the military services

[62] Commission on Organization of the Executive Branch of the Government, *Task Force Report on Federal Medical Services* (January 1949), Append. O, pp. 70–71.
[63] *Ibid.*, pp. 87–89.

abandon their numerous activities relating to products and services that could be obtained from private business firms. With regard to research in the military services, it strongly supported the contract system that had come into being. In its judgment,

research and development and design operations are, in general, best performed by civilian agencies. Since the close of World War II, the Military Departments have greatly expanded their facilities and personnel for the operations of research and development. The operations performed there are generally at a lower level of effectiveness than could be realized if suitably placed in the civilian economy. The Task Force Subcommittee estimates that in 1954 there was a $125 million volume of such work that was susceptible to shift into the civilian economy.[64]

It was further suggested that

even where operations must be done in military installations, frequently increased effectiveness and efficiency will be realized through operations by civilian organizations.

The task force subcommittee singled out the Department of the Air Force for commendation of its policy of relying upon private contractors. The commission pointed out, however, that at a minimum some 30 percent of R&D expenditures "would and must be expended within Government in vital areas," and further noted that the necessary personnel must be of the highest competence.

The views of the commission on the undesirability of government operations in areas that could be supplied by private institutions were already established as DOD policy[65] and were soon to be adopted as administration policy. In 1955 the Bureau of the Budget, undoubtedly reflecting President Eisenhower's views, instructed the executive agencies that "commercial-industrial activities were not to be started or conducted if the product or service involved could be procured from private enterprise."[66] Exceptions

[64] Commission on Organization of the Executive Branch of the Government, *Research and Development in the Government,* Report no. 14 (1955), p. 16.

[65] The Department of Defense in September 1952 issued a directive expressing its policy against the continued operation or the establishment of new commercial and industrial facilities when requirements could be met effectively and economically from private sources. The evolution of the government's policy in this area is reviewed in Eli E. Nobleman, *Government Competition with Private Enterprise,* Study prepared for the Senate Government Operations Committee, 88 Cong. 1 sess. (1963), pp. 12–37.

[66] Through its Bulletin 55-4.

were made for activities which involved jeopardy to national security if turned over to private industry and for those which could be procured through commercial sources only at higher costs.

The action of the Bureau of the Budget was directed specifically at the numerous routine activities such as bread-baking, ice cream manufacture, and paint production which had grown up within the government. With regard to such activities the bureau's action established procurement from private sources as standard policy and placed upon the agency the burden of proving that an exception to that procedure was warranted. The bureau's policy also clearly applied to some of the activities of such installations as the Army's manufacturing arsenals and the Navy's shipyards. The directive implementing the bureau's order within the DOD defined commercial or industrial activities as "those providing products or services which normally can be obtained from private enterprise through ordinary business channels."[67] Many if not most of the R&D activities of the services had long been justified on the grounds that they were services essential to military needs and that they were unique and unavailable from any private source. The application of the DOD's directive to R&D was then uncertain. The directive supported though it did not make mandatory the practice already established in some agencies of turning first to private sources. If the project involved something that private firms did not normally do they were queried as to their interest and capability for undertaking it. Only if such queries produced negative results would in-house performance be undertaken.

The Budget Bureau's action as interpreted by the agencies represented a long step in reducing agency discretion and a further hardening of policy in favor of contracting for a wide variety of services other than R&D. The presumption of the desirability of government performance which underlay the prewar R&D policies had been removed. Instead the procurement of R&D would be from private sources unless no private source could be found.

Since the policy of contracting for R&D was already well established on its own merits, the effect of the policies discussed was, on occasion, to encourage employment of contractors on projects that, in the agency's judgment, might have been better carried on by an expansion of in-house facilities. An additional important

---

[67] Nobleman, *Government Competition with Private Enterprise*, p. 9.

effect of personnel ceilings was to extend the use of the contract into many areas other than R&D.

To the agencies the contract has provided the solution to the problem posed by congressional disapproval of a civil service increasing as federal expenditures increase. The willingness of Congress to approve appropriations substantially in excess of the provisions for salaries has been construed as an invitation by the Congress to the agencies to employ contracts to accomplish their programs.

Constraints upon Contracting

With the creation of a device that gave the agencies great freedom in the methods that they could apply to the pursuit of their objectives and the establishment of controls over personnel which forced use of the contract, the need for establishing constraints was to be met by critical examination of experience and the pragmatic establishment of criteria. In this process the Congress played the role of critic of the experiments of the administrative agencies. The role of the Bureau of the Budget was that of appraising the broad problems and results of contracting, partly on the basis of opinions expressed by Congress, and establishing broad administrative policy for agency guidance. The General Accounting Office, on the other hand, dealt with specific situations in detail. Since congressional policy was clearly in process of change, the General Accounting Office reported its findings for action by the Congress although it was also a direct source of some mild restraints on agency action.

The General Accounting Office usually acts on its own initiative although it has frequently responded to requests from congressional committees and on a few occasions has responded to a protest by the Civil Service Commission. The numerous laws relating to the civil service had long been held by the GAO to constitute a policy or rule (but not positive law) that "purely personal services may not be engaged by the Government on a nonpersonal contract but are required to be performed by Federal personnel under Government supervision."[68] The General Accounting Office has found itself the interpreter of possible conflicts

[68] 33 Comp. Gen. 170–71 (1953).

between statutes relating to the civil service and statutes authorizing the agencies to contract. While the long-standing rule cited remains unaltered, the General Accounting Office in 1952 adopted a
policy which was consistent with the changing attitude of the Congress toward the use of the contract. That policy was that "where
it is administratively determined that it would be substantially
more economical, feasible, or necessary by reason of unusual circumstances, to have the work involving personal services performed by non-Government parties, and that it is clearly de-
monstrable, this Office will not object to the procurement of such
work through proper contract management."[69]

The General Accounting Office has necessarily dealt cautiously
with contracts in the R&D area since congressional policy has
clearly been one of encouraging the agencies to secure the services
of the best qualified individuals or group, whatever their institutional affiliation.

Among the numerous General Accounting Office reports which
have had some influence upon agency operations most have dealt
with the more or less routine operations of the contracting system
and have affected the operation of the system rather than its structure. The agency has, however, on occasion sought to set limits on
the applicability of contracting. Perhaps its most important effort
of this kind was its criticism of contracts calling for the management of the development of complex weapon systems, on the
grounds that such contracts constituted an excessive delegation of
government responsibilities and authority to private institutions.
The leading case involved a contract between the Air Force and
the Ramo-Wooldridge Corporation in which its subsidiary, Space
Technology Laboratory, performed the function of system manager for a number of Air Force missile programs. Among Space
Technology Laboratory's contracted duties was that of advising a
number of other contractors as to the technical alternatives in the
development of the missiles.

In the opinion of the General Accounting Office such decision-
making was a non-delegable responsibility of the government.[70]

[69] 31 Comp. Gen. 372–73 (1952); 33 Comp. Gen. 170–71 (1953).
[70] Comptroller General of the United States, *Compilation of General Accounting
Office Findings and Recommendations for Improving Government Operations, Fiscal
Year 1960, Report to the Congress of the United States* (1961), p. 144. It should

The General Accounting Office view was an interpretation of the procurement statutes which neither provided for the contracted procurement of system management as such nor prohibited such contracts. In effect the General Accounting Office argued that a contract must be carried out precisely as described in the work statement from which changes could be made only with the approval of the government. Delegation of the authority to refine or otherwise change the work statement was unacceptable.

The congressional reaction to the General Accounting Office report was pragmatic rather than ideological. The General Accounting Office recommendation was not accepted; instead the concept of contracting for system management found substantial support. However, an attempt to provide statutory authority for contracting for system management failed to reach the floor of Congress.[71]

The Ramo-Wooldridge case also presented a conflict of interest problem. The company served as a principal adviser on an Air Force program but was interested in bidding on related production contracts. The House Committee on Government Operations held that an unacceptable conflict of interest existed and suggested the idea of forming a nonprofit organization to perform the advisory function.[72] A General Accounting Office investigation released soon after the House report recommended that the Air Force acquire a staff competent to perform the complex technical functions required. However, the House committee accepted the Air Force's plan to create the nonprofit Aerospace Corporation to undertake those services under contract.[73]

---

be noted that the GAO ruled that contracting for weapon systems was illegal, an issue that had been debated for some time. See, for example, Robert F. S. Homann, "Weapon System Concepts and Their Pattern in Procurement," *Federal Bar Journal,* vol. 17 (1957), p. 406.

[71] *Military Procurement,* Hearings on S. 500 [Saltonstall bill] before the Senate Armed Services Committee, 86 Cong. 1 sess. (1959); and in the 86 Cong. 2 sess. (1960), *Procurement Study* and S. Rept. 1900.

[72] *Organization and Management of Missile Programs,* H. Rept. 1121, 86 Cong. 1 sess. (1959), p. 99.

[73] *Ibid.;* and *Air Force Ballistic Missile Management* [formation of Aerospace Corporation], H. Rept. 234, 87 Cong. 1 sess. (1961). The House Post Office and Civil Service Committee had instigated the GAO investigation in 1959 and tended to support the GAO in the view that the Air Force should develop an in-house capability. See the committee's *Survey of Certain Aspects of the Ballistic Missile Program of the Department of the Air Force* (1960).

The General Accounting Office has also been concerned with the use of the contract to secure a very wide variety of services other than R&D. As has been pointed out, contracts are used to secure stenographic services, the inspection of products offered for delivery, and the maintenance of equipment, and also such operations as the writing of technical manuals, and the processing of highly sophisticated data such as those obtained from satellites. The General Accounting Office has expressed disapproval of contracts which in its judgment evaded or violated civil service laws, manpower ceilings or fiscal restrictions, or which constituted a delegation of management responsibility.[74] It has approved contracts for messenger services on the grounds of economy, for management surveys on the grounds of the need for independent, outside expertise, and inspection services as a part of the facilities rendered available by a contractor.[75] It drew a clear line in a 1952 case which involved the practice of Navy field officers of employing contracts to assist in administering procurement contracts, including the application of financial controls and audits.[76] The General Accounting Office expressed the opinion that the practice, followed during World War II and until 1950, of performing the functions of these offices by firms and individuals under cost-plus-fixed-fee contracts was not justified either by emergency conditions or by the First War Powers Act. It was suggested that the contractual arrangements might be in violation of laws relating to government employment.

In the case cited, as in most others of this nature, the General Accounting Office rendered an opinion without recommending such action as the cancellation of a contract, refusal to make payment, or the recoupment of funds. It has occasionally ordered a practice terminated. The General Accounting Office's principal function has been to report to the Congress those situations which it believes call for further investigation and possible action. In the absence of action by the Congress or protests from the Civil Service Commission, the General Accounting Office has contributed modestly to establishing specific limits of contracting out. In view of the pragmatic attitude of the Congress and the absence of guide-

[74] 32 Comp. Gen. 127 (1952); 427 (1953).
[75] 36 Comp. Gen. 338 (1956); 33 Comp. Gen. 143 (1953).
[76] 32 Comp. Gen. 18 (1952).

lines, the General Accounting Office's defense of the boundaries of "work traditionally performed by government employees" has been highly permissive.

Critics of contracting have not been wholly absent in the Congress and some congressional groups have sought to supply, or to stimulate the executive to supply, clearer "metes and bounds" for contracting. Congressional committees have occasionally called for the formulation of a policy to guide the agencies in determining what work should be performed by the government and suggested that there was need for government-wide coordination of standards and policies applicable to contract awards and administration. Suggestions have been made that the Bureau of the Budget establish an office to provide such standards and to coordinate and review all contracts entered into by government agencies with private organizations.

No immediate action was taken on these recommendations. The Bureau of the Budget did routinely review agency proposals and activities including contract programs. However, as noted above, instead of moving to restrict the use of the contract, the Bureau, following the apparent wishes of Congress and the views of the administration as well as the guidance of the Hoover Commission, was moving toward support of wider application of contracting. The Bureau moved pragmatically to develop its policy on the basis of evaluation of agency experience and congressional reactions as these might be interpreted and blended into traditional practices.

The Bureau of the Budget made an effort as early as 1955 to develop guidelines for agency use of the contract, but it was not until 1961 that it published its Circular A-49 entitled "Use of Management and Operating Contracts." That title referred to cost-reimbursement contracts between the government and non-profit institutions, private businesses or universities "(a) to administer, on behalf of the Government, research or development establishments wholly devoted to Government work or Government research or development programs; (b) to administer and operate Government-owned or leased industrial facilities; or (c) to provide such personal or professional services as are authorized by law."

The circular, "based upon the most successful agency experience," suggested that contracts have been found particularly useful for the performance of functions requiring specialized knowledge and experience in large-scale industrial management or in the conduct of research, and where unusual speed was required in the organization of a new program or service. A contract was to be regarded as unsuitable (1) unless contractor operations would be more economical than direct operations or (2) unless the probable higher cost of a contractor would be outweighed by increased effectiveness of operation; (3) unless the agency had no essential need for the "in-service capability" which would be acquired if agency personnel performed the function; (4) the agency did not have a capability of the standard of excellence required; or (5) unless qualified contractors are known to be available and willing to assume full management responsibility. The agency was called upon to make a finding that the product or service could not be procured from private enterprise through normal channels.

The circular also listed a number of governmental functions which were not to be contracted out.

1. Functions involving the direction, supervision and control of government personnel, except for supervision incidental to training;

2. Functions involving the exercise of police and regulatory powers in the name of government, exclusive of guard and protection services;

3. Functions of determining basic government policies;

4. The day-to-day staff and management functions of the agency, or any element thereof, such as internal personnel administration and budget preparation (other than specialized studies of an intermittent nature relating to the analysis of organization, personnel administration, and management systems).

With minor changes, these regulations were restated in 1966 in Bureau of the Budget Circular No. A-76.

These regulations reflected congressional views, revealed in part as congressional committees commented on agency operations. There were also other issues with which Congress from time to time showed some concern.

It was recognized as early as 1953 by the Senate Committee on Post Office and Civil Service that personnel ceilings stimulated reliance upon contracting to accomplish agency missions.[77] Although

---

[77] *Manpower Utilization by the Federal Government through the Use of Private Contract Labor*, S. Doc. 32, 83 Cong. 1 sess. (1953), pp. 13–15.

the Congress has from time to time been concerned that the contract method may be higher in cost, no action has followed. In areas where the contract is used to procure services other than R&D, generalizations regarding comparative salaries and wages are sometimes difficult. In R&D, cost is a consideration clearly secondary to the quality of proposals, of the capability available, and of results. Aside from the difficulties of appraising qualitative differences there is the further difficulty to the government of securing satisfactory cost data. In some areas services can be obtained at less cost by contract, in others contract costs appear to be higher.

A basic principle upon which there is agreement among all parties is that administrative responsibility should not be delegated by contract to a private institution. The application of that principle, however, permits wide differences of opinion as to where the limit lies. Agency spokesmen have unanimously and invariably insisted that they retain the final decision-making authority. They insist also that they maintain levels of staff possessing the technical and scientific capabilities necessary to support their ability to make final decisions on the basis of independent and objective evaluation of the data available to them. The wide differences in such staff capabilities among the agencies and among different programs in the same agency, both at the management and performance levels, raise questions as to what constitutes a minimum capability necessary to support independent judgments.

Congress has from time to time expressed doubts that an agency possesses the technical competence necessary to make independent and informed judgments on contractor proposals and performance. If the Congress has on many occasions accepted a situation representing heavy dependence of the government on private management and technical services on the grounds of immediate need, it has at the same time expressed concern that no steps were taken to develop the government's competence. A House committee, for example, complained that some contracts represent a farming out of administrative and executive responsibilities and even the technical direction of programs to the point that the government is often unable to obtain qualified employees to carry out functions of critical importance because most of the available supply has been "cornered by the very firms holding Government contracts."[78] The problems presented by such questions relating to the competence of government personnel to deal with novel problems generated by R&D are exceedingly difficult as well as perennial. They involve not only the technical aspects of a proposal or an established project but the necessity also of evaluating the relevance of still-distant technical developments to possible applications.

Occasionally a congressional committee has been aroused by the titles or general nature of contractual projects to examine them in some detail. In some cases the good judgment of the responsible agency has been challenged and doubts have been expressed that specific contracts or grants should have been made, on the grounds that the subject-matter or the objectives were unworthy of the expenditure of public funds.

There have also been criticisms of contracts on the grounds that the work, though not of a management character, is nevertheless of the type that should be carried on within the agency. Thus, the committees concerned with foreign relations have on numerous occasions expressed disapproval of the Department of Defense contract with the Military Assistance Institute on the ground that the training functions performed should be an inhouse responsibility.[79] The committees objected also to the fact that the officials of the institute were retired military officers and therefore, in its opinion, ineligible to hold this contractual position.

As has been noted, the Subcommittee on Labor Utilization in the Federal Government of the House Committee on Post Office and Civil Service has been a consistent critic of contracting, primarily outside the R&D area. In some part it has served as a spokesman for labor organizations representing federal employees on whom it relied to provide examples of contracting for services which had

[78] House Post Office and Civil Service Committee, *Preliminary Report on Aspects of the Missile Program in the Departments of the Navy and Air Force,* 86 Cong. 1 sess. (1959).

[79] The Military Assistance Institute is an organization which provides training for military personnel assigned to overseas posts in the military assistance program. It is operated under contract by the American Research Institute. See *Mutual Security Act of 1959,* Hearings before the Senate Foreign Relations Committee, 86 Cong. 1 sess. (1959), p. 723; *Mutual Security Act of 1959,* Hearings before the House Foreign Affairs Committee, 86 Cong. 1 sess. (1959), p. 1252, and 86 Cong. 2 sess. (1960), p. 146.

been performed by government employees. Over a period of time the committee found numerous examples of contracting to secure services which it considered to be traditional responsibilities of civil service employees. While the committee occasionally questioned the cost data which presumably supported a shift from direct hire to contracting, it made no attempt to dispute the contracting guides as supplied by Bureau of the Budget Circular A-49.

The appropriations committees have occasionally contributed critical comments of the same kind. In its report on the Department of Defense Appropriations Act for Fiscal Year 1960 the House Appropriations Committee "took note of the increasing tendency to utilize contractors for the performance of largely personal service functions which have been, or should be, performed by Government employees." It referred "to the type of contract wherein the contractor undertakes to supply principally personnel for the accomplishment of an administrative or managerial task, as opposed to individual contracts with consultants, technicians, or specialists and as opposed to contracts for routine labor tasks for maintenance, such as painting, plumbing, carpentry, or the like."[80]

Such criticism no doubt has had some effect upon the agencies, but in the large majority of instances explanations of the projects have muted if not fully satisfied the critics. While Congress has reached no consensus critical of contracting, comments of the kind cited are nevertheless warnings that the use of the contract may have been extended excessively. Such warnings are also invitations to the affected agencies to take such action as they deem possible. The passage of the salary legislation of 1962 and 1964, discussed a few pages below, might be interpreted as reducing the incentive to employ contractual performers, although it is more likely that it will make possible more effective administration of programs that continue to rely upon private institutions.

There appear to be some groups in the Congress, however, willing to consider agency personnel ceilings as an excessively arbi-

_____

[80] *Department of Defense Appropriation Bill, 1960*, H. Rept. 408, 86 Cong. 1 sess. (1959), p. 44. Cf. *Contracting Out Government Responsibility for Administrative, Management and Other Services*, First Intermediate Report of the Subcommittee on Manpower Utilization [Davis subcommittee] of House Post Office and Civil Service Committee, 86 Cong. 1 sess. (1959).

trary control device involving unnecessary expense without compensating gain. In 1965, the time seemed propitious to establish some guidelines which would more precisely delineate the areas in which contracting was and was not acceptable. It was against this background that the Subcommittee on Manpower of the House Committee on Post Office and Civil Service requested a ruling by the General Accounting Office of an action of the Civil Service Commission. The case involved technical personnel supplied by a contractor for work in an Air Force facility. The work was not a group effort but of a personal nature, the contractual employees frequently working side by side with civil service employees. Day-to-day assignments and immediate supervision were performed by civil service employees. The contracts had been extended by renewal over a period of years, eliminating justification on the grounds of emergency.

The General Accounting Office ruled that the contract and all others of a similar nature were illegal and were to be terminated as soon as possible.[81] As a result of the ruling, contractor personnel can no longer be used if they are physically intermingled with government employees and if they are supervised by government personnel.[82] One reaction is the restructuring of contracts to place

[81] The Civil Service Commission had found that ". . . these contract technicians can only be employed in the work of Department of the Air Force after they are approved by the contracting officer who is, of course, a Federal employee, and who has the power to remove them; that the supervision of their daily work is performed by a Federal employee; and that, unquestionably, the contract technician is performing a Federal function. Positions whose incumbents have these characteristics should be Federal positions and the incumbents themselves should be Federal employees appointed and paid as such under applicable Federal personnel statutes. The fact that these contract technicians have not been appointed as Federal employees and that their services have been used in such positions without regard to the applicable Federal personnel statutes, established the illegality of the contract under which they have served." *Use of Contract Personnel in Department of Defense*, H. Rept. 129, 89 Cong. 1 sess. (1965), and Supplement, *Decision of the Comptroller General of the United States Regarding Contractor Technical Services*, H. Rept. 188, 89 Cong. 1 sess. (1965), p. 3.

[82] In the Department of Defense, the GAO action resulted in the identification of 10,500 positions supplied by contractors that required conversion to direct hire. The criteria applied by the Department included, in addition to those cited above, comparative costs of direct-hire versus contractual supply as well as military readiness. See Assistant Secretary of Defense Paul R. Ignatius, "Contracts for Technical Services," *Defense Industry Bulletin*, vol. 3 (August 1967), pp. 9–11.

fuller responsibilities upon the contractor. In other situations the performance of the work will henceforth be done by civil service employees. The end result of the GAO action is the establishment of a clearer boundary between contractual and direct-hire employment.

Toward More Specific Policies for R&D Contracting

The slow emergence of clearer constraints on contracting practices described above has been of significance primarily in areas other than R&D. Much the largest portion of the government's expenditures for contractual services has been for R&D objectives and members of Congress have frequently expressed uneasiness and occasionally dissatisfaction with the manner in which the programs were administered. There was also concern within the executive branch, and in 1962 the administration launched a multipronged review of R&D contracting. This included a reexamination of general policy with regard to the utilization of contracts in the area, a restatement of policies on problems of conflict of interest, a review of civil service salary scales, and an appraisal of agency programs relating to the working conditions provided the government's scientific and technical personnel. In essence, the effort sought to establish a rationale for the use of the contract and the relationships of contractual to inhouse operations based on grounds more rational than simple expediency or the fear of a growing body of federal employees.

The reexamination of general policy was undertaken in 1961–62 upon the request of the President by a task force chaired by David E. Bell, then director of the Bureau of the Budget. The President requested that the group "review the experience of the Government in using contracts with private institutions and enterprises to obtain research and development work needed for public purposes" with specific objectives of recommending "criteria that should be used in determining whether to perform a function through a contractor or through direct Federal operations"; and to recommend "actions needed to increase the Government's ability to review contractor operations and to perform scientific and technical work; and on policies which should be followed by the Government in obtaining maximum efficiency from contractor operations and in reviewing contractor performance and costs."[83]

In its report to the President the members of the Bell task force stated that "there is no doubt that the Government must continue to rely on the private sector for the major share of the scientific and technical work it requires."[84] They accepted as desirable the existing high degree of interdependence and collaboration between government and private institutions which "was in the national interest because it affords the largest opportunity for initiative and the competition of ideas from all elements of the technical community."[85]

It was held to be desirable that many kinds of arrangements be available by which the government could and should "mobilize the talent and facilities needed" to carry out its R&D effort. Though the Bell report did not say so explicitly, it implied that the use of the contract to avoid increasing federal payrolls should be rejected. Choice between direct-hire or contractual performers in any instance should be discriminating, based primarily on two considerations: "1. Getting the job done effectively and efficiently with due regard to the long-term strength of the Nation's scientific and technical resources, and 2. avoiding assignments of work

---

[83] The Report to the President on Government Contracting for Research and Development (April 30, 1962) was printed as Appendix 1 in *Systems Development and Management*, Hearings before the House Government Operations Committee, 87 Cong. 2 sess. (1962), pt. 1, pp. 191–337; the quotation is from p. 251. The House committee print is cited, but the report was also published as *Report to the President on Government Contracting for Research and Development*, S. Doc. 94, 87 Cong. 2 sess. (May 1962).

Simultaneously a private group chaired by Helge Holst of Arthur D. Little & Co. undertook a similar study, also printed in *Systems Development and Management*. The Holst report differed from the Bell report in a lesser concern with intramural laboratories and in some minor points. The two reports were, in general, very similar in analysis and conclusions.

[84] *Ibid.*, p. 203. In addition to David Bell, the report was signed by the Secretary of Defense, the chairman of the Atomic Energy Commission, the administrator of NASA, the director of the National Science Foundation, the chairman of the Civil Service Commission, and the Special Assistant to the President for Science and

[85] *Ibid.*, pp. 209–10.

which would create inherent conflicts of interest."[86] There were
certain functions which should under no circumstances be contracted out. Management and control of the federal research and
development effort must be firmly in the hands of full-time government officials responsible to the President and the Congress.

The Bell report thus accepted the general situation that had developed in the R&D area and in a sense went further in that in-
house performance was defended not for its own sake but as a necessary support for the more effective management of the system.
The ability to apply adequate management controls was seen to
rest upon the competence to make informed and objective decisions. The report pointed out that there must be sufficient technical competence within the government so that outside technical
advice does not become *de facto* technical decision-making. Even
the best qualified government managers need to obtain technical
advice from specialists. Arrangements for advice obtained from
sources outside the government were to be made in the light of a
recent memorandum from the President entitled "Preventing
Conflicts of Interest on the Part of Advisers and Consultants to the
Government."[87] Government-operated laboratories should also be
sources of such advice. The report suggested further that it was
necessary to be "particularly sensitive to the cumulative effects of
contracting out the government's work. A series of actions which
might be clearly justified individually might, when taken together,
erode the government's ability to manage its programs."[88]

For these reasons the report focused strongly on the need to
strengthen the "Government's competence as a 'sophisticated
buyer.' "[89] While the report indicated that there were improvements possible in the administrative procedures employed, as in

[86] *Ibid.*, p. 214.
[87] Text appears in *ibid.*, pp. 34–41.
[88] *Ibid.*, p. 218.
[89] *Ibid.*, p. 228. The Bell report was transmitted by the President to Congress.
In the House, the Government Operations Committee held extensive hearings
which have frequently been cited in this chapter under the heading of *Systems
Development and Management*. In those hearings congressional reaction was sym-
pathetic. The committee issued no report which broadly covered the information
it had received. Instead it chose to concentrate on a single aspect and issued a
thoughtful analysis of the thorny problems of conflict of interest (*Avoiding Conflicts
of Interest in Defense Contracting and Employment*, H. Rept. 917, 88 Cong. 1 sess.
[1963]).

greater use of feasibility studies preceding the letting of large development contracts, and in greater use of incentive provisions in contracts, it suggested that the fundamental need was to strengthen inhouse technical capability. The strengthening needed was of R&D performance capability, not primarily for its own sake but as necessary to maintain an adequate level of competence available for application by management to independent, objective decision-making within the government. To some degree this strengthening could be accomplished by removing administrative restrictions which hampered research effectiveness, by the assignment of significant and challenging work, and by the continual upgrading of the capabilities of federal personnel through education and training.

Effective strengthening of the government's ability to manage the systems rested primarily upon a solution to the major problem of civil service salaries for scientific and technical positions particularly regarding the upper levels. Such salaries had persistently lagged behind those paid by private institutions and the problem was now judged to be acute. The Bell report therefore threw its support to the President's recommendation, then before the Congress, for adjustments in the civil service salary schedules for higher professional and technical jobs in the federal service based on comparability with private pay levels.[90]

With the support of data from both governmental and nongovernmental sources the Civil Service Commission was able to convince the Congress of the need for substantial revision. In the Federal Salary Reform Act of 1962 the Congress abolished the limitations it had placed on the number of positions in the supergrades (16, 17, and 18). The act also endorsed the principle that "Fed-

---

In the Senate, no hearings were held. Senator John L. McClellan, chairman of the Government Operations Committee, in his letter of transmittal observed of the report that the committee had "made recommendations of similar import to the Congress and to the President on April 17, 1958 ('Science and Technology Act of 1958,' S. Doc. 90, 85th Cong., pp. 41–45, 66–68), and on September 9, 1958 ('Progress Report on Science Programs of the Federal Government,' S. Rept. 2498, 85th Cong., pp. 30–34), and on March 23, 1959 ('Science Program—86th Congress,' S. Rept. 120, pp. 41–58)" (*Report to the President on Government Contracting for Research and Development*, S. Doc. 94, 87 Cong. 2 sess. [1962], p. iii).

[90] A position further supported by a report by the Federal Council for Science and Technology, *Studies on Factors Affecting Federal Employment of Scientific Personnel* (1962), cited in *Systems Development and Management*, pp. 403–31.

eral salary rates shall be comparable with private enterprise salary rates for the same levels of work." New salary schedules were established on the basis of the information furnished by the executive in support of the bill and continued application of the principle was provided by a requirement for annual studies and reports to Congress on private salary scales.

The Congress, however, postponed the application of the comparability principle to salaries in excess of $15,000. It recognized the critical importance of some action on these grades but was reluctant to increase salaries above that level since the result would be that some civil servants would have salaries higher than the salaries of their politically appointed superiors. The Senate Committee on Post Office and Civil Service, however, requested that the President recommend a salary plan applying not only to those higher civil service grades but also to politically appointed executives, members of Congress, and judges, and maintaining appropriate differentials. Such a plan was submitted by the President's Advisory Panel on Federal Salary Systems. In the Federal Pay Reform Act of 1964, while Congress considerably modified the plan submitted, salary adjustments were made for most categories, resulting in a top civil service salary of $25,500.[91]

The Contract in Government Operations

Over the past two decades, the federal government has established objectives and pursued policies resting upon relationships between the government and the rest of society which differ markedly from those which many years of experience had previously established as standard. Under that standard system all of the federal government's activities were carried on by personnel employed by a government agency. The goods and common services needed by such personnel in the performance of their assignments were procured from private sources under statutes which required that the items be described in such detail that invitations to quote prices could be issued to all interested suppliers. If such specifications could not be readily prepared, the government undertook the work necessary. When work of this kind, now classified as research and de-

[91] The principal features of the 1962 and 1964 legislation on federal salaries are conveniently analyzed in the *Monthly Labor Review* (October 1964), pp. 1155–64.

velopment, was beyond the skills and resources to be found among government employees, the agency either requested authority to make special arrangements, sought to meet its needs through informal relations with private institutions, made do with what was available on the market, or did without. Public objectives not obtainable through these means were supported by grants of federal funds in aid of programs carried out by the state governments.

The objectives and programs established since World War II, and changes in the controlling statutes and in congressional authorizations, have given an important role to a third method. The government now makes large expenditures to accomplish incompletely defined objectives by means that cannot be precisely specified in advance. It must be assumed that the supplier will apply his best effort. The specifications describing the work are frequently the major contribution of the supplier. While there is frequently vigorous competition, selection of the contractor is not based on lowest price but upon judgment regarding the best value. Procurement of this nature has come to constitute an important part of government expenditures and is the characteristic of the way in which important programs are administered. After two decades of experience, programs calling for this type of procurement have acquired a large and permanent place in the government's activities.

The relative importance of the new types of procurement are shown in Chart 5, which divides the estimated obligations of the federal government for 1966—totaling $148 billion—into principal object classes. Personal services and benefits at $32.9 billion; acquisition of capital assets at $28.3 billion; supplies and materials at $20.7 billion; and rent, transportation, utilities and similar items at $8.5 billion represent the standard types of resources applied to government programs. Together these account for about 63 percent of federal obligations.

Personal services are obtained under statutes establishing rates of compensation, fringe benefits, and work classification. Items in the other categories are purchased primarily through competitive bidding procedures, at prices established by public regulatory agencies, or at prices negotiated with such regulated prices as a base. These are the conventional and long-established methods by which the government has obtained its requirements.

CHART 5

Federal Obligations by Principal Object Classification in the Administrative Budget for Fiscal Year 1966

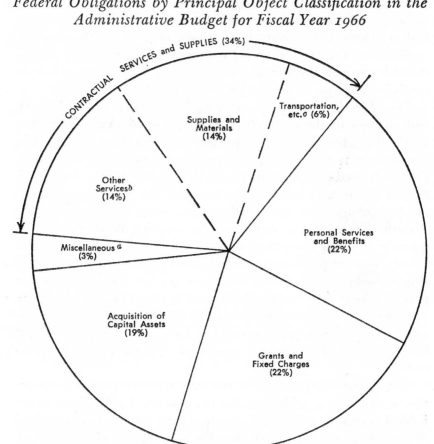

Source: U. S. Bureau of the Budget, *Special Analysis on Obligations by Object: Budget for Fiscal Year 1966* (June 1965), p. 7.

a. Includes funds proposed for separate transmittal and those not distributed otherwise.

b. Since grants for research are considered to be contracts in this study, the NIH and NSF research project grant funds are included in this category.

c. Includes rent, communications, utilities, printing costs, services of other agencies, and payments to specified accounts.

This third type of purchase is shown in Chart 5 as "other services." The $21 billion of estimated obligations for 1966 comprehend a great variety of services that prior to 1940 were provided, if at all, by direct-hire employees working within government-owned facilities with purchased supplies and equipment, or through grants to the states.

The major component of "other services" is the very wide variety of activities which since World War II have been classified as "research, development, testing, and evaluation." Federal obligations for 1966 for RDT&E are estimated to be $15.4 billion. It was anticipated that 75 percent of that amount or about $12.0 billion would be spent with private institutions.

The RDT&E area is also the major one in which new relationships between the government and private institutions have been established since World War II. The government's R&D programs claim a very large part of the nation's available resources, perhaps more than any other broad category. The growth of contractual R&D has had major impacts upon the government as purchaser and upon private institutions as suppliers. Furthermore the results that have flowed from R&D contractual programs must be expected to have a long-range impact upon the nation's technology and therefore the society in a wide variety of relationships.

Government Responsibility in Research and Development

The government now experiences very little difficulty in arousing the interest of private institutions in formulating programs, contributing proposals, or accepting contracts for R&D projects. There have been occasions when an agency has not succeeded in arousing interest as widely as it wished and has had to solicit the participation of private institutions in its programs. Normally, however, indication of government interest stimulates a sufficient flow of proposals that agencies can be selective and can formulate programs with confidence that the objectives can be accomplished.

From the point of view of the government the contractual system, particularly in its project form, has a number of characteristics that are highly advantageous.

1. The government at various levels is able to maintain continuing contact with the relevant research capabilities and activities of the nation, and much of the world.

2. It is possible for a federal agency to identify worthy new objectives or public goals at an early stage of scientific thinking on a subject. The agency may take the initiative in appraising possibili-

ties or, as the system has evolved, specific proposals may come to the agency after the possibilities have been the subject of discussion among private groups.

3. The system maximizes the agency's ability to choose among alternative approaches to any given problem. The system also permits the consolidation of ideas from a variety of sources into a single program, thereby both economizing on costs and accelerating the development process. If such consolidation is not possible or is judged undesirable, two or more approaches to an objective can be undertaken.

4. The proposal system also automatically identifies potential R&D contractors and makes it possible to measure their qualifications and degree of interest.

5. In considering new projects the agency normally selects from among a number of possible performers, but in choosing one it does not lose interest in the others. The contractual relationship has created some very large and complex private organizations, particularly in the field of defense materiel. Furthermore, long-continued relationships between a research institution and the government are common. Such relationships are not the result of any "arrangements" between the government and the private institution but are the product of continuing mutual interests and adaptations in capabilities expressed through contract awards and renewals, terminations, or completions. The sequence is renewed in new contracts as new programs are allocated funds and as new project proposals are accepted.

By this process the government shifts to private institutions the tasks of adjusting resources to the requirements of changing programs, increasing and reorganizing staff as new contracts are let, and then reducing personnel as program needs diminish. Adjustments of this kind have been frequent and sometimes on a large scale in the defense industries.

6. Research and development by private institutions assures that those institutions have the opportunity of considering the possibilities of applying new knowledge and technology generated by work on contracts for one agency to the problems of another agency or to objectives of interest to the private sector of society.

These characteristics emphasize the vital role of the government agency as decision-maker—in the evaluation of the state of knowledge in a field, in establishing program objectives, in identifying projects intended to further the objective, in inviting, evaluating and selecting proposals and performers, and in appraising projects and results. At all levels in an R&D program, from agency staff upward to Congress, judgments defining or affecting the public interest must be made, judgments which frequently involve highly technical issues characterized by uncertainties and requiring evaluations and estimates of probabilities. These often concern questions on which experts may reasonably differ. Ultimately the decision must be made by responsible officials appraising scientific and technical proposals against the broad perspective of the agency's role in promoting the interests of the government and of society.

The burden of decision-making is increased substantially because the proposing groups are inevitably advocates of their particular contributions. Such advocacy varies widely in the zeal with which it is pressed. Advocacy groups may at times bring pressure upon the government with regard to their objectives or to urge a course of action for reasons other than the purely technical. The involvement of private institutions, frequently in large numbers, means that the problem and the action taken on it may have strong and specific impact upon some significant private interests.

The formulation of research and, particularly, development programs, therefore, requires response to a wider range of forces than is characteristic of most government operations. It is under such circumstances that the administrator must formulate the program which will best fulfill the mission of his agency. Since some degree of uncertainty is always present, decisions rest upon the exercise of judgment and the acceptance of responsibility for such judgments. Decisions must be made by the relatively small group of high and accountable officials whose effectiveness will rest upon their own ability and the quality of staff support they receive in analyzing the alternatives before them.

The most striking adjustment within the structure of government to the growth of contractual R&D has been the concentration of responsibility for specific and specialized decisions at high administrative levels of the executive agencies. The administration of R&D programs is the central if not the sole function of some agencies, such as AEC, NIH, NSF and NASA, and is a high level responsibility in the Defense Department organization. The programs prepared in these agencies are subject to further revision for both feasibility and desirability by technically qualified staff and advisory counsel in the Executive Office of the President, a review that may be repeated by congressional committees and subcommittees.

The assignment of active participating responsibilities for development programs to high administrative levels has come about because of the importance attached to them and the large expenditures many of them entail, but particularly because of the nature of the problems calling for decision. In the process of achieving a performance objective, numerous important alternatives must be considered, and decisions must be made. The knowledge available, or that which seems likely to become available, must be matched with needs and appraised for opportunities. Such decisions are influenced by experience with preceding programs since these form the framework for the execution of proposed programs.

As in other complex activities, the responsible administrator must have the support of staff qualified in the area of interest to evaluate new knowledge for its significance to agency responsibilities, to provide analyses and evaluations of programs, of components of the programs, and of the proposals made in furtherance of objectives, and to evaluate progress made. The work involved increases with the capability of private institutions to submit proposals and with the complexity and technical sophistication of the objectives. Advisory committees composed of private citizens are useful and widely employed but they supplement rather than substitute for agency staff qualified to evaluate alternative courses of action, except in some areas of research. Such staff functions require the technical competence that comes from intimate contact with R&D work as well as the ability to give objective consideration to the alternatives that are presented in proposals, or that require decisions as they arise in the course of work.

While the importance—to the government and to the system as a whole—of staff highly qualified to assist in the administration of R&D programs is obvious, the importance of government organizations' doing R&D work is less clear. Some of these organizations are clearly essential in that they maintain unique R&D performing capabilities not available from private sources. Others are primarily engaged in testing and operational evaluation of the work of contractual performers, work which, at least in its final stages, must be done within the government. Other government organizations conducting R&D are continuations of historical practices. Their continuance may be justified as providing a source competitive with and alternative to contractual suppliers, more sensitive to agency needs than outsiders, and also more objective. An important justification made for these organizations is that they are a source of personnel for R&D management staffs.

These considerations are important. However, the variety of arrangements which exist among the agencies prohibits any broad generalizations regarding the optimal relationship of R&D performance to R&D management within the government. It is clear, however, that none of these considerations is well met unless the quality of the staff of the government's R&D organizations is comparable to that available to private institutions. It remains to be seen whether recent actions with regard to salaries and working conditions will be adequate to that end.

Conclusion

The contract and grant have made the research and technical resources of the nation readily accessible to government agencies. While at any one time the R&D capability available has seemed to be clearly limited, such capabilities have demonstrated a great capacity for growth in response to increased demands. They have also demonstrated a high degree of flexibility in adapting to agencies' interests and objectives.

If the capacity of R&D performing institutions has not served to restrict the growth of R&D expenditures, the ease with which a large number of agencies with diffuse and overlapping responsibilities have been able to establish programs and the strong tendency of such programs to enlarge rapidly have posed difficult problems of choice and have suggested the need for constraints. These have proved very difficult to apply. The conclusive decisions are made in the last analysis in the budget process, but the choices that must be made involve important considerations, some of which are foreign to traditional analytical procedures.

After two decades of experience, the government's commitment to R&D programs continues to broaden and with it its reliance upon private R&D contractors. Some minor constraints upon the use of the contract in areas other than R&D have appeared. However, the principle of utilizing private institutions as sources of ideas as well as of performance of R&D projects has withstood all challenges.

This is not to say that the system has reached a maturity in that existing relationships are optimal and that administrative issues can be handled routinely within a framework of practices that have been thoroughly tested. On the contrary, there are numerous difficulties which continue to demand attention. The rapid growth of R&D, facilitated by the ease with which resources could be commanded by contract, has required substantial adjustments in the government's organization and procedures and has suggested the need for more effective controls over agency assignments, programs, and budgets. These are taken up in Chapters IV and V. The corresponding evolution in the relationships between the agencies and those actually conducting its R&D operations is discussed in Chapters VI through IX.

CHAPTER IV

Organizing To Administer Innovation

Until World War II, the federal government had had little experience either in establishing technological goals requiring elaborate development efforts or in administering large scientific and technical programs. The government's experience in arranging with private institutions to contribute proposals and do the work on such programs was also very limited. As has been pointed out in Chapter II, the nature of the postwar programs and the manner in which they were to be accomplished presented problems of organization and procedure that were novel.

In the process of debate and experimentation which has marked the evolution of the system three principal types of administrative problems have required solution.

1. The establishment of organizations and procedures to administer programs directed to the accumulation of new knowledge. The end product of research of this kind is a scientific or technical report which is generally available to the interested public. This category includes what is customarily referred to as basic and, to some degree, applied research in the sciences, particularly the physical and medical sciences.

2. The setting up of organizations and procedures to apply research results to the development of devices and techniques relevant to the accomplishment of an agency's primary mission. This category includes the larger portion of the government's expendi-

tures and is represented principally by the programs of the military services and NASA, though there are many others of smaller magnitudes.

3. The establishment of procedures which, while preserving the multifaceted nature of the government's programs and the diffusion of responsibility among numerous agencies, supplement the budget process in establishing effective presidential and congressional control over agency programs. Related procedures are also needed for the identification of problems not adequately dealt with at the operating agency level, the assignment of priorities, and the coordination of multi-agency efforts.

Programmed Objectives and the Project System

The assignment of research and development responsibilities to an agency is typically expressed in terms of an area of responsibility and of goals to be sought. The agency response is one that "is built from the ground up."[1] The agency's administrative officials guide the agency staff in the formulation of this detailed program. With regard to all components of a program, it is essential that the agency have the opportunity to consider all possible solutions to the problem at hand. The agency must also estimate the probable results of work which is intended to extend the existing state of knowledge. The fact that numerous alternatives can be considered follows from the nature of the contractual R&D process, which can make available the proposals of more or less numerous private organizations. As the number of possible alternatives increases, however, the problem of choice among them becomes more complex. Unless the administrator has highly qualified technical staff to analyze proposals and to provide advice, the validity of any decision may be doubtful. The administrator alone cannot weigh the probabilities that any given effort will make the optimal contribution to the goals sought. A valid decision requires that the alternatives considered represent all possibilities that merit serious consideration; it requires also the constant exercise of judgment in selecting from the alternatives suggested and in developing a cohesive program.

[1] The phrase is David Beckler's in "Strategic Federal Decision-Making on R&D," *Proceedings of the Nineteenth National Conference on the Administration of Research* (Denver Research Institute, 1965), p. 113.

The organization of the R&D process involves many opportunities to make choices. The work units of research are stepping-stones from the known into the unknown, as well as means to the development of the successive groupings of operations which bring into existence increasingly effective devices. These units of planned work—to which popular usage has given the name projects—are highly flexible. The scope of a project in any given situation is determined by the ability of scientists and engineers to visualize the results of a proposed course of action.[2] Projects vary from a simple to an exceedingly complex sequence of activities and may be defined loosely or in precise detail. A project may involve from one to many hundreds, and on occasion thousands, of scientific and technical workers. It may have a very short time schedule or call for work over a period of years. Consequently, the financial requirements may vary from a few hundred to many millions of dollars. Normally each project is closely identified with an investigator or an organization, frequently, though not necessarily, private, that has assumed the initiative or contributed in some large measure to its formulation. Such a contributing organization is likely to be the best qualified to conduct the work of the project. The project concept is not limited to scientific and technical development, but is conveniently applied also to such functions as policy analysis, organization and management surveys, testing, evaluation, and operational applications.

As is pointed out in Chapter II, the system as it now exists recognizes that the knowledge and skills necessary to analyze an R&D problem, to prepare proposals for projects intended to contribute to the objective of a program, and to do the work required may be widely scattered. Relevant skills may be held by self-employed individuals and they may exist in a variety of forms of organization. If the government agency administrating an R&D program is to guide its operations with maximum effectiveness and speed, it must seek assurance that the project ideas that come to it represent the most advanced thinking of the most highly qualified scientists and engineers. The government administrator must be free to combine ideas, regardless of source, into a whole which rep-

---

[2] The terms "project" and "program" are used interchangeably in some agencies. The more common usage, followed in this text, conceives of the project as the smaller unit and the program as a group of implicitly or explicitly related projects. The term "task" is sometimes used to mean some part of a project.

resents an optimized program for attaining an objective—an objective that frequently reaches beyond proven knowledge. Having thus specified its objective and the steps by which it is to be sought, the agency must be able to engage the most effective work force possible, whether from private or public organizations.

The project is also a useful device in subdividing the work required in a large program. Project organization permits private groups to identify the portions of a program to which they can hope to contribute. The project system thus permits the employment of the specialized ideas and abilities of a large number of potential contributors to meet very broad program objectives. It is important to note that in the process each participating group acquires an interest in the program as a whole. Though a group's individual contribution may be small, the program as such becomes the essential vehicle by which its interest can be furthered.

One effect of the policy of inviting private institutions to suggest R&D projects is a heavy flow of proposals, both solicited and unsolicited. Jerome Wiesner has observed that "every day the Government receives many more proposals for work on interesting projects than we can possibly fund, or find people to do. . . . The government could, if resources were available, fund five times the number of really substantial and good applied research or development contracts that it now does."[3]

To deal with this flow, every agency engaged in some aspect of R&D requires staff qualified to analyze and appraise complex technical proposals. However, the depth of such staff capabilities, the work loads placed upon them, and the confidence which the administrator places in them varies widely from agency to agency. Extensive use is also made of advisory groups composed of private individuals. Such groups may be consulted on broad questions of merit and feasibility as well as on specific problems to be anticipated in the formulation of a program. Advisory groups may be consulted at various staff levels as a program moves forward; they may also be consulted by top management as critical points of decision are reached.

[3] Jerome B. Wiesner, "The Impact of Scientific Technology upon Industry and Society," *NASA Conference on Space, Science, and Urban Life*, NASA SP–37 (1963), pp. 69–70.

Wide public participation in the technical aspects of this area of public administration also leads to the participation of private groups in the political side of the process. The establishment of objectives and of programs to effectuate them and the year-to-year reconsideration of the level of expenditures of each program require that decisions be made about the expenditure of limited public funds—decisions based on judgments regarding the relevance of each program to the public interest. Whether in the deliberations of small groups or in public debate, those who feel themselves deeply involved are drawn into the discussion and affect the decision-making process.

The Evolution of Organization for R&D

It was recognized early in the history of government-sponsored R&D that these characteristics of R&D programs, together with the importance attached to R&D objectives, required appropriate administrative organization and procedures. One step that was taken, quickly in some areas, slowly in others, was the separation of the overall administration of R&D programs from the administration of the work itself. Such a separation already existed in the well established programs of the Department of Agriculture. The identification of overall administration as a function distinct from performance was sharply drawn in the legislation creating the Atomic Energy Commission, the first independent agency with clear responsibility for pursuing technological objectives.

Broadly speaking, the present organization of the executive branch of the government for the management of R&D has evolved slowly as responsibility for R&D has been administratively separated from procurement and as research has been separated from development, development from evaluation, and evaluation from operational application. The programming of R&D objectives was quickly recognized as too important to be left with technical staffs and was seen to require constant attention at policy making levels. As time went on, the highest levels of agency administrations, and of the government, assumed more responsibility for actively directing research and, particularly, development.

This was accomplished by statute in the formation of new agencies with specific responsibilities such as the National Science Foundation, the National Institutes of Health, and the National Aeronautics and Space Administration.

In other agencies, established R&D functions were reorganized and made the responsibility of high agency officials as was also the procedure when new functions were undertaken. In the AEC in 1954 the position of general manager, created by the organizing act, was supplemented by that of an assistant general manager for research and development, paralleling an office which had been established earlier for manufacturing operations. The centralization of responsibility for R&D may also be seen in the creation of such new posts as that of Science Advisor to the Secretary, Department of the Interior (1961), and Assistant Secretary for Science and Technology in the Department of Commerce (1962), as well as in the establishment of the Office of Research and Engineering in the Post Office Department (1956), and the Office of Research and Development in the Maritime Administration (1960). Similar offices now exist in the Patent Office (1956), the Department of Labor (1957), the Office of the Assistant Commissioner (Planning and Research), Internal Revenue Service (1958), the Coast and Geodetic Survey (1960), and Aviation Research and Development Service, Federal Aviation Agency (1961).

The importance of science and technology in the nation's international relations received formal recognition in 1958 with the establishment of the post of Science Advisor to the Secretary of State with the responsibility of advising on matters of science policy that affect foreign policy and of assisting in the utilization of science and scientists in international affairs. These functions were given greater recognition in 1962 with the appointment of a Director of International Scientific and Technological Affairs, whose office was to "participate actively in general foreign policy development" as well as to "advise and assist the Secretary of State . . . on matters having scientific and technological implications."[4]

[4] Activities of the State Department relating to science are analyzed in Eugene B. Skolnikoff, *Science, Technology, and American Foreign Policy* (The MIT Press, 1967).

The Administration of Development Programs— the Military Agencies and NASA

The military services pioneered in the assumption of R&D programs that covered the full gamut from basic research to very complex development objectives. The services have consistently maintained the largest and most varied of R&D programs. They have faced a very wide variety of problems in organizing for project selection and in dealing with contractors, and as a result have developed organizations and procedures which offer useful precedents to other agencies. For these reasons the following discussion focuses on the evolution and present character of Defense Department practices in dealing with development. There are some differences in NASA's procedures but on the whole they are similar to those of the Defense agencies. Other agencies follow procedures which reflect their statutory authorities and their special problems and objectives.[5]

The process of defining R&D objectives, assigning responsibilities for them, and establishing appropriate organizations to pursue them within the three services proved to be a difficult and time-consuming problem. Some centralized control was exercised following the end of World War II, but the effective assumption of responsibilities at a central point evolved slowly and was to have major impact upon the organization of the military establishment and the three services.

Many problems relating to postwar organization of the military services were resolved in 1947 with the passage of the National Security Act, which created a national military establishment composed of the three departments, Army, Navy, and Air Force. The three services were distinguished by mission assignments for operations applying the technologies relating to air, water, and land environments. In each case the assignments ranged from responsi-

---

[5] A useful summary of agency authorities, organization, and procedures relating to R&D is *Contract Policies and Procedures for Research and Development*, Report of the Select Committee on Government Research, H. Rept. 1942, 88 Cong. 2 sess. (1964), pp. 3–72.

bility for military operations through procurement back to development and research.

The Secretary of Defense was given broad responsibilities for unifying the activities of the three military departments. Their efforts were to be supported by three staff organizations: the Joint Chiefs of Staff for operations, the Munitions Board for procurement of common items, and the Research and Development Board. Specifically the Secretary of Defense was to establish general policies, to exercise general direction, authority and control over the military establishment, to eliminate unnecessary duplication in a number of specified areas including research, and to supervise and coordinate the preparation of budget estimates of the agencies comprising the national military establishment. At the same time the independence of each of the three services was protected by provisions that each department was to be administered separately. The secretary of each department was given administrative responsibilities and could make reports and recommendations directly to the President after informing the Secretary of Defense. Under the National Security Act, funds continued to be appropriated directly to each service department. The departments also retained all powers not specifically conferred upon the Secretary of Defense.

The internal organization of the noncombat functions of the Army and Navy was not affected by the 1947 legislation. The organization of the newly created Department of the Air Force was modeled on that of its predecessor, the Army Air Corps. Within each service the development of new devices remained the responsibility, usually statutory, of the procurement organizations—the Army's technical services, the Navy's bureaus and the Air Force's commands. Among their responsibilities were those for maintaining knowledge of technical developments of possible relevance to service operations, formulating development proposals, combining these proposals into programs and budgets, reporting progress on approved and funded projects, and submitting prototypes for testing and evaluation. The procurement organizations have proved sufficiently flexible that with the assistance of the technical resources available by contracts and advisory committees they have been able to assume the initiative in exploring the relevance of the new and emerging technologies to the roles and missions of their services.[6]

At times, the ability of the R&D branches of the procurement organizations to generate development proposals have created severe problems of management for the responsible administrative officials in each service. The proposals coming to their desks for approval have not always been coordinated with proposals from other procurement branches. They may reflect an interpretation of strategic requirements not in accord with current department views and they may fail to consider the possibility of developments in some areas. Moreover, requested funds always amount to some multiple of the current budget.

The development of a department R&D program and of its budget requires a selection of proposals based upon a set of priorities which reflect current strategic requirements together with a technical evaluation of each proposal. Involved in the formulation of such programs are appraisals of the strategic or tactical significance of each device that has become technically feasible; an anticipation of its operational applications and limitations which require that realistic operational specifications be established; the assignment of responsibilities for carrying out such decisions; and the determination of the most effective way of organizing complex development efforts. These are functions that require, as Vannevar Bush pointed out in 1945, "technical planning at the top . . . to give affirmative direction and drive to new developments and their use."

The evolution of the military R&D also brought problems between the services. Each service interpreted new technical developments in terms of its responsibilities for carrying out its mission, broadly defined. The result was a profusion of parallel if not duplicating efforts. It could not be otherwise when missiles were viewed by the Army as a new form of artillery and by the Air Force as a type of pilotless aircraft. All three services consequently supported large programs to develop strategic ballistic missiles.

By 1950 none of the services was so organized as to permit the exercise of the functions cited in expeditious and effective fashion. The difficulties were noted both in statue and in traditional prac-

---

⁶ There were some 557 boards, committees, councils, and organized groups in the Office of the Secretary of Defense and the three services in 1959. Of these approximately half were public advisory committees, of which the Army was the largest user. For a list, see *Impact of Defense Procurement*, Hearings before the Joint Economic Committee, 86 Cong. 2 sess. (1960), pp. 80–106.

tices; as Bush pointed out, "our techniques have outrun our organization for handling them." Within the Army and Navy, operations and procurement were only loosely related. Within each, there were a number of procurement agencies, also independent, established by statute and receiving their own appropriations. The solution to common problems traditionally had been sought through ad hoc committees on which each interested service had been represented. Such committees normally recommended that the Army Chief of Staff or the Navy's Chief of Naval Operations approve an action of a procurement agency only as they reached unanimous decisions.

In providing a Secretary of Defense with broad responsibilities for R&D, the Congress had taken the first step toward organizational adjustments called for by massive development programs. While the services took some steps looking to more effective organization, it was the pressure by OSD upon the service secretaries for clearer and more specific plans for operations and development, for sounder technical evaluations, and for coordinated programs, which weakened the barriers to organizational adaptation, thereby recognizing the nature and importance of development programs in the Defense structure. These adjustments were made only slowly in the face of strong opposition. However, the problems presented by the new technology and the management of R&D have contributed in large measure to the fact that the Department of Defense in 1968 is a far different organization than it was in 1946.

The need for detailed guidance as to assignments and as to priorities was clear from the beginning. Secretary Forrestal sought to secure the preparation of detailed plans based upon strategic requirements which would supply detailed guidelines to the services.[7] Since then, much progress has been made in the develop-

---

[7] Secretary Louis Johnson expressed James Forrestal's view in writing: "The entire operation revolves around the preparation of the master plan of R&D. The plan is based upon strategic operational categories such as sea combat operations, land combat operations, strategic air operations, etc., to which the Joint Chiefs of Staff have assigned ratings reflecting relative importance from the strategic planning standpoint.

"Under each operational category are listed technical objectives which comprise all the various weapons, devices, and techniques necessary to that type of operation. Each of these objectives carries a rating reflecting its relative strategic importance, its military adequacy in its current state of development, and the promise for

ment of overall long-range plans, founded upon strategic considerations, and of a specificity suitable for the guidance of R&D programs. However, R&D programs must remain fluid, subject to periodic changes of direction as the nation reacts to political events in the world at large, and to scientific and technical achievements at home and abroad as these have been interpreted by each of the services in their program and budget proposals.

The legislation of 1947 provided for a Research and Development Board to aid the Secretary of Defense in coordinating the activities of the three services. The Board was to have statutory responsibilities for preparing a complete, integrated R&D program, including the coordination of R&D activities among the three departments. It was given policy-making authority over the military's relationships with other agencies in R&D activities, and also assigned some advisory functions as in advising the Joint Chiefs of Staff on R&D matters related to military strategy. Its responsibilities were defined as extending to the point of the availability and approval of equipment for use by the military services. The responsibility for the procurement, production, and supply of approved equipment for service use was assigned to the Munitions Board.

The Research and Development Board given the responsibility of overseeing the R&D program of the military establishment consisted of two representatives from each of the services, plus the chairman. The work of the Board was performed by a small permanent staff and some 15 technical committees which operated through numerous panels (76 in 1949, more than 100 in 1953).

---

improvement or refinement under further development. The military departments furnish plans and military requirements and work with the R&D Board staff to establish these ratings. When the plan is completed, it is distributed among the interested defense agencies where it becomes the yardstick against which the R&D development programs of the military departments are measured.

"The military departments make up their preliminary budget estimates for R&D using the categories and objectives of the master plan. They also have the technical guidance reports of the R&D Board committees which result from the year long study by the committees of department activities within their respective fields. A significant advance in the preparation of more realistic budget estimates was realized this year when the Secretary of Defense issued planning figures that established definite monetary limits within which estimates were to be submitted" (U.S. Department of Defense, *Second Report of the Secretary of Defense* [1949], pp. 59–60).

Members of the panels (in 1949 about 2,500) were normally private scientists spending a few days per year on panel work.

The Board was preoccupied during the first year of Service unification with completing the task begun in 1946 of reviewing the OSRD projects begun by the joint board. Some 18,000 projects were reviewed of which 5,000 had been completed, suspended or canceled so that at the end of fiscal 1948 the R&D program of the national military establishment consisted of approximately 13,000 projects.

At the same time the Board laid the groundwork for a system of centralized control by establishing a standard reporting system for classifying R&D activities into categories and programs and for relating these to the operational needs of the military services. The Board also acted as a forum for consideration of the diverse viewpoints of the three services and for exchange of information on matters of common concern. It divided some activities between the services, assigning, for example, the support of basic research to the Navy and the administration of a unified technical information service to the Air Force.

The panels of the Research and Development Board were an effective device by which the military agencies could secure authoritative reviews of specific projects proposed by the services. They served also to point out duplications and overlaps, but the organization did not function effectively in providing advice on broad policy questions. A further difficulty was the fact that the equal division of representation of the services on the Board guaranteed that interservice rivalries arising from the impact of technical developments upon service roles and missions could not be resolved. In large part, the Board's limitations stemmed from the limited authority of the Secretary of Defense.

There followed a number of efforts to strengthen the Board, both directly and by increasing the powers of the Secretary. The 1949 amendments to the National Security Act made it possible for the Secretary of Defense to give the chairman of the Board power of decision in any matter on which other members of the Board were not unanimous. The composition of the Board was also changed. Formerly composed of two officers from each of the services, the Board was altered so that one of the two from each department was henceforth to be either an assistant or under secretary. Another step taken in 1949 was the provision in the Military Establishment Appropriation bill that no funds should be obligated for R&D or for industrial mobilization by any agency in the military establishment except in accordance with regulations issued by the Secretary of Defense.

Though these changes strengthened the Board they did little to allay dissatisfaction. The RDB did not supply leadership in providing the Department with an overall view of the developing weapons systems as they related to strategy but tended to concentrate on overlapping and duplicating activities. In consequence the RDB tended to flounder in detailed review of specific scientific programs. The committee system of part-time experts was organized by operational categories exploiting the areas of special competence but by that fact was unable to supply broad coordination and policy guidance. Though the Board was allocated funds so that it might initiate projects of its own, relatively little was accomplished.

The limitations of the RDB were pointed out by the Committee on the Organization of the Department of Defense appointed in 1953 by Secretary Wilson with Nelson Rockefeller as chairman. The Rockefeller report recommended that the RDB (as well as the Munitions Board) be abolished.[8] Their functions were to be transferred to the Secretary of Defense. Policy direction of research was to be consolidated under an assistant secretary of defense (R&D). The report recommended further that the function of appraising the suitability of new developments for possible production in quantity and operational use should be made the responsibility of another assistant secretary (Application Engineering). Their work would be supported by a strengthened Weapons Systems Evaluation Group. The report called for greatly strengthening the Joint Strategy Survey Group, an advisory body of the JCS charged with planning for the operational use of new weapons.

These recommendations were promptly adopted.[9] For the next

[8] Printed as *Report of the Rockefeller Committee on Department of Defense Organization,* by the Senate Armed Services Committee, 83 Cong. 1 sess. (1953).

[9] By Reorganization Plan No. 6 of 1953.

four years the two assistant secretaries mentioned served as the review and coordination centers of the DOD for R&D, operating through a policy council, coordination committees, and advisory panels staffed from the scientific and technical community. Although the Congress continued to appropriate funds directly to the three services, the assistant secretaries by means of recommendations to the Secretary of Defense exercised some control over the expenditure or obligation of these funds. The separation of R&D from engineering, however, proved unworkable and upon recommendation of the Hoover Commission these functions were consolidated in 1957 into a single Assistant Secretary for Research, Development and Engineering.

The problems of controlling the development programs of the procurement organizations were paralleled by the need to supplement the initiative of those organizations with positive guidance of their activities in terms of the nation's strategic needs and with sophisticated evaluations of new developments in scientific knowledge at the earliest possible time. It was highly desirable also to evaluate new weapons at the earliest possible stage of their development with regard to strategic uses and with regard to the alternatives they presented.

The function of guiding research in terms of strategic needs was assigned to the Joint Chiefs of Staff, supported by planning groups in each of the services. Because security requirements necessarily shroud such activity, little can be said about it. It appears, however, that defense-wide, long-range planning has only slowly become a significant factor in these operations. Contractual groups in some areas have strongly influenced the development of national strategy as in the case of the Rand Corporation's contribution to the establishment, first of the Strategic Air Command, and later to programs leading to the development of intercontinental ballistic missiles.

The evaluation of new weapons has been a more immediate problem, though difficult because of the complex and novel technical issues presented. Traditionally such evaluations have been performed by the procuring organizations working in cooperation with the operating groups that might be affected. The inadequacies of that system were made apparent on many occasions before and during World War II. Since operations were unified under the JCS, strategic planning which gave consideration to new weapons could be done only if there were available qualified and objective evaluations of proposals made by the services.

A Weapons Systems Evaluation Group had been established within the JCS to supply such technical evaluations. It remained small partly because of uncertainties regarding its status and role and with subsequent difficulties in recruiting men with the necessary qualifications. It was, in the opinion of the second Hoover Commission task force, inadequate to the task and the commission recommended that the JCS arrange to secure the assistance it needed by contract.[10] This was accomplished by the formation under the auspices of a group of universities of a nonprofit corporation, the Institute for Defense Analyses.

There were parallel efforts to adjust the internal organizations of the services to increase central control over development efforts. In each of the services, the effective establishment of service-wide machinery to consider policy, programs and budgets faced difficulties that resulted from the independent and overlapping functions of the procurement agencies. Relationships which would be responsive to the service-wide needs and to the Secretary of Defense involved reorganization of procurement assignments and functions. In each service, responsibility for such functions was assigned to a Chief of Research and Development and to an Assistant Secretary (R&D).

The operation of these organizational arrangements continued to invite criticism. The guidance provided by the National Security Council and by the Joint Chiefs of Staff was judged by the second Hoover Commission to fall short of providing a clear and integrated national policy.[11] The planning function which Forrestal had visualized as central to all other operations had not been successfully undertaken as, for example, in the face of the anxiety of the three services to place new technology—particularly in missiles —into production and use.

[10] U. S. Commission on Organization of the Executive Branch of the Government, *Subcommittee Report on Research Activities in the Department of Defense and Defense Related Agencies* (1953), p. 30. The *Report of the Rockefeller Committee on Department of Defense Organization* was also critical of WSEG's operations.

[11] U. S. Commission on Organization of the Executive Branch of the Government, *Defense Procurement: The Vital Role of the National Security Council and the Joint Chiefs of Staff* (1955), p. 19.

The evolution of new technology embroiled the three services in numerous disputes, particularly concerning jurisdiction over various types of missiles, but also over numerous other questions such as Air Force support of Army airborne operations or carrier versus land-based aviation. These disputes Secretary Wilson sought to resolve by the technique of reclarification of missions in 1953, 1956, and 1957.[12] The results, in the opinion of the House Appropriations Committee, were unsatisfactory. The Committee observed:

> Each service, it would seem, is striving to acquire an arsenal of weapons complete in itself to carry out any and all possible missions. It is the firm belief of the committee that this matter of rivalry is getting completely out of control. It is expensive and undesirable and points up the need for more effective control and direction.[13]

Secretary Wilson responded to such criticism by establishing in 1957 the position of Director of Guided Missiles with responsibility for overall coordination of the program. Shortly after assuming office, Secretary McElroy assigned to the Advanced Research Projects Agency responsibility for managing all research and early development projects related to antimissiles and satellites. But further reorganization was clearly necessary. President Eisenhower laid down the general objectives he visualized in his State of the Union message in 1958. These included full coordination in the development, production and use of national resources, particularly with respect to newer weapons.[14] There followed a report of a panel headed by Nelson Rockefeller which concluded that drastic changes in the numerous areas of the defense organization were necessary.[15]

Many of the Rockefeller panel recommendations were incorporated in a defense reorganization plan submitted by President Eisenhower to Congress in April 1958. The proposals related to the establishment of truly unified commands, clearer channels of oper-

[12] U. S. Library of Congress, Legislative Reference Service, *United States Defense Policies in 1957*, by Charles H. Donnelly, 85 Cong. 2 sess. (1958), pp. 106–19.

[13] *Ibid.*, p. 83.

[14] *Congressional Record*, vol. 104, 85 Cong. 2 sess. (Jan. 9, 1958), p. 173.

[15] *International Security—the Military Aspect,* Report of Panel II of the Special Studies Project, America at Mid-Century Series (Rockefeller Bros. Fund, 1958).

ational command, the strengthening of the Joint Chiefs of Staff, the improvement of administration within the Department of Defense, and research and development. The Congress accepted the recommended separation of operational functions from those of procurement logistics, manpower and training. The line of operational command henceforth ran from the President to the Secretary of Defense, the Joint Chiefs of Staff and to the unified commands. Support activities, including research and development, were now the principal functions of the departmental secretaries and the chiefs of the services.

The 1958 reorganization also created the new post of Director of Defense Research and Engineering in place of the former Assistant Secretary of Defense for Research and Engineering. The duties of the DDRE were to "supervise all research and engineering activities in the Department of Defense" and to "direct and control" (including their assignment or reassignment) research and engineering activities that the Secretary of Defense judged to require centralized management. The Office of the Director of Guided Missiles as well as the Advanced Research Projects Agency were brought under the DDRE in 1960. These changes made possible a significant change in budget procedure. In 1960 the military budget was presented by the President in terms of major programs rather than by departments.

The status of the nation's military technology and its preparedness were an issue in the 1960 presidential campaign and further proposals for reorganization were studied.[16] The new Secretary of Defense, Robert S. McNamara, however, chose to postpone consideration of reorganization and to apply the powers already available to him, to develop more effective procedures and to consider new organizational arrangements as experience might suggest.[17]

On the horizon were problems in the R&D area arising from the fact that continuing technical developments produce successive generations of a given device, each suitable for operational appli-

[16] Senate Operations Committee [the Jackson subcommittee], *Organizing for National Security* (1961).

[17] Most influential was the work of a group of RAND economists. Their basic ideas were expressed in Charles J. Hitch and Roland N. McKean, *The Economics of Defense in the Nuclear Age* (Harvard University Press, 1960).

cation though the newer may be in some way superior to the older. They may be subject to quick obsolescence, but there may also be doubt that improvement is worth the cost. Difficult decisions must then be made as to the urgency of operational application as against the economy of continuing development toward more highly perfected devices.[18] A case in point is the choice between building more nuclear-powered naval vessels utilizing existing technology or waiting until the technology has been more highly perfected and has become more competitive in cost with conventional propulsion sources. Still other problems arose from the results of research and exploratory development which required decisions as to whether or not the more expensive operational development effort should be undertaken as in the case of Nike X, the antimissile missile system.[19]

As experience accumulated, it was obvious that projects typically had cost much more than estimated and also required more time for completion than had been forecast. The progress made on some projects was so disappointing as to require thorough reappraisal. In such reappraisals, some projects were judged to have been ill-conceived, either from a technical or from a strategic point of view;[20] in others, accumulated costs relative to progress made were judged excessive and cancellations followed. Some items which had been developed and put to operational use proved to be less satisfactory than the equipment they were intended to replace.[21] Some items brought to completion were obso-

---

[18] See *Nuclear Propulsion for Naval Surface Vessels,* Hearings before the Joint Committee on Atomic Energy, 88 Cong. 1 sess. (1963).

[19] See the discussion scattered through much of *Military Procurement Authorization, Fiscal Year 1966,* Hearings of the Senate Armed Services Committee, 89 Cong. 1 sess. (1965); and also the hearings of the House Armed Services and Appropriations committees for the same period.

[20] One was the Manned Aircraft Nuclear Powered (ANP) program, a joint effort of the Atomic Energy Commission and the Department of Defense, principally the Air Force. Over the period from its establishment in 1946 to its termination in 1961, an estimated $1,040 million had been spent on the project. See Comptroller General of the United States, *Review of Manned Aircraft Nuclear Propulsion Program, Atomic Energy Commission and Department of Defense* (February 1963).

[21] One example is the Davy Crockett, the Army's mortar-like, short-range weapon able to fire nuclear or conventional warheads. The weapon after being deployed proved to be less accurate than the 155 mm. howitzer. The howitzer also requires less special handling and is less dangerous to front-line troops. *New York Times,* May 28, 1965.

lete—technically or economically—before being available for use; others quickly became obsolete as new R&D projects yielded significant improvements.[22] Between 1952 and 1963, approximately sixty large development projects were terminated by the Department of Defense before completion or completed but never made operational. The costs incurred by these projects are estimated at $6 billion; no estimate is available for smaller projects.[23]

It is inherent in the development process, whether conducted to public or private account, that changing conditions may arise that require termination short of planned objectives. It does not follow that failure to achieve an objective means a waste of funds; much may have been learned that is applicable to other programs. The rough estimate made with regard to the terminated Dyna-Soar program that about one-quarter of the $400 million spent represented a gain in knowledge and skills does indicate strongly that considerable misallocation of resources may occur.[24] The problem of terminating development programs is one of the most difficult that arise in the R&D process, whether public or private.

The Army's La Crosse, a longer-range weapon also designed for nuclear or conventional warheads, has been criticized for its inaccuracy and the problems presented in its use. The General Accounting Office declared the La Crosse to be a $300 million mistake, a judgment denied by the Army. *New York Times,* Feb. 21, 1964.

[22] The Army's Mauler program is an example. After five years and an expenditure of $200 million, another $180 million was estimated as the cost of completion. Meanwhile, improvements in the Hawk missile system became operational and the Chapparal promised to provide the objective of protection of front-line troops from high-speed aircraft and short range missiles. *Army Research and Development Newsmagazine* (September 1965), p. 18.

[23] Harold Brown, Department of Defense press release, April 28, 1965. A list of projects terminated by the Department of Defense from 1952 to 1963 is in *Military Procurement Authorization, Fiscal Year 1965,* Hearings before the Senate Appropriations Committee, 88 Cong. 2 sess. (1964), pp. 178–79. Some corrections to that list appear in the same committee's appropriations hearings for fiscal year 1966 on p. 467. Principal reasons for cancellation of most of the projects listed above together with the contractor affected may be found in *Congressional Record,* vol. 109, 88 Cong. 1 sess. (Dec. 13, 1963), pp. 23352–56.

It should be noted that private industry also experiences a high rate of failures in developing new products for markets. One study concludes that of 27,000 new products introduced in a typical year by firms in "major manufacturing categories" only 20 percent were successful (Johan Bjorksten, "Why New Products Fail," *Drug and Cosmetic Industry,* vol. 97 [September 1965], p. 334).

[24] Secretary McNamara, in responding to a question regarding the possibility of using information gathered during projects now cancelled, said, using Dyna-

The Control of Change in Military Technology

It had become clear by 1960 that the military services had not made the adjustments necessary to effective planning for and utilization of new technology and that the procedures by which technological changes were achieved were inefficient. One problem was the obsolescence of the division of responsibilities among the services by mission assignment.

Defense Secretary McNamara met this problem by a restatement of the functions of the Department in broad categories: strategic forces, continental air and missile defense forces, sealift and airlift forces, general purpose, reserve, general support, and research and development. The classification extended to the procurement functions of the services the integration that had already been achieved in military operations through the Joint Chiefs of Staff. Assignments could now be made by the Secretary to the service best qualified to undertake a task. This classification also permitted the OSD to develop more readily the information it needed to make decisions relating to the weapons systems required to carry out missions demanded by national security objectives.

There followed a new approach to budgeting. The first step was planning—the determination of goals based on a review of requirements resting on military-economic studies that assessed alternative ways of attaining security objectives. Such studies included comparisons between alternative proposals of estimates of costs for development, production, and utilization over a period of time. Planning also permitted the establishment of priorities between competing proposals.

Planning was followed by programming—the formulation and review of programs extending over a considerable period of time

Soar as an example: "I would guess $100 million worth of work out of the $400 million is salvageable. This is the roughest kind of judgment because we have advanced the state of the art in certain materials. For example, we have certainly increased our knowledge of the effect of changes in form of reentry controls; we have learned a lot about reentry but I am just guessing it when I say $100 million out of $400 million." *Military Procurement Authorization, Fiscal Year 1965*, Hearings, pp. 177, 180.

(five to ten years); and the "packaging" of interrelated program elements on the basis of a common mission or set of objectives; for example, the strategic retaliatory forces are composed of a combination of Polaris submarines, B-52's, and ICBM's, the number of each balanced against the number and special capabilities and limitations of each of the others. The resulting programs, determined at the highest levels, when approved, became items in the budget.[25]

In the years following World War II, new procedures were established to control the process whereby R&D proposals were evaluated and undertaken. While numerous considerations were involved, much of the control machinery was built around a classification of R&D activities which has been of great influence. This classification was as follows:[26]

Research: all efforts directed toward acquiring new knowledge of natural and environmental phenomena. In the DOD, the research programs are organized by disciplines such as materials or chemistry. Emphasis in selecting research projects is placed upon problems of special interest to defense, but the range of interest is very wide.

Exploratory development: effort pointed toward the expansion of technological knowledge, directed to the solution of specific problems. The emphasis is on invention and the preliminary exploration of the feasibility of new ideas, short of the point where hardware components and subsystems are produced. In 1966 there were more than eight hundred DOD projects in this category.[27]

Advanced development: effort directed toward projects involving defense-related items for experimentation and operational test. Contractors are supplied with performance specifications, innovation is encouraged, and heavy reliance is placed upon ideas contributed by

[25] This is a very brief summary of a very important development in the federal government's planning and budgeting operations. An account of the rationale and evolution of the system is presented by one of its architects, Charles J. Hitch, in *Decision-Making for Defense* (University of California Press, 1965). It is discussed in more detail and with reference to its applications to other agencies in David Novick (ed.), *Program Budgeting, Program Analysis, and the Federal Budget* (Government Printing Office, 1965).

[26] For more formal definitions, see Armed Services Procurement Regulations, sec. IV, para. 201, "Definitions."

[27] Secretary McNamara's testimony for the fiscal year 1968 budget is reproduced in *Defense Industry Bulletin*, vol. 3 (February 1967), p. 31.

private R&D performers. Preliminary evaluation is made of possible military applications and costs of application are explored.

Engineering development: effort directed to engineering components and systems suitable for operational testing although not yet approved for production or operation. Contractors are provided design specifications selected from the advanced development stage. The end products of such efforts are detailed specifications and one or more advanced prototypes suitable for testing under operational conditions. This area includes the determination of specific operational requirements as well as the cost-effectiveness of the system.

Operational system development: effort directed to further development, engineering, and testing of systems, support programs, and items that have been approved for production and service deployment. Design specifications are detailed and the goals and time-schedules are established.

In this classification the first two processes are sources of knowledge. Expenditures on each project are relatively small, and the programs are administered by staff organizations under broad level-of-effort controls. The third step—advanced development—represents a search for feasibility of application and, with the first two, prepares the way for the subsequent steps. However, because advanced development projects are more expensive than others, they are administered as line items in the budget and program control is exercised by individual review. Projects classified as engineering development or operational systems development usually involve very large sums. They are therefore budgeted as major line items and are reviewed accordingly.

It should be noted that the first three categories—through advanced development—though increasingly specific are exploratory in nature. They permit the support of R&D projects that could not be clearly defended under the traditional procedure which demanded that firm military requirements be established before a proposed development could be approved.[28]

---

[28] The military requirements procedure has been attacked as an obstacle to technological development and hence a threat to the nation's military position; see James T. Ramey, "The Requirements Merry-Go-Round in Government Research and Development," Atomic Energy Commission press release, April 20, 1964.

Harold Brown, Director of Defense Research and Engineering, has pointed out that in the Department of Defense ". . . outlays for research and exploratory development have now passed the $1.5 billion mark. This $1.5 billion-plus is

Reorganization for Development

From the point of view of management concerned with development relating to the mission of an agency, the ultimate objective of the development process is to present a proposal in sufficient specific detail that it can be evaluated for its contribution to the mission. In the defense area this means projecting the contribution that a device proposed for development offers in comparison with existing weapons, and other proposals. Consideration must also be given to the growth of technology and, with knowledge, of its long-range as well as its immediate operational costs. In the DOD system, this appraisal is made when consideration is being given to embarking upon engineering development and is made at the Secretary level.

The line of authority for development projects had been established by a series of statutory provisions culminating in the legislation of 1958. Effective application of that authority was made only after the new procedures were in use and only after the three services were reorganized in such manner as to be responsive to the control of the Secretary of Defense. The Director of Defense Research and Engineering, an office established in 1958, held responsibilities for directing and controlling all R&D programs. The authority of DDR&E is exercised both through the budget and through reporting procedures which embrace the wide-ranging technical efforts throughout the military establishment. That authority is exercised primarily through the assistant secretaries for research and development in each of the three service departments. These officials, in turn, are responsible for the R&D appropriations of their departments as they are also responsible for tech-

spent for projects which are not required to have a detailed justification in terms of end use before approval. On the contrary, we usually fund research on a level-of-effort basis, and ask only for general relevance in exploratory development. . . .

"There is another $800 million in the Advanced Development category earmarked for innovations in experimental hardware. This money is intended for hardware developments which might evolve into large systems. About half of this is required to pass the test of good probability of evolution into new military systems. Thus, overall, nearly $2 billion a year, in the Department of Defense alone, is not subjected to the test of a high probability of immediate or clearly foreseeable utility" (Department of Defense press release, April 28, 1965). See also the testimony of Secretary McNamara in Senate *Military Procurement Authorization, Fiscal Year 1966*, pp. 132–35.

nical review. It is important to point out also that R&D funds are budgeted and appropriated separately from procurement.

During the early 1960's, each of the services made changes in organization to reflect the research and development patterns cited above, to utilize the procedures established by the Office of the Secretary of Defense, and to respond more effectively to its requirements. Each service established a high level center of responsibility for research and another for development.[29]

The Air Force was first to concentrate responsibilities for the overall management of its development effort. It did so in 1961 by consolidating the Air Research and Development Command and the Air Materiel Command into the Air Force Systems Command. This command is organized internally along technological lines with divisions of electronics, ballistics, and aeronautics.[30]

The problems of establishing central control over development programs were more difficult in the Army and Navy than in the Air Force, since both the Army and Navy procurement and combat organizations traditionally cherished high degrees of independence.[31] Proposals to reorganize the Army's procurement functions had been made from time to time. In 1962, as a result of a painstaking review of its structure and functions, the Army transferred the procurement functions that had been performed by its technical services to an Army Materiel Command.[32] The AMC was organized into nine commodity commands representing the major areas of technology covered by the Army's development opera-

[29] There has been much discussion of the increasing centralization of responsibility in the Office of the Secretary of Defense as a result of Secretary McNamara's policies. These policies have imposed upon the services more disciplined procedures in gathering data and in reaching decisions than had been customary. They have also placed the responsibility for decision-making in the offices of the civilian Secretary and his immediate assistants. See Eugene M. Zuckert, "The Service Secretary: Has He a Useful Role?" *Foreign Affairs*, April 1966, pp. 458–79.

[30] A description of Air Force organization is contained in N. Warren Graves, "The Air Force R&D Acquisition Process," *Defense Industry Bulletin*, vol. 1 (September 1965), pp. 13–14. Brief descriptions of agency organizations for development as well as for research may be found in *Contract Policies and Procedures for Research and Development*, H. Rept. 1942, pp. 21–54.

[31] B. Marlin, "The Framework of Army Research and Development," *Defense Industry Bulletin*, vol. 2 (May 1966), pp. 14–16, 22–23.

[32] U. S. Department of the Army, *Report on the Reorganization of the Department of the Army* [the Hoelscher report] (1961).

tions. Technical testing and evaluation was assigned to an independent command—the Army Combat Developments Command.

In the Navy, the development of new material remained the responsibility of the long-established bureaus (Weapons, Ships, Yards and Docks, and Supplies and Accounts). Like the Army, the Navy experienced difficulties in coordinating its efforts when confronted with complex requirements and also found it difficult to meet the requirements of the OSD that its development plans be appraised in the light of DOD-wide considerations. A reorganization in 1963 maintained the responsibilities of the four long-established bureaus but brought them together as the Naval Material Support Establishment under the centralized control of a Chief of Naval Material responsible to the Secretary of the Navy. The Chief of Naval Operations held a parallel position. Material development and procurement and naval operations were linked in a complex set of organizational arrangements.

The Naval Material Support Establishment had scarcely had time to become fully operational before it was superseded. In 1966 there was a more drastic reorganization, closely resembling the 1962 action of the Army. The four bureaus were abolished and replaced by six systems commands (Air, Ships, Electronic, Ordnance, Supply and Facilities Engineering) each with comprehensive responsibilities beginning with exploratory development. The systems commands reported to the Chief of Naval Material, who was now subordinated to the Chief of Naval Operations. Like the Army, the Navy has followed the practice of selecting a number of its most difficult or highest priority areas for special management, having them report directly to the Chief of Naval Material. In 1966 there were eleven such Project Managed programs.[33]

Managing the Development Process

The management of development programs is a complex process in which an agency staff working with private contractors seeks step by step to bring an idea to fruition. Responsible management

[33] B. H. Andrews, "The Planning and Management of the Navy RDT&E Program," *Defense Industry Bulletin*, vol. 2 (February 1966), pp. 22–23, 25; and "Navy Reorganizes Material Command Structure," *Defense Industry Bulletin*, vol. 2 (April 1966), pp. 12–13. A complete account is in U. S. Department of the Navy, *RDT&E Management Guide* (Government Printing Office, 1966).

reviews the progress at each step, evaluating and selecting for the next step as needs, promise, and cost suggest.

Development projects normally emerge when some new knowledge or some new mix of knowledge is perceived as offering possibilities for application. These perceptions may occur almost anywhere in the knowledgeable community. It is the responsibility of agency development staffs to appraise new knowledge constantly in terms of the operational requirements of the agency. However, as private institutions have built up their R&D capabilities and as they have become familiar with government programs and goals, they have become increasingly important sources of perceptions of development possibilities. Such ideas come to the interested government agency in the form of suggestions or project proposals, formal or informal. Proposals may be prepared in response to an expression of interest by the agency or because a private group believes that a specific project will stimulate an interest not previously expressed.

The ideas involved usually have a complex history. Some may have originated with the agency's operating personnel, with the intramural RDT&E staff or with private individuals and groups. The source is not significant except for the possibility that the prestige of the initiating group may be such as to carry substantial weight in the decision-making process. Responsibility for initiating the consideration of a proposal rests with the technical staff. It is the essence of the programming function that all ideas be considered and that judgments be made regarding their relevance to the agency's mission, the degree of feasibility, and the cost. In the process the proposal will be compared with others directed to similar ends. It is possible that it will be discussed with an advisory committee. If the proposal survives it becomes a part of the proposed budget of the responsible subdivision of the agency and then moves upward as the higher administrators make the selections which will constitute the agency-wide program and budget request.

While very important gains follow from the availability of numerous proposals, the appraisal, blending, and selection of these proposals also pose very difficult tasks for the technical and managerial talent within government. This is particularly true in the defense and space area which are unique in the federal structure with respect to the breadth of their interest and responsibilities and the magnitude of their operation. Their responsibilities include operating new military systems and technologies, previewing them, testing them, developing them, researching them, and identifying the new ideas to be developed. Most other agencies of the government have an interest in only one or two of these stages.

To be considered for inclusion in a program and therefore in the budget, a development proposal must contribute in some meaningful way to the needs of the agency as identified in its intermediate- and long-range planning. The proposal must rest upon a body of knowledge and skills so that its feasibility can be demonstrated sufficiently and so that the uncertainties can be identified and appraised. The nature of the evaluation and appraisal of the proposal will depend upon the stage that has been reached, and will range from the suggestion that modest sums be spent in exploration to a recommendation that an operational model be sought, looking forward to its testing and evaluation for use.

In the Department of Defense, budget requests are submitted both in traditional appropriation categories and in terms of the mission categories. If two, or all three, of the military departments submit requests for an essentially identical item, the requests are considered as possible national military alternatives rather than as individual service needs. The program package budgeting concept also provides an effective framework within which the Director of Defense Research and Engineering (DDR&E) can exercise the responsibilities of his office relating to choice. The R&D program package comes under direct supervision of the DDR&E. The other program packages define broad needs toward which defense R&D is oriented. Programs are then assigned to the services or to the DDR&E's own Advanced Research Projects Agency as exclusive, integrated and budgeted units called program packages.

The analytical effort given to a proposal varies with its classification and the funds involved. In the case of exploratory development the sums involved are relatively small, and the concepts are such that only a general appraisal of its utility or relevance is possible. Such projects are therefore not subjected to intense scrutiny but are handled as relatively short-term contracts, periodically reappraised for continuation, termination, or reclassification. Projects classified as advanced development tend to be much larger and since they have been identified as possible sources of new hardware are given more attention.

The determination that sufficient knowledge has accumulated to make an engineering development effort feasible raises difficult questions. The presumption that what is possible should be undertaken must be analyzed in the light of limited funds, numerous development proposals from which selection must be made, and the question of probable returns in relation to the costs. In some cases, costs can be compared with the benefits anticipated to provide a basis for judgment. In other cases, benefits are not readily measurable, or, as in the health area, are assumed to be so desirable that costs are ruled out of consideration. In the health area, the presumption is that development will be undertaken as possibilities arise. In the case of defense, the knowledge or belief that other nations are working towards an objective may be determining. If other nations have no such program the decision is a more difficult one but some further work may be programmed so that knowledge of the particular problem area can be maintained and added to at relatively low levels of expenditure.

In the Department of Defense, a project proposed for engineering development is subjected to an intensive review process. The first step is Concept Formulation, which is an attempt to determine whether the technical, military, and economic bases for a proposed effort exist and to be sure that alternative operational and technical approaches have been analyzed and that estimates of cost and operational effectiveness have been made. A conditional decision to initiate engineering development follows a favorable determination.

In the second or Contract Definition phase, the technical, cost, schedule, and management aspects of the project are intensively reviewed.[34] In this process it is determined that the needed technology is available and that the project requires engineering rather than experimental effort; that the nature and objectives of the mission are defined; that the best technical approaches have

[34] A brief account is in James W. Roach, "Management Trends in Defense R&D," *Defense Industry Bulletin*, vol. 2 (July 1966), pp. 11–13.

been selected; that the cost-effectiveness of the item compares favorably with competing items; and that the cost and schedule estimates are acceptable.[35]

If the analysis is favorable on all counts and validated on review at high levels, the final decision to undertake engineering development depends upon broad strategic considerations.

Contractor Selection

Given an approved engineering development, the process moves on to the selection of the contractor. The problem of selecting a working group differs with the classification of the project, the number of organizations qualified to undertake it, the source of the proposal, the dollar value of the work, and the ability of the agency to provide technical direction and supervision.

Throughout this process private contractors have contributed to the development program, doing the work on one stage and submitting proposals for next steps. In the earlier stages this work has been done under study contracts to carry out what were frequently proposals made by the contractor. Contractors who have not participated in these stages are unlikely to be serious competitors. Nevertheless, those with relevant capabilities have the right to an op-

[35] The National Aeronautics and Space Administration employs a "Phased Project Planning" concept. This is based on the normal character of a space flight project, which is generally along the following lines: first, a determination must be made that a specific mission objective is both valid and feasible, and then alternate means of achieving that objective must be detailed; second, from analyses and studies of these alternates, the best single approach must be selected, one that fits into the overall program in terms of resources, schedule, and end results; third, a complete plan that includes system design, bread-boarding of critical components, and firm cost and manpower projections must be developed and reviewed. The last step is to implement the final plan by flight hardware development fabrication, test, and operation. In keeping with the foregoing, Phased Project Planning provides that major projects will normally be conducted in four sequential phases, each of which must be approved by agency top management: Phase A—Advanced Studies; Phase B—Project Definition; Phase C—Design; Phase D—Development/Operations. The National Aeronautics and Space Administration's Phase Project Planning is focused on the planning and definition phases of activity that precede full-scale hardware development, and provides a disciplined basis for management to (1) evaluate project planning efforts at critical points; (2) be cognizant of, and thereby in a position to preserve, significant future options; and (3) optimize the payoff of the effort in relation to other activities and their combined contribution to overall agency objectives.

portunity to participate. Accordingly, requests for proposals are usually sent to all firms known to be interested. Trade journals give further publicity to the subject. "Bidders briefings," as well as more general reviews of agency plans, are offered to interested and qualified parties for the purpose of increasing the responsiveness of contractors' proposals to agency needs.

The principal elements of a proposal are the technical section including a statement of the work to be done, a manning schedule including a list of key personnel who will supervise and carry out the work, a management section describing the organization, techniques and procedures to be applied, and the detailed sequence of work to be followed along with cost and time estimates for each major task in this sequence. There are usually detailed separate treatments of the technical proposal and of the management proposal. Proposals vary considerably with the scope and nature of the project or program and with the particular strategy of source selection. For a small-scale effort, the proposal may be brief and very general in describing what is proposed to be done. A major development system, moving into engineering development, will require proposals set forth in great detail encompassing volumes of system definitions, work plans, drawings, engineering analysis, organization and management, facilities, cost estimates, etc.

Agencies normally seek competitive proposals from two or more qualified sources. A proposal may, however, be of such nature that only a single source is qualified to do the work, in which case a justification for sole source procurement must be prepared, and a search made to verify the recommendation. Procurement without effort to secure alternative sources is, however, normal when the agency decides to support an unsolicited proposal. The preferred position acquired by a firm via an unsolicited proposal may continue when the work on the project it involves is continued in successive steps. When the stage of engineering development is reached the firm that has produced the earlier work may possess much superior capabilities.

It is common practice when competition is possible for the agencies to use source evaluation procedures to determine the qualifications of the firms involved. The proposals of the firms that are deemed qualified are then considered by a source selection board or committee.

In the case of large and costly projects, a multiple-step—usually a two-step—proposal procedure is frequently used. The first procedure is an open invitation to contractors to indicate their interest and to submit statements describing their qualifications as indicated by their past experience, existing organization, and competence, along with a statement of the key personnel who would be involved and a generalized description of their proposed approach to the problem at hand. At this stage, the agency's principal interest is in the technical aspects of the situation and it may request detailed technical proposals.

After the agency staff has selected from the responses the best qualified firms in the field—two or six or eight contractors—step two of the process follows. The selected contractors are invited to submit proposals to include detailed technical plans and detailed cost and time figures. Sometimes there is a further narrowing of the field to two contractors and further proposal submission by the contractors.

Particularly with respect to larger systems development, the final contractor selection process, once a more or less technical evaluation of the product models, has become a complex analytical task involving numerous technical factors, management problems, cost factors, and development risks.[36] Despite such preliminary planning and analysis, the precise technical approach to be followed is frequently not clear at the time of the contract award.

The final decision process typically involves two specialized panels, one concerned with the technical side and the other with the management side of the proposals. Though weighted check lists may be employed, human judgment remains very important. Evaluators must weigh all principal elements of each contractor's written proposal as well as the technical competence available to do the work. Past performance of the competing firms has some bearing on the evaluation but the current capability is more directly relevant.

Such selection procedures result in a recommendation to the

[36] In the case of the C-5a total-package procurement competition, five contractors, making up the two competing groups, submitted detailed support of their proposals weighing over thirty-five tons. "Over 400 people spent two and one half months—a total of 132,000 manhours—reading and evaluating the proposals" (Lieutenant General W. A. Davis, "Management Systems for Package Procurement," *Defense Industry Bulletin,* vol. 2 [December 1966] p. 3).

agency's responsible official. In the case of larger contracts, the recommendation may be submitted to the head of the agency, with the final decision made by him, his immediate assistant, or some group of high level officials.

Contract Negotiation

After the selection of contractors or contractor teams, the representatives of an R&D sponsoring agency proceed to negotiate contracts. In the Department of Defense and the National Aeronautics and Space Administration, the issues subject to negotiation are closely defined by the provisions of the Armed Services Procurement Regulations. However, contracting offices have a variety of techniques to draw upon in seeking to establish an effective contractual relationship.

The government is, in the case of R&D, by definition unable to specify precisely what it wants; indeed, detailed specifications are a part of the services which it seeks to procure. Fixed-price contracts are therefore inappropriate and some type of cost reimbursement arrangement is universally employed. In two types of contract there is no fee. One provides cost-reimbursement without fee and is used chiefly for research contracts with educational and other nonprofit institutions. The other is a cost-sharing without fee, which is appropriate in situations in which a commercial application of the desired development can be foreseen. However, this type of contract is little used.

Cost-reimbursement contracts employed in development contracts with business firms provide for either a fixed fee or an incentive fee.[37] The cost-plus-fixed-fee contract was until 1960 virtually standard in R&D, used "not sparingly but grudgingly."[38] It was a matter of necessity because of the uncertainties in the costs of attaining the performance objective desired, inexperience in administering the development process, and the pressure for quick results. Under CPFF contracts the government obligates itself to

[37] A detailed examination of the problem of introducing incentives into weapons contracts is in Frederic M. Scherer, *The Weapons Acquisition Process: Economic Incentives* (Harvard University, Graduate School of Business Administration, 1964).

[38] Statement by Assistant Secretary of Defense Perkins McGuire, cited in House Armed Services Committee, *Hearings Pursuant to Section 4, Public Law 86–89*, 86 Cong. 2 sess. (1960), p. 163.

reimburse the contractor for the allowable cost of doing the work agreed to in the work statement, regardless of the estimated cost, although the government did frequently set an expenditure ceiling. The contractor's obligation is to apply his best effort to completing the work agreed to within the stated maximum cost limits. If the project is incomplete when such expenditures have been made, he is under no obligation to continue. However, since the attainment of the objective is of prime importance, it has been very common for the agency to provide more money. If this is done by changing or extending the scope of the work, the contractor's fee is also adjusted.[39]

The cost-plus-fixed-fee contract is useful if not indispensable if an objective must be accomplished regardless of cost, and if there are uncertainties regarding the methods by which the performance objective can be accomplished. It is therefore, under current DOD policy, used for projects in the exploratory and advanced development categories. This type of contract permits the technical personnel involved, whether employees of the agency (under appropriate contractual provisions) or employees of the contractor, maximum freedom to experiment in searching for solutions relating to the objective. Under such conditions the contractor, even should he desire to demonstrate the efficiency of his operations, has little financial incentive to do so whereas he has every incentive to explore technical alternatives relating to the objective. Because this type of contract frequently provides for "technical direction" by the government or by such affiliated organizations as the non-profit systems managers (such as Applied Physics Laboratory, Aerospace Corporation, or Mitre) the contractor is frequently not in full control of his operations.

The very large overruns which have characterized many development projects have been in large part the product of underestimation of the technical difficulties involved, but they have also been the result in some measure of inadequate controls over the propensity of technical personnel to explore numerous alternatives and hence to increase costs. Improving the accuracy of estimates of the costs and difficulties of development efforts is an agency responsi-

---

[39] The matter of adjusted fees is explored in Frederick T. Moore, *Military Procurement and Contracting: An Analysis* (RAND Corporation, 1962), pp. 40–49.

bility that has been met by better planning as described above. Better planning also permits the government to enter into contracts which provide incentives for more cost-conscious management by the contractor.

Cost-reimbursable contracts with incentive fees were used prior to 1962 but on a relatively small scale.[40] Since that date both the Department of Defense and NASA have placed emphasis upon incentive contracts in which the fee varies above or below a target amount depending upon performance. Current DOD policy is to require the use of fixed-price agreements with or without incentive or cost-plus-incentive-fee contracts for projects classified as engineering development. Under incentive contracts, the contractor agrees to be held accountable for specified costs, delivery schedules, and the performance characteristics of the product. Weights assigned to these three variables are negotiated. In general, the contractor stands to gain additional profits over the agreed minimum if he does better than the agreed-upon standard for any of the three variables, and he is assessed agreed-upon penalties if he fails. Incentive fees are usually provided by a formula which provides for separate fees for performance with regard to costs, delivery schedules, and performance characteristics, the latter including such considerations as reliability. Since the more precise planning of both the government and the contractor has broken the project down into a series of milestones, incentive fees may be applied to each of the items suggested for each milestone. Such planning introduces an important element of discipline into the work. In seeking to maximize his overall fee, the contractor retains a degree of freedom in that he can sacrifice some fee in one area in order to attain higher fees in others.

Mention should also be made of efforts by the government to encourage contractors to reduce the cost and increase the reliability and maintainability of the end product without affecting performance. Many contracts now include provisions whereby the contractor shares in the savings that can be made by undertaking the additional operation of value-appraisal of all elements as the

[40] The Army's contract with the Wright brothers for the development of the first airplane was an incentive contract, providing a reward or penalty for performance above or below 40 miles per hour (*Army Research and Development Magazine*, vol. 3 [November 1962], p. 3).

work proceeds, the objective being to reduce costs while retaining all performance characteristics.

While the incentive contract concept just described is relatively simple, its reduction to practice can be complicated. In contracting for a research and development project it is extremely difficult to establish a fair and realistic median in each of the three variables—cost, performance, and schedule—from which to measure quality of performance for the fee determination formula. Under these circumstances NASA and the Navy have made extensive use of, and the Army and Air Force have experimented with, an incentive arrangement generally referred to as the Cost-Plus-Award-Fee (CPAF) contract. This type of contract generally provides for a base fee lower than that which would be set under cost-plus-a-fixed-fee (CPFF) contracts for equivalent work. However, a higher target fee is also established. As periodic evaluations by the government may indicate, the contractor may then be awarded additional fees up to the limit contractually prescribed. For average performance, the fee is in the area of the normal CPFF fee. For superior performance, the fee does in fact become an "award." Evaluations are conducted at the government project office or division level, with ultimate fee determination made by an Award Fee Board composed of high-level management people. The contractor is apprised of the evaluations and is afforded the opportunity to make known his viewpoints on them prior to fee determination. The CPAF system differs basically from other types of incentive arrangements in that, unlike the CPIF, there is no mathematical formula established at the outset, application of which then determines the fee. Instead, the evaluation of performance and the determination of an award above the base fee is essentially a subjective and unilateral action by the agency (rather than objective as in the case of formula incentive-fee contracts).

Both NASA and the Navy believe that under this system there has been better communication and understanding between the contractor and government, greater management participation and interest in work progress on both sides, and earlier recognition and resolution of problems. While it is still in an evolutionary state, this type of contract management technique holds promise for the future. The terms of such a contract also include, along with a large number of standard clauses, a variety of provisions that require administrative decision. Among them are agreements covering the technical data to be supplied the agency, the amount of subcontracting, "set-asides" for small business, and "set-asides for depressed areas."

The contract will include provisions for reporting progress made and costs incurred. The reporting requirements at minimum may be a standard package. In the case of large, technically difficult projects of special importance to the agency, the contract may require that the contractor schedule the work and expenditures in detail. Management control of production and development has long used some form of scheduling based upon milestones over a period of time but the government will specify the type of reporting system it desires.[41]

A cost-plus-fixed-fee contract confronts the government with the necessity of assuring itself as the work proceeds that the end product, its components and subcomponents, will meet established technical standards. It is recognized that even with the greatest care in planning, the design which the contractor is converting into a device will be incomplete, containing what are frequently no more than the best conjectures possible at the time. Some parts of the design are sure to prove unsatisfactory or unworkable, and others will prove to have lost importance as a result of the work being done. It is a characteristic of development, particularly under cost-plus-fixed-fee contracts, that there will be numerous changes from the original work statement. In the case of large contracts such changes may number from one to two thousand and have been known to number twenty thousand or more per year.

---

[41] There are numerous reporting systems but the one that has attracted most attention is PERT (program evaluation and review technique), originally developed by the Navy to monitor the progress of the very complex Polaris against an urgent schedule. This serves to break down a complicated program containing elements of uncertainty into a number of precisely defined components, each of which is given a schedule for completion (and in some cases as to cost). Periodic reports as to progress from all suppliers provides a check on emerging problem areas. See Department of Defense and National Aeronautics and Space Administration, *DOD and NASA Guide, PERT Cost Systems Design* (June 1962); and National Aeronautics and Space Administration, *NASA, PERT and Companion Cost System Handbook* (October 1962).

Such changes may be recommended by the firm's technical staff or they may originate with the government's technical people. In either case, they must be approved by the government's responsible representative. While not all will represent increases in cost, most will, and the costs must be estimated and approved as amendments to the contract. At one time an estimated 40 percent of DOD R&D funds were being absorbed by the costs of changes in existing contracts.

As has been pointed out, the Defense Department has sought to control R&D programs by organizing the work to be done into successive steps, each a contracted project and each of greater specificity. It has also sought greater control over changes in contracts under way. This is possible through a "program change proposal" mechanism which requires a detailed consideration of change proposals at the top levels of the agency and approval by the service secretary or the Secretary of Defense, depending upon the dollar amounts involved.[42] By placing restraints upon post-award changes in a contract, the agency staff is forced into fuller technical and cost analysis before the contract is let. Such analysis also permits the greater use of cost-reimbursement-incentive contracts, which reinforce the restraints upon the agency in making changes by providing for frequent completion targets with the consequent necessity for checking the work accomplished and determination of the fee earned.

A cost-plus-fixed-fee contract also imposes upon the government the need to assure itself that the contractor's operations are efficiently and economically conducted. This has meant elaborate reporting requirements and auditing procedures that have been costly to the government and irritating to business management. With the incentive contract, the government has less need of such controls and some reduction in their application has occurred. Further reduction is taking place as the government applies its policy of relying more fully upon cost consideration. As incentive contracts impose greater cost consciousness upon management, the government is moving toward a reduction of its review and over-

[42] Explanations of the system can be found in such service publications as Department of the Navy, *Program Change Control System in the Department of the Navy* (1962).

head audit controls in the case of firms with a large proportion of high risk contracts.[43]

Contract Management

Once a contract is signed, the program management function is essentially one of maintaining a flow of technical and financial data sufficient so that the agency can hold the contractor or contractors responsible for performing as proposed, and can consider recommending courses of action for coping with deviations. Responsibility for monitoring small projects continues to be normally assigned to the staff of the originating program office.

Monitorship of a large project is, in the majority of cases, made the responsibility of a project or program manager. In the earlier experience of the government with development programs, authority and responsibility were diffused among requirements officers, plant representatives, technical personnel, auditors, and numerous others. Problems of continuity and responsibility were further aggravated in that nominal control was transferred from time to time from planning officers, to research officers, to development officers, to procurement officers, and to operations people.

In very complex programs, the monitorship function requires the full-time attention of large numbers of specialists and more elaborate methods for implementing a program and for maintaining control may be applied. One approach is to have a project officer operating under a program manager. Arrangements vary, but perhaps the most effective is one in which such managers are delegated the authority of the responsible agency official to accomplish the objectives of the program within a time and money budget. The program manager's principal responsibility is to assure that the program progresses in accordance with the approved time schedule and cost budgets for subgoals and remains consistent with the performance goals in the approved program statement. If and when significant deviations occur, the policy-level officials are alerted and take such action as seems appropriate.

[43] See Robert D. Lyons, "Contractors' Weighted Average Share Concept," *Defense Industry Bulletin,* vol. 3 (1967) pp. 5–6. This is a method of measuring the proportions of a firm's high and low risk business. The purpose is "to eliminate administrative controls and reasonableness overhead audits on those contractors who attain a verifiable 'weighted average share of risk' which meets a prescribed threshold."

Other Development Programs

The Department of Defense, the National Aeronautics and Space Administration, and the Atomic Energy Commission in 1965 accounted for about 98 percent of federal expenditures on development programs. Although the expenditures of other agencies for development programs are relatively small, they increased from less than $50 million in 1960 to about $500 million in 1967. This rapid rise follows in some small measure from agency efforts to develop new technology for their internal use—as in the case of the Post Office, the Food and Drug Administration, and the Environmental Science Services Administration. The major factor, however, is the increasing commitment to accelerating the application of knowledge gained from research and technology to objectives that may benefit society at large. The principal component of the recent increase of development expenditures by these agencies is FAA's programs relating to civilian aviation, particularly the supersonic transport. Water pollution, high-speed surface transportation, desalination of water, and the poverty program are recent and substantial programs. There are a variety of others which though of small magnitude also show some growth, as in commercial fisheries, vocational rehabilitation, coal, arms control, housing, and manpower.

The administrative procedures applied to these programs reflect the extensive and varied experience of DOD and, to a lesser degree, that of NASA and AEC. The most sweeping application of DOD experience was President Johnson's instructions to many agencies in 1965 that they apply the planning-programming-budgeting system (PPBS) developed by DOD to their operations.[44]

The President's directive requires that agency heads submit to the Bureau of the Budget each year a five-year financial plan together with program memoranda that are the basic planning documents for each major activity. These documents require agency heads to define their primary missions and objectives more explic-

[44] The President's statement on the government-wide planning-programming-budgeting system together with the Budget Bureau's guidelines are conveniently assembled in Senate Committee on Government Operations, *Planning-Programming-Budgeting: Official Documents,* 90 Cong. 1 sess. (1967).

itly, in greater detail, and in a longer time perspective than they have in the past and to do so in quantitative terms whenever possible. The program memoranda include comparisons of alternative programs and of alternative ways in which programs might be accomplished. The consideration of alternatives means that existing programs and procedures are placed in competition with new proposals. After the program memoranda have been discussed with the interested agencies of the Executive Office, they constitute the foundation upon which budget requests are prepared.

Much of what is incorporated in the PPBS procedure has been done in the past. The significance of the more formalized requirements upon agency technical development programs remains uncertain. In identifying more precisely alternative goals and programs together with long-range costs and expected benefits, the procedure reacts to the widening range of opportunities and needs that form the government as it also supports and contributes to the government's commitment to promoting technical gains.

There is usually an understanding, formal or informal, between the congressional committees of jurisdiction and the agency as to how an approved and funded program is to be carried out. The contractual arrangements are governed by the Federal Property and Administrative Services Act of 1949 administered by General Services Administration and interpreted in Federal Procurement Regulations. GSA has generally delegated its authority to the agencies and these in turn have developed procurement regulations based upon FPR. While there are some differences in the basic statutory authority, the FPR as it relates to R&D contracting is very similar to ASPA, although less detailed. The FPR, indeed, draws heavily upon DOD experience.[45]

The management of approved and funded development programs intended for incorporation in an agency's internal operations does not differ markedly from the procedures followed by the DOD, recognizing that such efforts are comparatively small and that they have limited and specific objectives. Much the same is true of agency sponsored development projects intended for use

[45] A brief analysis is in House Select Committee on Government Research, *Contract Policies and Procedures for Research and Development*, Study Number VII, H. Rept. 1942, 88 Cong. 2 sess. (1964), pp. 17–18.

by the public. However, the latter type of project presents problems that affect the contractual relationship since the transfer of new technology to private institutions must be arranged in an effective and equitable manner to the benefit of the public.

The basic contribution of agency programs to the advancement of technology is made by the circulation of technical reports. All agencies impose a requirement in their contracts calling for the submission of technical reports, a requirement that may present administrative problems even though the transmission of such reports is a routine function of many agencies. The effectiveness of such reports depends upon the capacity of the industry to absorb new information and also upon the character of the technology involved.

In an increasing number of areas, the transmission of new information is being judged as insufficient to stimulate the technological change that seems to be possible. An agency may then seek to stimulate development by offering to finance the preparation of new designs as the FAA did unsuccessfully in the case of a replacement for the DC-3.[46] It may contract for a demonstration project or for the building and operation of experimental demonstration plans as in the case of water desalination. It may enter into cost-sharing arrangements with a private firm to stimulate the utilization of known technology as in the case of the high-speed North East Corridor rail transportation project of the Department of Transportation.

The most advanced form of government promotion of technology for private use is the FAA's program to develop the supersonic transport. This project has followed the DOD pattern of successive competitive feasibility and design contracts. It is unique in that the government is not only the development sponsor but serves also as financial underwriter, bearing many though not all the risks inherent in any development effort. Recoupment of the government's investment is planned from sales of the completed aircraft to the airlines.[47]

[46] A brief account of the DC-3 replacement project is in Senate Committee on Aeronautical and Space Sciences, *Policy Planning for Aeronautical Research and Development*, 89 Cong. 2 sess. (1966), pp. 237–39.

[47] *Ibid.*, pp. 215–16.

The Administration of Research Programs

Federal obligations for research as distinguished from development in 1967 were $5.5 billion. About one-third went for basic research defined by the National Science Foundation as "research in which the primary aim of the investigator is fuller knowledge or understanding of the subject under study, . . . rather than a practical application as is the case with applied research." The other two-thirds of the research was classified as "applied" in that "the aims of the inquiry are clear and the possibility that these goals can be realized with the basic knowledge available is accepted but the actual means by which the goals are to be reached are as yet undefined. The main purpose of the applied research is to identify and explore such means and to determine which of them are likely to be of most use in the later development phase when an actual end product or process is to be created."[48]

No clear line separates basic research from applied. The NSF, for example, classifies its Mohole project for drilling through the earth's mantle as basic research. On the other hand, the applied research category includes NASA's Gemini and Apollo manned space flight programs and investigation of possible future advanced missions, comprehensive programs of unmanned investigation of earth, moon, sun, and planets, development of meteorological and communications satellite systems and research and technical developments to support the agency's aeronautical and space programs.

Federal programs in research are of three general types, differing in origin and objectives. One type is directed solely to the acquisition of new knowledge, leaving application for others to explore. Only one agency, the National Science Foundation, has the specific and limited responsibility of stimulating research activity for the unqualified purpose of increasing knowledge. The Foundation in 1965 provided about 11 percent of the federal funds allocated to basic research and about 4 percent of the funds available for all research.

[48] National Science Foundation definitions are given in *Federal Funds for Research, Development, and Other Scientific Activities: Fiscal Years 1963, 1964, and 1965*, vol. 13 (1965), pp. 10, 18.

A second type of program seeks to apply knowledge derived from basic research to an objective. The programs of the Atomic Energy Commission and the National Institutes of Health, the Department of Agriculture and many others are generally of this nature.

A third type of research program has its origin in current and long-range development programs, as in the military departments. Here research interests in some degree arise out of needs exposed in pursuing development objectives, but there is also interest in the results of research because of their relevance to long-range plans. The military agencies feel it necessary that the major development contractors have personnel who maintain an intimate knowledge of ongoing research over a broad spectrum. Through such personnel, subjects of special interest can be identified which may require more basic research or more vigorous applied research. Defense Department programs in research are thus intended to contribute to the opportunities or the needs that appear to exist in areas relevant to the long-range planning of the services.

Both the magnitude of federal research programs and their composition have evolved pragmatically and piecemeal. While the importance of research is not challenged, its relationship to development objectives is unclear.[49] No criteria have been evolved which would suggest an optimal overall level of research effort or an ideal distribution among possible fields. By and large, basic and applied research have received federal support most readily when an agency has identified a reasonably close relationship between its problems in meeting its development responsibilities and the possibility that such problems might be resolved by research.

The formulation of research programs varies greatly depending upon the specificity of the ends sought, the nature of the scientific area involved, and the purposes to be served. An agency, such as the National Institutes of Health, may limit its program formulation to the broadest terms, the specifics being supplied to private conceptualizations of its problems as they appear in research pro-

[49] The interplay between science and technology is obvious, but the relationships are complex and are by no means causal in one direction. See Derek J. de Solla Price, "Is Technology Historically Independent of Science? A Study in Statistical Historiography," *Technology and Culture,* vol. 6 (1965), pp. 533–68.

posals submitted to it.[50] There is then little research that is directed by the agency to accomplish narrow, well-defined objectives, and emphasis is placed upon the accumulation of large amounts of knowledge of far-reaching implications in many directions. Other agencies seek to structure their programs to their technological objectives by identifying problems that call for solution through research, ranking them in some rough order of priority, estimating costs, and trying to appraise the value of solutions.[51]

In either case, the agency will then seek to identify that segment of the qualified manpower available that might be stimulated to contribute to the program and that would also contribute to the further definition of the problems and of priorities. The result, repeated periodically, constitutes the agency's program as a guide to project selection. Part of the program will be applied and directed research. The agency will seek to arouse interest and to invite proposals focused on problems and projects of its selection and will consider unsolicited proposals primarily in terms of immediacy of relevance to those problems. Contracts will be used for much of this work. Part may be devoted to supporting research that is concerned with increasing fundamental knowledge broadly relevant to the agency's mission.

The budgets that follow may on occasion reflect an effort to employ all of the nation's well-qualified manpower in this area and to train more. More likely the agency will seek to support some percentage of that qualified manpower, contributing its share to the overall federal effort.

Organizing Basic and Medical Research

Discussion of the government's organization for support of basic research at one time centered upon the proposal that the National Science Foundation be given control over all support of the type of research that might be performed by universities. The concept

[50] For one explanation of the NIH point of view and for criticism of the agency's lack of planning, see House Committee on Interstate and Foreign Commerce, *Investigation of HEW*, H. Rept. 2266, 89 Cong. 2 sess. (1966), pp. 111, 120.

[51] An interesting effort at such cost-effectiveness analysis is U. S. Department of Health, Education and Welfare, Office of the Assistant Secretary for Program Coordination, *Selected Disease Control Programs* (September 1966).

of a single centralized agency for basic research foundered on the fact that the AEC and NIH already had full statutory responsibility for large programs of research in universities, and in addition, each of the military departments had established important programs of university research. During the debate over the National Science Foundation, the Army anticipated transferring its basic research to the proposed organization, but other agencies sought assurances that their R&D activities be continued on the grounds that they were oriented to their needs. Such agencies as Interior and Commerce also sought to protect their established research functions. The result was that the idea of a military division within NSF to serve military requirements was abandoned as was that of a medical division. However, NSF was charged with coordinating responsibilities.

The National Science Foundation was established to support basic research by grants or contracts to private institutions and was prohibited from operating its own laboratories. The Atomic Energy Commission chose to continue to operate through contractual arrangements. While the military services have some intramural facilities for research, they maintain their contractual programs to provide contacts with university scientists and to direct to military needs the skills to be found in the universities and in the private institutions.

The Navy's way of administering basic research both in its own laboratories and by contract through a separate and substantially independent Office of Naval Research has been continued and expanded over the years. Until 1950, Army research support functions were scattered among the technical services and administered as a part of their procurement operations. However, in that year, the Ordnance Department, which accounted for the largest part of the Army's expenditures for research, consolidated its basic research programs in the Ordnance Research Office, separately budgeted and administered from an office maintained under contract on the campus of Duke University. In 1960 the Army consolidated most of the basic research programs of the technical services, the Ordnance establishment becoming the Army Research Office. The ARO has responsibilities for all Army-oriented basic research in the physical and mathematical sciences, whether carried on intramurally or by contract. The Air Force has continued its long dependence on the intramural facilities of NACA for basic research in aeronautics but also, in 1949, established an Office of Air Research to oversee a program of contractual research as well as operating its own laboratories. After its establishment, NASA also developed a large mission-oriented program in support of university research.

Developments in the field of medical research have followed a similar path. The proposal that NSF be assigned full responsibilities in the area were abandoned in the light of the rapid growth of the National Institutes of Health within the Public Health Service. Although NSF has maintained programs in the biological-medical area, NIH has become the government's principal agency in medical research. Its growth has been characterized by the establishment of new institutes with larger and more specific responsibilities for designated areas.

Other agencies have broadened old programs in medical research or established new ones. The problems presented by nuclear radiation have stimulated AEC support of a large program, carried on almost entirely by grants and contracts. Another program which has grown significantly since World War II is that of the Veterans Administration. In 1946 the Veterans Administration, recognizing the medical problems of its very large hospital population, established a medical research program. During its earlier years the program relied heavily upon contracts to accomplish its objectives. As the VA assembled a qualified staff, attracted in part by research opportunities, it was able to release staff time for research and the program became predominantly an intramural operation even though some studies continue to be performed on contract.[52] This shift from extra- to intramural research performance makes the VA program unique among government programs.

Meanwhile, each of the military services has maintained programs in mission-related medical research, in all cases supplementing intramural programs with research grants and contracts. There is also a NASA program in space medicine and a number of other agencies have small programs in areas of special interest.

[52] Administrator of Veterans Affairs, *Annual Report,* for the years 1946–54.

The Management of Research Programs

In research, as in development, the formulation of an agency's program is influenced by the trends that can be ascertained in scientific research, in large part as reflected in the suggestions of scientists associated with a variety of institutions. The institutional organization of research is complex compared with that of development programs in which only a relatively small number of business firms are possible contractors. The work required to carry out an agency program will be performed by one or more among four possible types of organization.

The traditional source of research performance—administratively the simplest—is an intramural organization which is a part of the sponsoring agency or of some other government agency and to which full responsibility can be assigned. The character of work assigned to an intramural organization is normally described in broad program terms. Determination of the details of what should be done and how is left to the responsible laboratory director guided by discussions with the interested group in the agency. The agency may rely upon its laboratories as its sole research activity, may operate a laboratory parallel to but separate from other research programs, or may give the laboratory responsibility for administering a supplemental contract research program. Only a small percentage of federal research funds are now committed in this way.

A second method by which agencies support basic and applied research (and development to a degree) is by financial contributions to activities maintained by business firms in support of their interest in government programs.[53] The Defense Department, and to a limited extent NASA and AEC, employ this method. It is difficult in many situations to separate estimated research costs from costs incurred in the preparation of proposals, whether unsolicited or in response to a formal RFP. Such arrangements are financed by negotiated cost-sharing agreements under which a firm doing research relevant to government interests is permitted to charge a part of the cost to overhead on all its government development contracts. The formulation of such R&D programs is at the initia-

[53] See chapter VI.

tive of the firm, and the agency exercises no formal programming responsibilities. The functions performed by the agency are to review the firm's program and to determine by negotiation, sometimes in advance, the portion of the cost which the government will accept as a charge to contract overhead.

A third method is followed when a federal agency maintains one or more research centers which are wholly financed by the agency but managed by a private organization under a contract. Appropriate parts of an agency's research program are assigned during the formulation stage to such research centers. A large part of the AEC program is executed in this fashion. Similar arrangements are also maintained on a smaller scale by the military departments, by NASA, and by the NSF.

The fourth method of implementing a program is to invite research proposals from any interested institution for appraisal and possible award of a contract or grant. Invitations may be directed specifically to a possible research performer and are therefore solicited; alternatively, the agency may announce generally its interest in receiving unsolicited research proposals in specified fields. In either case, the agency has the task of selecting from the resulting proposals those to which it will give financial support.

The project approach is employed by almost all agencies, sometimes as the sole method of implementing its research programs, sometimes as a parallel to other procedures and sometimes as a supplement. Competitive project research accounts for about 80 percent of the government's expenditures for basic and applied research.

The project approach places a heavier administrative burden on the sponsoring agency than do the other three methods in that it must select from among proposals, sometimes numerous, those which it will support. This is, in essence, the purchase of research at retail. Although the contract or grant will be with an institution, the proposals are made by individual scientists. The average dollar value of the contract is comparatively small and its duration is also relatively short (roughly one to one and a half years for the Department of Defense and less than three years for other agencies). Most unsolicited research proposals come from university scientists although proposals may also come from scientists employed by business firms, noneducational research organizations, and government laboratories.

An agency makes known its research interest by means of brochures sent to a mailing list, announcements in the specialized professional journals, personal contact as by staff attendance at meetings of professional groups, meetings sponsored by the agency, and sometimes through the work of traveling liaison personnel. Such measures are effective in stimulating a flow of proposals and there have been few complaints; nevertheless it is not certain that these procedures are always wholly effective in reaching all qualified and potentially interested personnel.

After having attracted research proposals, the agency faces then the problem of evaluating them. With its broadly defined mission of supporting scientific endeavor, the National Science Foundation seeks to select on the basis of quality over a broad spectrum of subject matter. In the other agencies, projects are submitted in the classifications representing the agency's areas of interest, and are evaluated in terms of relevance to agency objectives, the likelihood that knowledge will be significantly increased, and the prospect that the work proposed will be done effectively. An agency which has operated for some years will have a large portion of its annual appropriation committed to grants of two or three years' duration. It will also have a substantial number of requests for renewals. Under these circumstances, the funds available for considering wholly new proposals are relatively small.

Appraising the significance of the contribution which might be made by a proposed research project as well as the feasibility of proposed procedures rests upon intimate familiarity with the most recent additions to knowledge in the area, awareness of research under way, and experience in the techniques of evaluation. Some agencies (for example, Office of Naval Research) rely upon their permanent staffs to maintain the knowledge necessary to permit sophisticated evaluation. Some (for example, NIH) rely entirely upon study groups and advisory committees of private citizens qualified by their scientific experience to provide such evaluations, making their awards according to the recommendations of such committees. Others (for example, Army Research Office) may arrange for evaluations by private groups as a first step toward applying their own staff evaluations.[54]

[54] Agency procedures in evaluating proposals are described in U. S. Bureau of the Budget, *The Administration of Government Supported Research at Universities* (1966), chap. 4.

A common procedure is to classify all proposals in a number of groups, the projects within each group then being ranked in order by some qualitative criteria expressed ultimately as the judgment of the examiners. Proposals approved as to their scientific objectives and procedures are then considered in the light of the funds available. Proposals that rank high on scientific or technical grounds, however, may be rejected because of cost relative to probable results. The agency staff may consider a costly project desirable, but the funds available may be insufficient to meet the proposed budget. The staff may conclude that the work can be done for less than the financing requested and offer the proposer a smaller amount.[55]

Most research-sponsoring agencies coordinate with established mechanisms to some degree to avoid undesirable duplication of research. Maintaining effective listings of and access to the results of work done and of work underway is a difficult task that is attracting increasing attention.[56] In selecting projects, however, all agencies rely on the knowledge of specialists regarding work going on in their fields and on the reluctance of scientists to duplicate the work of others.

The legal instrument formalizing the acceptance of proposals and authorizing the transfer of funds is a cost-reimbursement contract of stated amount which normally specifies the work to be done as described in the contractor's proposal, and which approves the submitted budget in whole or in part. The legal form of the contract differs among agencies depending upon the agency's legal authority and the requirements of a particular project. The principal forms are the standard contract, modifications thereof, and the grant. The differences between the two are discussed at greater length in Chapter VII. It is sufficient to point out here that al-

[55] One study indicates that the amounts granted to successful new proposals ranged from 65 percent of the amounts requested to more than 100 percent; for renewals, from 49 percent to 100 percent. Agencies differed considerably in this respect with the Defense agencies and NASA tending to meet requested budgets while NSF grants averaged about two-thirds. National Science Foundation, *A Case Study of Support of Scientific and Engineering Research Proposals* (1963), p. 19.

[56] See House Select Committee on Government Research, *Documentation and Dissemination of Research and Development Results*, Study No. 4, 88 Cong. 2 sess. (1964); Senate Select Committee on Small Business, *Policy Planning for Technology Transfer*, 90 Cong. 1 sess. (1967).

though the grant is a limited cost-reimbursement contract, it is a simpler instrument than the standard contract in that it imposes fewer restrictions upon the recipient. Though differing somewhat between agencies, all grants impose a statutory cost-sharing requirement. The contract may, but does not necessarily, impose more specific restrictions upon the contractor than does the grant. Thus the contract may require the approval of the sponsoring agency if the researcher determines that he should follow a course of investigation differing from that outlined in his proposals. In the case of the grant the agency would normally request that it be apprised of such a change but would not require that its approval be sought in advance.

The NIH is required by statute to use grants in sponsoring unsolicited proposals from nonprofit institutions; the NSF uses grants as an administrative policy. The AEC uses cost-reimbursement contracts with limitations on the overhead acceptable. Other agencies had no authority to use grants before 1958; since that time all agencies which have authority to contract for research may also use grants.[57] However, the preference of many nonprofit institutions for the contract has restrained the wider use of grants.

The agencies administering research programs have a variety of procedures for monitoring research in progress. These include periodic progress reports from researchers, visits to their laboratories, and participation in scientific meetings. The final administrative steps for research programs consist of providing for the dissemination of results. Agencies like AEC and DOD may review the results of projects they sponsor to determine security classification. Some agencies require formal final reports. Others have no requirement but anticipate that results will be published in appropriate professional journals.

Summary

The government's organization and procedure for administering the contract system of R&D is the product of an evolution in which numerous congressional groups and executive agencies have participated. This evolution has been marked by disruptive exter-

[57] By P.L. 85–934 (1958).

nal influences like the Korean war and Sputnik and by the introduction of new programs, some of which constituted experiments
in organization. It is significant, however, that the basic principle
established immediately after World War II of reliance upon the
R&D capabilities of private institutions has not been seriously
questioned but has instead been steadily extended. The advantage
of the contract system in making readily available to the government almost any source of scientific and technical capabilities has
been demonstrated to be so great that extensive use of the contract
seems essential to the achievement of the objectives which the government has established.

At the same time there are problems. The launching of a development project is no longer simply a matter for bureaucratic action in the isolation of the lower echelons of a multilayered organization. Instead it involves a variety of interested parties outside
the agency most directly concerned, including other arms of the
government and numerous private organizations. As a consequence, the nature of the objective may be visualized in a number
of ways, numerous alternative routes to its accomplishment may be
proposed, presenting the need for difficult evaluations, and the
participants in the discussion may be numerous. The government,
in order to draw effectively upon a wider variety of abilities, must
have a heightened capacity to guide the scientific and technical resources available to it. As the ultimate decision-maker the government must be highly discriminating in its selection of objectives,
programs, and performers and it must be wise and prudent in the
terms of participation it offers.

It is obvious that reliance upon contractors to formulate R&D
proposals and to do R&D work places the government in a position of intimacy with outside researchers as well as in a position of
dependence upon them. Historically, such relationships were minimized by restricting the government's contacts with private institutions. Government employees did most of the government's
work and private institutions were called upon only through contracts let on competitive price bids. The government was not, of
course, as isolated or as self-sufficient as the governing statutes
might suggest. It was, however, sufficiently isolated that the limitations of the system could be clearly demonstrated (see Chapter
II). What is more important is the fact that in responding to its

own needs and those of society by assuming the initiative in important areas of R&D, the government could assure itself of maximizing its effectiveness only if it had unrestricted access to all relevant capabilities. In acquiring this, it necessarily assumed the risks inherent in intimate relationships with private institutions.

Over the past two decades public administration has evolved a new dimension as these problems have been faced. The new dimension in administration deals with uncertainties in objectives and methods, with qualitative rather than quantitative differences, and operates in an intimacy with private institutions which historically would have been considered intolerable.

The system works effectively insofar as the government is able to channel the energies of the contributors to the technical issues and to control the formulation of large and expensive development projects so that both need and feasibility are clear. The government has made extensive adjustments in organization and procedure to deal with these problems. On their part, the private research institutions have acquired considerable experience and have become better equipped to suggest new development objectives and to specify the methods by which they might be accomplished. The government has created a complex structure both for generating ideas and for performance. Its basic control problem is to utilize that structure to formulate objectives that are in the public interest and to pursue them effectively and economically.

The possibility of achieving greater efficiency in managing approved programs has properly been given considerable attention and further efforts in that direction may be anticipated as experience accumulates. While numerous improvements may be possible, it seems clear that a sense of urgency can be both a source of rapid and effective accomplishment and a source of great inefficiency. The experiences of the past two decades have been analyzed only in part.

A much more difficult problem relates to the determination that something should or should not be incorporated in a government program. The problem of determining that a development objective should or should not be sought is not affected in any fundamental way by the source of the ideas or by the governmental or private character of the people doing the work. What does differ is that calling in private institutions expands the technical abilities directed to the problem, increases the alternatives to be considered, and may generate more participation by private groups and individuals in the debate. Decision-making is then both enriched and made more involved. On balance there can be little doubt that broader participation is in the public interest. It is equally true that the determination of the public interest has required more attention by highly placed responsible public officials and has placed heavy burdens upon them. It is also clear that private individuals and organizations participating in the research and development programs of the government thereby become affected with a public interest, which they must recognize and respect in their relationships with the government if the system is to work acceptably. Recognition of and respect for the public interest are common in periods of great national emergency such as that under which the present system has grown. The real challenge to the government's ability to administer the system will come if and when the sense of emergency fades.

CHAPTER V

The Role of the President and the Congress in Research and Development

The R&D operations of the executive agencies involve both the President and the Congress at many points. At a minimum, this contact relates to the agency programs which, when presented in the form of a budget request, move to the President for approval and incorporation into his legislative program and his budget for submission to the Congress. There are also numerous contacts which may bear not only on the formulation of the budget but also on the programs and projects involved, the organization of the agency, and the effectiveness with which it conducts its operations.

The President and the Executive Office

Agency proposals for legislation and appropriations do not in the aggregate or necessarily in all their details constitute a program that is well designed and integrated for the effective application of scientific and technological possibilities to the nation's needs. There may be duplications in the programs, or there may be undesirable gaps, while the possibility exists that some areas of science or technology may receive excessive and others inadequate attention. Development programs, frequently very expensive, must be evaluated from a broader point of view and in the light of considerations that may be more inclusive than is possible in the originating agency. The division of responsibilities among the agencies, the rapid growth of expenditures, and the multiplicity of sources of suggestions for R&D programs have created numerous problems in the coordination of agency programs, technical evaluation of particularly expensive programs and, in effect, the proper allocation of a large proportion of the nation's resources of scientific and technical personnel. Though some of these problems relate to the mission of a single agency, others involve several or perhaps all of the agencies conducting R&D activities.

The Bureau of the Budget

The President's connection with the development of the nation's R&D policy is chiefly and, in any case, ultimately, through the Bureau of the Budget. In this area the President's staff organization, the Bureau of the Budget, has carried the burden of reviewing agency proposals for their conformity with his policies. Agency priorities as between funds for operations, procurement, development, and research may, for example, differ from that believed desirable in terms of the President's view of national requirements as such views have been formulated and applied by the Bureau of the Budget in the budget review process. From this process there emerges what are, perforce, the federal government's policies and programs with regard to R&D. The federal budget for R&D is an aggregate reflecting judgments that have been made of the R&D proposals of the agencies. In its preparation, decisions have been made on thousands of projects. Some of the items have been of a size and importance that required the President's personal attention; most rest upon a faith in the technical competence of the proposing agency and represent a judgment regarding the public interest in the expenditure requested.

The determination of priorities among scientific and technical areas and of the overall level of expenditures for scientific and technical objectives is the function of the Bureau of the Budget as the staff assisting the President. Testifying on the role of the Bureau of the Budget, Elmer Staats, its Deputy Director, observed that the Bureau "is deeply concerned that research programs are properly planned, that research funds are not misapplied through unnecessary duplication, that the Federal Government is properly organized to administer its research and development activities—including provision of clear lines of authority—and that the research and development itself is of high quality." Staats emphasized that "in reviewing research and development programs and budgets, the Bureau of the Budget draws liberally upon the resources of the Office of Science and Technology which, like the Bureau, is part of the Executive Office of the President. In addition, we draw upon the expertise of the line departments and agencies wherever appropriate."

Staats observed further that "the Bureau of the Budget does not review in detail nor pass final judgment on the worth of every research and development project—nor does the President or the Congress expect us to do so. Instead, chiefly through our budget review process, we make an informed judgment as to how strong a case the departments and agencies have made for the levels and types of expenditures" they propose.[1]

In reviewing proposals for research and development programs the Bureau considers a variety of factors. In his testimony Elmer Staats indicated that, broadly speaking, they were as follows:

1. Relationship of the research and development program to demonstrated needs: Examples of recent emerging needs which require augmentation of research and development are assuring safe use of new families of pesticides, alleviating air and water pollution that endangers the public health, and policing the atmospheric test ban treaty. Because Federal research and development is preponderantly directed to support of agency missions, when the missions change to reflect changing national needs there are attendant adjustments needed in research and development programs. Part of our review is therefore ascertaining the extent to which proposed research and development programs are directed to recognized areas of national need.

[1] *Federal Research and Development Programs,* Hearings before the House Select Committee on Government Research, 88 Cong. 1 sess. (1963), pt. 1, p. 563. Harvey Brooks, a member of the President's Science Advisory Committee (PSAC), confirms this description of the role of the Bureau of the Budget, writing that "the President's Science Advisory Committee has strenuously resisted being put in a position of making the decision as to scientific priorities. Basically these priorities are still determined by the Bureau of the Budget, *de facto* . . ." ("The Interaction of Science and Technology: Another View," in Aaron W. Warner *et al.* [eds.], *The Impact of Science on Technology* [Columbia University Press, 1965], p. 48).

2. Scientific or technical merit of the program as evidenced by critical evaluation procedures in the agencies: While many programs involve exceedingly complex theoretical and technical questions that we can deal with only from an educated layman's point of view, we can make sure that the proposal has been critically scrutinized by experts in the field. We therefore review the procedures being used by agencies in developing their programs, including the use of panels of outstanding scientists from outside Government, and in addition we are helped greatly by independent evaluations furnished by the Office of Science and Technology. . . .

3. The relative emphasis to be given particular fields of science: The Federal Government is concerned not only with using science to meet national needs, but also with strengthening science as a national resource. Consequently, we are guided in budgetary decisions by the consensus of scientists as to what fields of science are most in need of support. These may be areas which have been neglected because they are not of immediate concern to the operational missions of particular Federal agencies. They may be fields which appear to be ripe for large scientific breakthroughs with some additional effort. In assessing the level of support for a scientific field, we are concerned with the availability of competent research manpower and research tools, as well as the needs of the field. In some instances qualified manpower is more of a limiting factor than funds. . . .

4. Special factors of timing and opportunity for maximum research impact: Sometimes opportunities arise that need to be exploited at once to take advantage of special physical phenomena and auspicious conditions. The circumstances presented by the International Geophysical Year and the so-called International Year of the Quiet Sun are cases at point.

5. The current assessment of research and development values: It is of course necessary to maintain a continuing review of ongoing programs to determine whether support should be continued or withdrawn. It may be that the current technological approach in view of recent experience now appears to be unsound. Related technological advances may cast doubt on the wisdom of proceeding with the current approach. The objectives of the original program may have changed sufficiently to make the existing research and development program obsolete. . . . These kinds of decisions are not easy but must be made to make way for new avenues of research that are competing for scarce dollars.

6. Relative urgency, in the context of budgetary limitations on the one hand and a demonstrated national need on the other: The deter-

mination of priorities is probably the most difficult aspect of our problem. For instance, a strong case can be made at any time for substantial investment in cardiovascular research to reduce the prodigious economic and human waste caused by such illness. But if the budget is tight, a choice may have to be made between a buildup of such research and a new research effort on the causes of mental retardation, another area requiring greater scientific investigation.[2]

Useful as such criteria may be, they do not lead to formulae that can be applied to secure clearly objective recommendations. Proposals calling for development are usually the most expensive but they are also subject to analysis in terms of costs compared with benefits and hence permit some comparison with alternative courses of action as well as with quite different sets of opportunities. The experience of the Department of Defense in measuring the costs of alternative opportunities for accomplishing a specific objective has led the Bureau of the Budget to encourage the use of cost-effectiveness analysis in a very wide variety of development problems.[3] To some degree, applied research can also be subjected to such quantitative analysis. It is true, however, that subjective judgment remains an essential element in the process. A highly experienced member of the Bureau of the Budget staff observes that

in government, as elsewhere, decisions about what to (or not to) do in research and development are opportunistic in the sense that they flow from the bargaining process common to all problems of choice in allocating resources. . . .

No matter how far we may go with innovations in Federal budgeting, designed to increase its rational inputs, nothing we do is likely to repeal either the bargaining factor or the political judgments that accompany it—including such value notions, if you will, as national prestige, keeping a scientific or technological edge over the Soviets, and the itch to respond to opportunities. . . .

---

[2] *Federal Research and Development Programs,* Hearings, pt. 1, pp. 563–65. See also Staats, "Making the 1967 Science Budget," in Harold Orlans (ed.), *Science Policy and the University* (Brookings Institution, 1968).

[3] A new planning-programming-budgeting system was instituted in 1965 for use by government agencies by Bureau of the Budget Bulletin No. 66-3 and a supplement of Feb. 21, 1966. The purpose of PPBS is to assure more systematic decision-making throughout the government by identifying national goals with greater precision and as a continuous process, selecting the most urgent goals, selecting from among alternative means those that are most effective at least cost (costs being considered over at least a five-year period), and measuring the results of the programs.

In all types of bargaining, guidelines help immensely to produce acceptable outcomes. But where research and development is concerned—notwithstanding the prolific funding of late years—we still do not have enough criteria to illuminate many of our judgments about priorities. Still, R&D priorities manage to be decided despite the imperfect structure of decision-making.

If you ask me how they are arrived at, I can only answer that they emerge from a variety of analytical reviews, trading procedures, and an uncertain mix of intuition and judgment. Technological dead-ends, resource shortages, and opportunity considerations are just some of the justifications that produce public priorities for R&D investment.[4]

The Bureau of the Budget must deal also with many problems raised by R&D programs which are not in themselves of a scientific or technical nature but which influence the character of federal R&D programs and their management. The Bureau reviews questionnaires directed to the public arising from research projects sponsored by the government.[5] The Bureau promotes interagency coordination, as, for example, in the field of federal meteorological services, when the Bureau assigned to the Department of Commerce the responsibility for preparing and applying plans for the efficient utilization of meteorological services and related research. The Bureau of the Budget has also acted to encourage uniform administrative procedures among the agencies. For example, the Bureau was instrumental in defining agency-wide policy on contracted overhead allowances and, more recently, on policy regarding university cost-sharing on research grants.

The Office of Science and Technology

It is clear from the foregoing discussion of the functions of the Bureau of the Budget as staff to the President that the issues on which decisions must be made rest upon an understanding of scientific and technical matters adequate to permit intelligent

[4] William D. Carey, Executive Assistant Director, U. S. Bureau of the Budget, "Decisions on Research and Development: Viewpoint from the Bureau of the Budget," *Proceedings of the Nineteenth National Conference on the Administration of Research* (Denver Research Institute, University of Denver, 1965), pp. 107–8.

[5] That is, questionnaires arising from work conducted at the explicit request of a government agency. See House Committee on Government Operations, *The Use of Social Research in Federal Domestic Programs,* 90 Cong. 1 sess. (1967), pt. 4, pp. 16–17, 459–80.

judgments regarding the usefulness, feasibility, and relative costs of the proposals which are competing for federal funds. While the Bureau of the Budget has acquired a high level of expertise in analyzing the fiscal and administrative aspects of agency programs, the Bureau has not been staffed to provide technical appraisals and has resisted suggestions that it do so.[6]

One of the objectives of the adjustments in organization and management of the executive agencies, described in the preceding chapter, was to improve the quality of the information on which presidential decisions are made. While the quality of the relevant information has been improved and the number of issues coming to the President may be reduced, there remain inevitably a wide variety of difficult and complex problems. It is the President who must ultimately make the decisions with regard to the very large development proposals, and it is to the President that the agencies transfer pressures placed upon them by private groups for approval of proposals of interest to them. The decisions are particularly difficult if, for example, there is reason to believe that the cost estimates are of doubtful validity, if there is reason to doubt the technical feasibility of a proposal, if scientific and technical advice is conflicting, if an immediate need must be assessed against the possibility of more effective developments at some future date, or if a choice must be made between proposals of generally equal appeal and political support.

In the area of basic science, coordinating functions had been envisaged for the National Science Foundation in the 1950 legislation and had been reiterated by executive order in 1954. That order specifically instructed the National Science Foundation to recommend policies for strengthening the nation's scientific effort. However, the executive order also recognized the desirability of the basic research programs then functioning in other agencies and called for their continuance. The NSF was given no additional powers to support its assignment to make recommendations regarding the basic research programs of other agencies.

There had existed since 1947 an Interdepartmental Committee on Scientific Research and Development. The executive order establishing the committee directed its activities principally to the

---

[6] Address by William D. Carey, reprinted in *Congressional Record*, vol. 109, Appendix, 88 Cong. 1 sess. (Sept. 20, 1963), p. A 6107.

problems of increasing the efficiency of administration of scientific research and development programs, though much of the effort of this group was directed to the problems of scientific manpower, specifically within the federal government. By its nature the committee served as a forum and was not a source of advice on specific policy issues.

One such issue became critical after the U.S.S.R., in 1957, boosted a satellite into space. The character of the nation's response was a problem that called for a presidential proposal to Congress based upon the best qualified advice that could be obtained. The missile development program of the military services involved many conflicts and uncertainties. Some of them, particularly such very large proposals as the development of Polaris, required presidential action. A very different problem arose in 1959 involving a conflict between two departments over the significance of the fact that much of the nation's cranberry crop had been treated with a weed-killer, a substance which had been discovered to have carcinogenic effects.[7] Among the more recent problems that are known to have required special attention at the presidential level have been the decisions with regard to the Midwestern Universities Research Association,[8] the supersonic transport, the manned orbiting laboratory, and a variety of efforts by the Joint Committee on Atomic Energy to promote expensive projects involving the application of nuclear energy.[9] Other issues that have required presi-

[7] At that time the President was advised by the Department of Agriculture that there was no conceivable danger from the material (aminotriazole), while the Secretary of Health, Education and Welfare was insisting that the material had carcinogenic effects and was therefore to be outlawed, regardless of the low probability of deleterious effects on human beings. The decision as to what action, if any, to take was one for the government—in this case, the President—to make. That decision had to be based on an evaluation of the scientific evidence and the possible interpretations of it. See "A Scientist in the White House," an interview with George B. Kistiakowsky, *International Science and Technology*, October 1964, p. 50.

[8] The Midwestern Universities Research Association had proposed an AEC-sponsored high intensity accelerator budgeted at $170 million. The project represented a major effort by midwestern scientists to achieve greater participation in high energy physics programs, an effort which had mobilized considerable political support. The decision not to fund the program was made by the President, who at the same time offered the interested group an opportunity for increased participation in the operations of the Argonne laboratory. See "The MURA Accelerator: Compromise for the Mid-west," *Science*, vol. 143 (Jan. 31, 1964), pp. 450–52.

[9] Howard Margolis, "R&D on Capitol Hill," *Bulletin of the Atomic Scientists*, May 1964, pp. 34–37.

dential attention involved broad problems such as the utilization of scientific and technical manpower, educational policy relating to scientists and engineers, the broad relationship of government to private institutions, and the impact of technical change upon government policy as well as upon society.

The wide variety of problems facing the President requires that there be available to him a source of advice technically qualified as well as independent of the agencies. In 1950 the President took a first step toward obtaining advice on scientific and technical matters independently of the executive agencies by establishing a Science Advisory Committee. Administratively, the committee was placed in the Office of Defense Mobilization. Though little used, two of its panels produced very influential reports. In 1954 the Technical Capabilities Panel chaired by James Killian urged expansion of the ballistic missile program. The famed Gaither report was produced by a group of private citizens commissioned by the Security Resources Panel in 1957.[10] The crisis presented by the Soviet success with Sputnik spotlighted the need of the presidency for more readily accessible advice. In response, the President created the post of Special Assistant to the President for Science and Technology within the White House office.[11] At the same time, the Science Advisory Committee was elevated to become the President's Science Advisory Committee.

The President's Science Advisory Committee consists of eighteen scientists and engineers drawn from private life and appointed by the President for three-year terms. This body undertakes stud-

[10] Jerome B. Wiesner, *Where Science and Politics Meet* (McGraw-Hill, 1965), p. 44; Morton H. Halperin, "The Gaither Committee and the Policy Process," *World Politics*, vol. 13 (1961) pp. 360–84. On the Gaither report and its influence, see Dwight D. Eisenhower, *Waging Peace, 1956–61* (Doubleday & Co., 1965), pp. 219–22.

[11] Jerome B. Wiesner observes that "one of the great revolutions in Washington during the past decade has been the slow, but genuine, recognition on the part of recent presidents of the fact that they were handicapped in their work without a continuing scientific input provided by someone responsible to them rather than an operating agency with its vested interest. The position of Special Assistant for Science and Technology which I occupied under Presidents Kennedy and Johnson was created by President Eisenhower after he recognized that he was a captive of vested interest groups in the Defense Department and Atomic Energy Commission whom he couldn't expect to provide objective advice on technical issues affecting defense and foreign policy when their local interests were also involved" ("Technology and World Politics," in *Motivation and Support of R&D To Achieve National Goals,* Proceedings of a National Security Industry Association Symposium [Government Printing Office, 1965], p. 21).

ies in response to specific presidential requests as well as on its own initiative, provides scientific advice and analysis, reviews studies by other advisory groups such as the Federal Council for Science and Technology and the National Academy of Sciences, and is concerned with the effect of federal scientific and technical policy and programs upon the nation. For some years after its establishment, PSAC devoted much of its time to defense problems. As the Department of Defense, through its Director of Defense Research and Engineering, gained increased control over its problems, PSAC's interests shifted to other areas.[12] It plays an important role in blending and integrating governmental and nongovernmental views to achieve an approach to problems involving science and government that is comprehensive of a field.[13] Most of the work of the committee is accomplished through a number of panels, which include regular committee members as well as scientists and engineers selected from outside the committee.[14] Some are standing panels; others are established to study a specific subject

[12] See "On Planning Science, Thinking Ahead with . . . Donald Hornig," *International Science and Technology*, January 1966, pp. 66–70. Jerome Wiesner, after leaving the post of Chairman of PSAC, reported that a very large part of his time was spent on "technological issues which had a major impact on foreign affairs and much of this went to providing the President with more options than the military would permit him" ("Technology and World Politics," in *Motivation and Support of R&D To Achieve National Goals*, p. 21).

[13] The President's Science Advisory Committee has issued some highly influential reports, including *Scientific Progress, the Universities, and the Federal Government* (1960); *Meeting Manpower Needs in Science and Technology* (1962); *Strengthening the Behavioral Sciences* (1962); and *Some New Technologies and Their Promise for the Life Sciences* (1963); *Restoring the Quality of Our Environment* (1965).

[14] Typically the membership of the panels is secret to enable the participants to give the most objective advice possible, free of the pressures that would follow from public knowledge of their role. As an organization of presumably great power and particularly because it is the epitome of scientists exercising political power, the Office of Science and Technology and its affiliates have attracted much attention whetted by the secrecy of panel membership. See Christopher Wright, "Scientists and the Establishment of Science Affairs," and Harvey Brooks, "The Scientific Adviser," in Robert Gilpin and Christopher Wright (eds.), *Scientists and National Policy Making* (Columbia University Press, 1964); M. Greenfield, "Science Goes to Washington," *Science*, vol. 142 (Oct. 18, 1963), pp. 361–67; Avery Leiserson, "Scientists and the Policy Process," *American Political Science Review*, vol. 59 (June 1965), pp. 408–16. For a discussion of the desirability of separating PSAC and OST, see Philip H. Abelson, "The President's Science Advisers," *Minerva*, vol. 3 (Winter 1965), pp. 150–57, and the comments of Harvey Brooks and Abelson's reply in the subsequent issue of the same journal (Spring 1965), pp. 392–98; and Don K. Price, *The Scientific Estate* (Belknap Press, 1965).

and disband upon completion of their work. One of the first tasks given to PSAC was to study the ways the federal government could best maintain and advance the vigor and excellence of United States' science and technology. Since that time panel reports have ranged from studies of specific proposals to studies of education as related to increasing scientific manpower.

In 1959, in response to a recommendation of the President's Science Advisory Committee, the President established the Federal Council for Science and Technology (FCST) and abolished the Interdepartmental Committee.[15] The effort to give higher status to the consideration of interagency problems in science and technology is reflected in the FCST's membership. The council is composed of the Special Assistant to the President for Science and Technology and a policy level official representing the Departments of Defense, Interior, Agriculture, Commerce, and Health, Education and Welfare, the National Science Foundation, the National Aeronautics and Space Administration, and the Atomic Energy Commission.

The functions of the Federal Council are to make recommendations regarding problems and developments in the fields of science and technology and related activities affecting more than one federal agency or concerning the overall advancement of the nation's science and technology. The council is responsible for recommendations that will result in more effective planning and administration of federal science and technology programs, for identifying research needs including areas of research requiring additional emphasis, for achieving more effective utilization of the scientific and technological resources and facilities of federal agencies, including the elimination of unnecessary duplication, and for furthering international cooperation in science and technology.[16]

In developing such policies and measures the council considers the effects of federal R&D policies and programs on nonfederal programs and institutions, long-range program plans designed to meet the scientific and technological needs of the federal government, including manpower and capital requirements, and the ef-

[15] By Executive Order 10807 (March 13, 1959).
[16] On the Federal Council for Science and Technology, see testimony of its executive secretary, Edward Wenk, Jr., in *Federal Research and Development Programs*, Hearings, pt. 1, pp. 217–54.

fects of nonfederal programs in science and technology upon federal R&D policies and programs. Because the statutory authority is vested in the agencies, the council has no policy-making or executive powers. It does provide a focus for interagency discussions, and through a number of its committees prepares studies and reports which form recommendations to the Special Assistant to the President for Science and Technology on planning and policy matters and provide guidelines for agency programs or management of R&D activities.[17]

Further steps were taken in 1962 to strengthen the President's role and at the same time improve the lines of communication between the executive and the Congress by the establishment of the Office of Science and Technology (OST) in the Executive Office of the President to provide staff functions for the Federal Council for Science and Technology and the President's Science Advisory Committee.

The Office of Science and Technology is intended to have a broad perspective from which to rationalize the government's scientific and technical activities. The OST is the highest technical office in the government with responsibilities relating to the formulation and review of national science and technology programs. It provides such advice as scientists, each with a detailed knowledge of one field and general awareness of others, can contribute to the task of giving direction and control to federal activities. Operating with a small staff of scientific specialists, but with numerous advisory groups, OST reports to and advises the President directly and through the Bureau of the Budget on virtually any question relating to the government's role in the nation's research and development activities as well as those involving the policies and programs of the various agencies. The office has no operational functions but is the focal point for all problems and all sources of advice relating to the government's R&D programs.[18] As

[17] For example, the first FCST report, "Research and Development on Natural Resources" (May 1963), was prepared in close collaboration with the National Academy of Sciences and about ninety scientists in government.

[18] A comprehensive review of actions and procedures dealing with substantive R&D problems at the level of the Executive Office is *The Office of Science and Technology*, A Report Prepared by the Science Policy Research Division of the Legislative Reference Service for the House Committee on Government Operations, 90 Cong. 1 sess. (1967), esp. pp. 154–58. For a staff member's view of OST operations, see William L. Hooper, "The Role of OST in Program Selection," in Walter L.

has been pointed out, OST does not determine priorities between scientific areas nor does it determine the level of expenditures for scientific and technical objectives. Such determination remains the function of the Bureau of the Budget as the staff assisting the President.[19]

All three offices—OST, FCST, and PSAC—until the present time have been headed by the same man, who also acts as Special Assistant to the President. As Special Assistant, he advises the President on such matters as priorities and level of expenditures of various programs. The director of OST is available to present testimony to the Congress, a function that the Special Assistant to the President cannot perform. An important avenue of communication between the executive and legislative branches on scientific and technical matters has thus been established and it has been well used.[20]

Other organizations within the Executive Office of the President have specialized interests and responsibilities for science and technology. The National Aeronautics and Space Council has been active in formulating space policy and in coordinating the overlapping missions and functions of NASA and the Department of Defense. The responsibilities of the Office of Emergency Planning for telecommunications—the nation's communication system—include the sponsorship of research of broad scope. The Council of Economic Advisers as well as the National Security Council may also advise on R&D policy related to their special areas of interest. The Federal Radiation Council is an interagency organization that advises the President on radiation problems.

Ad hoc committees are frequently of considerable influence. An

---

Johnson (ed.), *The Management of Aerospace Programs* (AAS Science and Technology Series, vol. 12 [American Astronautical Society, 1966]), pp. 13–25. See also Donald Hornig's testimony before the House Committee on Science and Astronautics, 89 Cong. 1 sess., *Government and Science: Review of the National Science Foundation* (1965), no. 6, vol. 1, p. 114.

[19] In the view of one close observer of the government's R&D operations, "OST is influential not because it intrinsically has power but because it has acquired the confidence of the Bureau of the Budget, and when the Budget speaks federal agencies listen" (D. S. Greenberg, "Research Administration: Study Urges Universities To Improve Methods," *Science*, vol. 152 [April 29, 1966], p. 626).

[20] The director of OST made sixty-one appearances before eighteen different congressional committees in the years 1962–66; see *The Office of Science and Technology*, p. 36.

interagency committee chaired by the director of the Bureau of the Budget, David Bell, in 1962 prepared the influential report on the government's contracting policies referred to earlier. In 1965, a committee of private scientists established at the request of the President through OST conducted a detailed study and evaluation of the programs and procedures of the National Institutes of Health.[21] The President's actions to encourage cost reduction in the space and defense industries have also influenced the character of federal contracting programs. Similarly, actions by the Executive Office to reduce or limit the number of direct federal employees often have the immediate result of inducing more work by contract.

From time to time the idea of a Department of Science has been advocated.[22] Most of the government's science programs are oriented to an agency's mission, and the concept has met strong objections from the agencies conducting programs that would be affected. While some scientists continue to urge such a department, others have objected to the creation of a monolithic organization, preferring the opportunity to deal with a number of agencies. While a Department of Science might give the appearance of greater orderliness than does the present structure, it would be concerned with only a small fraction of the government's R&D programs and the contribution it might make to greater effectiveness is very unclear.[23]

[21] Office of Science and Technology, *Biomedical Science and Its Administration: A Study of the National Institutes of Health* [the Wooldridge report] (Government Printing Office, 1965).

[22] The subject of a Department of Science has been debated since the 1880's (see A. Hunter Dupree, *Science in the Federal Government* [Belknap Press, 1957], pp. 215–20). At that time and on various occasions since, it has been concluded that the government's scientific organization and interests are too complex for such a department to function effectively. The subject was revived in 1957 when hearings were held before the Senate Government Operations Committee on a Science and Technology Act of 1957 (85 Cong. 1 sess.), which continued into 1959 (*Commission on a Department of Science and Technology*, S. Rept. 408, 86 Cong. 1 sess. [1959]).

[23] The House Select Committee on Government Research collected extensive comment on the issue, almost all of it adverse (*Federal Research and Development Programs*, 88 Cong. 1 and 2 sess., pts. 1–3 [1963–64]). The committee concluded that "consolidating research and development into one or a few separate agencies— such as an often suggested Department of Science and Technology—would separate such work from the purposes for which it is performed, the committee believes, with devastating effects both to the work and to the capacities of agencies to carry out their missions" (House Select Committee on Government Research, *National Goals and Policies*, Study No. 10, H. Rept. 1941, 88 Cong. 2 sess. [1964], p. 49).

Congress and Research and Development

Basically Congress deals with scientific research and development and the contractual system in conventional ways—it reacts to the President's program, the legislation requested, and the budget proposed. It does so in terms of committee jurisdiction over the agencies involved. Legislation involving an agency is considered by the legislative committee with jurisdiction in its area of operations. In those cases where the legislative committee has retained control over expenditures by requiring annual authorization or has established limits which are exceeded in the proposed budget, the proposed budget must be justified before it. The very large missile and aircraft programs of the Department of Defense, for example, must be justified annually before the two Committees on Armed Services, as the programs of NASA are considered by the Senate Committee on Aeronautical and Space Sciences and the House Committee on Science and Astronautics. The appropriations committees operate through subcommittees which have at times raised significant questions and exercised considerable influence on federal programs in these areas.

This is not to say that Congress has not made adjustments to deal with the problems of R&D programs. As new programs have emerged and as established programs have grown and have presented questions of policy as well as of management performance, Congress has sought to deal with its problems by the formation of new committees and has made extensive use of subcommittees of the regular committees. The importance of atomic energy and the novel problems it presents led the Congress to make special arrangements to oversee the program. Almost simultaneously with the passage of the Atomic Energy Act of 1946, the two houses agreed to the establishment of an eighteen-member Joint Committee on Atomic Energy. The committee has since maintained extraordinarily close surveillance over the Atomic Energy Commission. A high degree of continuity of committee members as well as of its staff has permitted the development of considerable expertise in the subject area.

In 1958, the problems presented by Sputnik again led both houses to form new regular committees. In the Senate a Special Committee on Space and Astronautics was continued as a permanent Committee on Aeronautical and Space Sciences with jurisdiction as indicated in the title. In the House, the Committee on Science and Astronautics was given somewhat broader responsibilities including not only astronautical research and development but also scientific research and development in general as well as science scholarships. The agencies over which the committee has jurisdiction include the National Aeronautics and Space Administration, the National Science Foundation, and the Bureau of Standards.

The three committees cited, as well as regular committees dealing with important R&D programs, have made extensive use of subcommittees, some of which have played key roles in developing information and in formulating policy. These organizational arrangements change from time to time. In the Eighty-ninth Congress, in the House, the former Special Subcommittee on Research and Development of the Committee on the Armed Services became a permanent subcommittee (Subcommittee No. 3), the Foreign Affairs Committee had a Subcommittee on National Security and Scientific Developments Affecting Foreign Policy, and the Merchant Marine and Fisheries Committee had a Subcommittee on Oceanography. In the House, the Subcommittee on Research and Technical Programs, and in the Senate, the Special Subcommittee on Government Research operated under the respective Government Operations Committees to deal with questions of federal science policy and procedures. Both the Senate and House Agriculture Committees had subcommittees concerned with agricultural research. The Senate Labor and Public Welfare Committee had a Special Subcommittee on Scientific Manpower Utilization and the Senate Select Committee on Small Business had a Subcommittee on Government Procurement and a Subcommittee on Science and Technology. The Subcommittee on Patents, Trademarks and Copyrights of the Senate Committee on the Judiciary gave considerable attention to patent policies applied to contracts. Among the Joint Committees, the Subcommittee on Federal Procurement and Regulations of the Joint Economic Committee explored various aspects of contracting extensively.[24]

[24] The wide range of subject matter reviewed by these committees is summarized in *Science, Technology, and Public Policy during the Eighty-Ninth Congress,* Report of the Committee on Science and Astronautics, 90 Cong. 1 sess. (1967).

The division of responsibilities among committees has the advantages of leading to specialization and, given a considerable continuity of committee membership, to the development of expertise in the affairs of one or a group of agency programs.[25]

The investigative function of Congress was not aggressively employed during the first decade of the present contractual system. Over the past decade, however, one or another congressional committee has explored a very wide variety of aspects of the structure which has developed, its objectives, and the effectiveness of its operations.[26] Such concern with the effective management of programs and its possible implications may be expressed by any committee to the agencies over which it has jurisdiction. The Armed Services Committees of both Senate and House undertook in 1960 the first comprehensive studies of post–World War II procurement policies. The two Committees on Government Operations, because of their broad jurisdiction and because of their relationship with the General Accounting Office, have been a particularly clear source of influence on contractual relationships. Two subcommittees of the House Government Operations Committee—on Military Operations and on Intergovernmental Relations—have explored specific R&D programs in considerable detail, and have contributed substantially to the establishment of criteria for contracting as well as to management organization of large contracts.

[25] On congressmen as specialists, see Charles L. Clapp, *The Congressman: His Work as He Sees It* (Brookings Institution, 1963), chap. 3, "The Congressman as Legislator."

[26] One analysis of the scope of congressional activities relating to research and development that included "only those topics and reports which are conspicuously related to science and technology, and which have their primary focus on research and development," identified 1,400 Senate and House publications in the years 1963–65—statutes, hearings, committee reports, special research studies, presidential reports, and messages and agency reports and requests (Senate Committee on Government Operations, *An Inventory of Congressional Concern with Research and Development* [88th and 89th Congresses], 89 Cong. 2 sess. [1966], p. iv).

While this volume of publications is impressive, it does not suggest that Congress is paying a disproportionate amount of attention to R&D. The 1,400 titles listed comprise about 15 percent of all congressional publications over the three-year period. Appropriations for R&D also approximated 15 percent of all federal expenditures over the same time. However, the definition of R&D applied to federal expenditures appears to be somewhat more restrictive than the definitions applied in the study of congressional publications. A quantitative study of this kind provides, of course, no measure of the substantive nature and impact of congressional interest and action.

Criticism of the use of the contract—not limited to R&D—has come most consistently from the Subcommittee on Manpower Utilization of the House Committee on Post Office and Civil Service, though also from the House Committee on Appropriations.

Congress also continues to concern itself with issues that suggest an emerging need for broad policy formulation—issues that, in its view are not satisfactorily dealt with by the executive branch, or that arise as substantive or managerial problems from the application of established policies. Among these are such problems as the coordination of agency programs, the availability and utilization of scientific and technical manpower, the gathering and dissemination of information resulting from research activities, the impacts of rapidly changing technology, the geographic distribution of R&D contracts, and the perennial problem of the desirable level of federal support for basic research, particularly in relation to the universities.

While such problems may attract the attention of one of the regular committees in the normal course of legislative review, the House in 1963 took two actions specifically directed toward broad policy questions of the nature suggested. One was the formation within the Committee on Science and Astronautics of the Subcommittee on Scientific Research and Development. The other was the action of the House Rules Committee sponsoring the establishment of a Select Committee on Government Research, which was given a one-year assignment to review the entire structure of federally financed research operations. The Select Committee, upon its dissolution at the end of its authorized life, recommended that further investigation be undertaken, and this recommendation led to the creation of the Research and Technical Programs Subcommittee of the House Government Operations Committee.

The Congress has clearly made substantial adjustments for dealing with the problems presented by R&D programs. Two criticisms merit attention here. One is that the Congress is not equipped to deal intelligently with requests for authorization and appropriations for highly technical programs. The other is that no procedure exists that permits a critical review of R&D programs as a whole, or even effective consideration of programs that overlap committee jurisdictions.

Doubt that Congress can deal intelligently with R&D proposals arises from the fact that few congressmen have scientific or technical backgrounds and from the fact that the executive branch, in preparing its proposals, has employed numerous sources of information and advice that are not, or at least not readily, available to Congress.[27] It has been argued at various times that Congress, in considering such requests, should seek the assistance of independent sources of scientific and technical advice, an argument that is occasionally advanced by a member of Congress but, more frequently, is put forth by men involved in such programs who may believe that their positions will be more readily accepted if the technical aspects are thoroughly understood.

It is true that congressmen rarely have backgrounds in science or engineering. Their position in this respect is no different than it is in many other areas in which they must make decisions without being experts—areas such as military strategy or economic policy. They must be able to understand the testimony of the expert, from whatever field, to evaluate the objectivity of such testimony, and, on occasion, to reconcile conflicting testimony. Since they must deal with courses of action to be followed in the future, congressmen must deal with predictions. They have found that scientists and technical people, like other experts, leave much to be desired when they undertake prediction and prophecy.[28]

It must be recognized also that the Congress is not primarily in-

[27] Douglass Cater, for example, suggests that the ". . . Congress lacks the capacity to assimilate this outpouring of experts" (*Power in Washington: A Critical Look at Today's Struggle To Govern in the Nation's Capital* [Random House, 1964], p. 133). The more serious charge is made that political leaders have abdicated their responsibilities and permitted technological elites to make decisions; see Hans J. Morgenthau, "Decision-Making in the Nuclear Age," *Bulletin of the Atomic Scientists*, December 1962, pp. 7–8. Criticism of a similar nature may be found in James Burnham, *Congress and the American Tradition* (Henry Regnery Co., 1959), pp. 190, 348; a more moderate view is given by Ralph Lapp, *The New Priesthood* (Harper & Row, 1965); and by D. S. Greenberg, "Science and Congress: Machinery Is Out of Date for Handling $12 Billion in Research Programs," *Science*, vol. 138 (Oct. 19, 1962), pp. 417–18.

[28] As, notably, in the cases of the development of the hydrogen bomb and the problems associated with the nuclear test ban; see Robert Gilpin, *American Scientists and Nuclear Weapons Policy* (Princeton University Press, 1962). On the debate over the danger from radioactive fallout, see James L. McCamy, *Science and Public Administration* (University of Alabama Press, 1960), pp. 185–95. The matter merits some study, but the author's impression is that many prominent scientists who have made predictions of a specific nature regarding scientific and technical developments have been proven wrong in one or more instances by subsequent events. A very useful review of the literature on technological forecasting is Erich Jantsch, *Technological Forecasting in Perspective* (Organization for Economic Cooperation and Development, 1967).

terested in science and technology *per se* but in the application of knowledge to recognized problems. Its major concern is to satisfy itself that a given problem is of sufficient importance to require federal action and that there is reasonable assurance that the proposed program will contribute to a solution.[29] For the most part Congress plays the role of disposing of what the executive has proposed. In the R&D area, however, the degree of initiative exercised by congressional committees has been noteworthy. Sometimes this takes the form of an expression of interest in the testimony of a witness, an expression that results in a subsequent year in the submission of a new or changed program by the agency involved. Among many other occasions when Congress has taken more obvious direction, only a few need be cited.

The Joint Committee on Atomic Energy has been a strong and aggressive proponent of numerous applications of nuclear energy, frequently pressing for support of larger programs than the administration recommended.[30] Congressman Chet Holifield, chairman of the Joint Committee on Atomic Energy, has stated that "it was Congress who took the lead in forcing the shift to nuclear power in submarines. It was Congress who took the lead in developing nuclear propulsion for surface warships. It was Congress who strongly supported the building of the three nuclear surface warships now in the fleet which have so ably demonstrated to the world the obvious capabilities of nuclear propulsion in warships."[31] These were successes. The same committee also supported the Manned Aircraft Nuclear Propulsion program which was ter-

[29] The confidence that congressmen can feel in agency presentations is therefore critical. See the chapter by Herbert Roback, "Presenting Scientific and Technical Programs to the Congress," in Harold Orlans (ed.), *Science Policy and the University* (Brookings Institution, 1968).

[30] As, for example, in the dispute between the Joint Committee on Atomic Energy and the Secretary of Defense over the building of more nuclear-powered aircraft carriers. The Secretary argued for postponing such construction, pending the development of more efficient power sources; the committee argued for the need for immediate construction (*Nuclear Propulsion for Naval Surface Vessels*, Hearings before the Joint Committee on Atomic Energy, 88 Cong. 1 sess. [1963], p. 173).

The Joint Committee on Atomic Energy's relationships to policy in its area are analyzed in Harold P. Green and Alan Rosenthal, *Government of the Atom: The Integration of Powers* (Atherton Press, 1963); Harold P. Green, "Nuclear Technology and the Fabric of Government," *George Washington Law Review*, vol. 33 (October 1964), pp. 121–61; and Harold Orlans, *Contracting for Atoms* (Brookings Institution, 1967), chap. 8.

[31] "Creation of a Nuclear Navy," *Vital Speeches*, vol. 32 (Feb. 14, 1966), pp. 261–62.

minated far short of its objective.[32] Its unique role and the way it has chosen to discharge its responsibilities have led to criticism that the Joint Committee violates the traditional separation of legislative and executive powers. Whatever the merits of that criticism, it is true that the Joint Committee serves as a powerful advocate within the Congress for nuclear R&D programs. By virtue of the Joint Committee's position, programs in nuclear energy and nuclear physics are dealt with in a narrower perspective than is applied to other programs.

The armed services committees have taken a keen interest in numerous development situations and in their application. The well-known controversy over the development of the B-70 aircraft grew out of differences in strategic concepts; the similar controversy over the operational application of the Nike-X system has reflected both strategic questions and differences of opinion on the desirability of continuing development efforts. Committee members frequently follow a development program with some care, questioning the level of effort programmed as well as potential operational uses.[33] One case among many is the survey conducted by the House Armed Services' Subcommittee on Research and Development with regard to vertical and short takeoff and landing aircraft (V/STOL). The committee doubted the adequacy of the level of effort being applied and urged that the military services "not overcommit themselves to the helicopter to the detriment and interests of the V/STOL transport aircraft when they become available."[34]

An area in which Congress has brought a sense of urgency about R&D objectives markedly exceeding that of the executive is that of health. In both houses, the appropriations subcommittees with jurisdiction over NIH have consistently sought more rapid growth over a wider range of programs in health research than the President has proposed. In 1966, for example, the House subcommittee refused to accept a leveling off of funds for medical research and an increased appropriation for medical services, arguing that "the

[32] See Clinton P. Anderson and James T. Ramey, "Congress and Research: Experience in Atomic Research and Development," *The Annals of the American Academy of Political and Social Science*, vol. 37 (January 1960), p. 88.

[33] See Raymond L. Dawson, "Congressional Innovation and Intervention in Defense Policy: Legislative Authorization of Weapons Systems," *American Political Science Review*, March 1962, p. 42.

[34] *Congressional Record*, daily ed., March 18, 1965, p. A 1264.

capability that now exists for earlier diagnosis and more effective treatment, and—most important—for preventing certain diseases and disabilities, is the direct result of research conducted in years past. The constant strengthening of this capability is wholly dependent on the maintenance of a vigorous research effort. If health research is allowed to lose momentum today the improvement in health services will inevitably lose momentum a few years hence. The time lost can never be made up—if research is allowed to lag, people will continue that much longer to succumb to diseases that might be prevented and some will die who might have been cured."[35]

Congressional committees have exercised similar positive influences in many other areas. The space programs have enjoyed strong support, though the committees of jurisdiction have from time to time explored the possibilities that there was neglect of what might be promising technical directions[36] and that future goals were not being developed. The urban transport research program of the Department of Commerce apparently originated in Congress although that Department's proposal for a civilian technology program met opposition for some time.[37] Although recognition of the importance of basic science is frequently acknowledged by Congress, the experience of the National Science Foundation suggests that Congress has difficulties visualizing the role of the agency established to support efforts in that area.[38] In general, the Congress finds it easiest to deal with programs directed to areas in which clear and immediate problems exist and has at times sought to goad the agencies into faster and more aggressive action.[39]

[35] *Departments of Labor, and Health, Education and Welfare and Related Agencies Appropriations Bill, 1967*, H. Rept. 1464, 89 Cong. 2 sess. (1966), p. 20.

[36] As, for example, congressional concern that NASA was neglecting the possibilities of solid fuel for space boosters; see James R. Kerr, "Congress and Space: Overview or Oversight?" *Public Administration Review*, vol. 25 (September 1965), pp. 185–91.

[37] See Senator Claiborne Pell's account of his efforts to secure passage of an urban transportation bill in *Megalopolis Unbound* (Praeger, 1966).

[38] But the House Committee on Science and Astronautics has made some effort to strengthen the Foundation and to expand its role; see the committee's reports, *The National Science Foundation: A General Review of Its First Fifteen Years* and *The National Science Foundation: Its Present and Future*, 89 Cong. 2 sess. (1966).

[39] As, for example, the conclusion of the House Government Operations Committee that some areas suffer from "too few initiatives from some program directors, . . . inadequate executive office initiatives to remedy weaknesses at program

The fact is that congressmen, particularly committee chairmen, acquire considerable expert knowledge from association with a program over a period of time.[40] Congressional committees frequently invite testimony from experts outside the government, and hear from critics of administration programs. Committees have also sponsored seminar presentations on scientific topics[41] and have employed the contract to secure independent studies of their own.[42]

---

level, [and] . . . insufficient cost-benefit comparisons made by executive office of competing claims to federal R&D." The report contrasted the situation in defense, space, and atomic energy with that in urban transportation, housing and hospital facilities, and water pollution control (*Federal Research and Development Programs: The Decision-making Process,* H. Rept. 1664, 89 Cong. 2 sess. [1966], pp. 26–36).

[40] R. F. Fenno, in "The House Appropriations Committee," *American Political Science Review,* June 1962, points out that the average member of the House Appropriations Committee had spent nine years on the committee and the fifteen professional staff employees had an average of nearly eleven years of service, tenures greatly exceeding those of the average senior official appointed by the President. See also Marver Bernstein, *The Job of the Federal Executive* (Brookings Institution, 1958), p. 86.

[41] The House Science and Astronautics Committee in 1960 established a Panel on Science and Technology, consisting of an advisory group of fifteen scientists, engineers, and educators. The panel has met at least annually and its proceedings are published by the committee.

[42] Congress ordinarily secures analytical studies from sources outside the government without cost by inviting testimony, although it recognizes the advocacy character of much such testimony. Occasionally, Congress has sought to secure expert and objective analysis and advice by studies prepared by private sources under contract. The 1963 contract between the House Science and Astronautics Committee and NAS-NRC has been mentioned. The Senate has made most use of the contract to secure such studies from independent sources. In 1956 the Senate, by resolution, established the Special Committee To Study the Foreign Aid Program and provided that "full use be made of the experience, knowledge and advice of private organizations, schools, institutions, and individuals." Contractual arrangements were then made with eleven organizations to make a corresponding number of studies.

In 1958 the Subcommittee on American Republic Affairs of the Senate Foreign Relations Committee contracted with six universities and independent nonprofit organizations for studies relating to Latin America. These were published as *United States–Latin American Relations,* S. Doc. 125, 86 Cong. 2 sess. (1960).

In 1960, the Senate Foreign Relations Committee again contracted for a dozen studies on various broader aspects of American foreign policy, which were later published as *United States Foreign Policy: A Compilation of Studies Prepared under the Direction of the Senate Foreign Relations Committee,* S. Doc. 24, 87 Cong. 1 sess. (1961).

Among others, the Subcommittee on Patents, Trademarks, and Copyrights of the Senate Judiciary Committee has commissioned a variety of studies under the

A degree of familiarity if not of expertise is necessary in understanding scientific and technical proposals and in communicating with expert witnesses. The role of Congress, however, is not that of providing another layer of scientific and technical appraisal.[43] The role of Congress is, first, that of assuring itself that it can have confidence in the scientific and technical quality of the proposals before it, and then that of determining against the broadest of perspectives the nature and magnitude of the public interest.

Congressman Edith Green, recognizing both the need for and the limitations of scientific testimony and expertise, points out that "in the last analysis, the crucial ingredient of legislation is social, not technological." Representative Green continues:

With all its difficulties, legislation in contemporary society differs only in degree, not in kind, from legislation in earlier, less complicated eras. Congress has always had to deal with a staggering variety of substantive problems and Congressmen have always, unavoidably, been amateurs in most of the matters they deal with. When Congress has legislated wisely and well, this has not been because of its expert knowledge of shoes and ships or sealing wax. Rather, it has been because Congress was able to bring to these matters a sound perspective of what the public interest requires.[44]

---

title of Patent Studies. The Senate Armed Services Committee contracted for *A Study of the Military Retired Pay System and Certain Related Subjects: A Report . . . by the Study Committee of the University of Michigan,* 87 Cong. 1 sess. (1961).

[43] A very perceptive discussion of the role of Congress may be found in chapter 7, "Professionals and Politicians," in Don K. Price, *The Scientific Estate* (Harvard University Press, 1965).

[44] "Legislating in an Age of Science," in Gerald W. Elbers and Paul Duncan (eds.), *The Scientific Revolution: Challenge and Promise* (Public Affairs Press, 1959), pp. 32–33. Congressman Benjamin S. Rosenthal explained his concept of the congressional function in similar terms: "I do not think any of my colleagues, or I myself, think of our role as requiring the capacity to analyze some of the technical decisions that have to be made. I do not think this is our function. Our role, rather, is to determine whether or not the executive has set up the appropriate machinery, has taken the appropriate initiatives, has established an overall program to make these decisions" (*The Federal Research and Development Programs: The Decisionmaking Process,* Hearings before the House Committee on Government Operations, 89 Cong. 2 sess. [1966], pp. 56–57). See also "The View from Congress: An Interview with Congressmen Emilio Daddario, Charles Mosher, and Weston Vivian," *International Science and Technology,* September 1966, pp. 69–76. Also relevant are the observations of Assistant Secretary of Commerce for Science and Technology, J. Herbert Hollomon, in *Federal Research and Development Programs,* Hearings, p. 294.

The nature of the information that congressmen have sought may properly be considered as a measure of the information that congressmen feel they need beyond that presented in documents and testimony by the executive branch. A study of the nature of congressional inquiries addressed to the Legislative Reference Service of the Library of Congress concluded that "the needs are not primarily for scientific knowledge, but for the facts relating to governmental scientific programs and operations in relation to the overall fabric of our civilization. It appears also that the great bulk of such programs and operations are more closely related to the field of engineering than to the field of pure science, since most government scientific programs are concerned primarily with the implementation of known scientific principles rather than with expanding basic knowledge."[45]

In the light of these and other findings, the Daddario subcommittee (on Scientific Research and Development) concluded that "few national issues, even those of a scientific nature, are resolved solely by technical decisions. Most are tempered by a multitude of other interests which in themselves do not present a clear-cut solution. The element of judgment and the weighing of all factors precludes the likelihood that Congress will find a ready answer, regardless of the methods of securing information and advice."[46] The Congress has made some efforts to make better use of existing sources of information.[47] The Daddario subcommittee in 1963 arranged with the House Committee on Administration for the establishment of a Science Policy Research Division in the Legislative Reference Service of the Library of Congress, staffed by a small group of scientific and technical specialists.[48] In addition, the

[45] House Committee on Science and Astronautics, *Scientific and Technical Advice for Congress: Needs and Sources,* Government and Science No. 3, 88 Cong. 2 sess. (1964), p. 58.

[46] *Ibid.,* p. 83.

[47] *Establishment of a Congressional Science Advisory Staff,* Hearings before the Subcommittee on Accounts of the House Committee on House Administration, 88 Cong. 1 sess. (1963).

[48] The first two major reports of the Science Policy Research Division of the Legislative Reference Service were *Government Weather Programs* for the House Committee on Government Operations and *The National Science Foundation: A General Review of Its First Fifteen Years* for the House Committee on Science and Astronautics. An appraisal of the SPRD's first year is given by George E. Lowe in "Congress and Scientific Advice," *Bulletin of the Atomic Scientists,* vol. 21, (December 1965), pp. 39–42.

Daddario subcommittee entered into a cost-reimbursement contractual arrangement with the National Academy of Sciences to prepare studies upon request.[49] The committee also urged the strengthening of congressional committee staffs with personnel of technical backgrounds, cautioning, however, "that the bulk of staff work even for technically oriented committees, requires more application of the social and political sciences than the purely physical ones."[50]

The division of responsibilities among committees and subcommittees is also sometimes looked upon as a fragmentation that makes it difficult if not impossible for the Congress to deal with science and technology in sufficiently broad scope. Committee jurisdictions, like agency mission assignments, do not always conform to the requirements of changing scientific and technical interests. Congressional organization, on occasion, makes it difficult to reach decisions regarding programs that cut across established fields and agencies. When an administration program calls for co-ordinated efforts by two or more agencies, it may encounter the difficulties of multiple committee jurisdictions. A case in point is the program in oceanography, which involves eight executive agencies, an interagency coordinating committee, twenty-two legislative subcommittees in Congress, and eight subcommittees of the two appropriations committees.[51]

[49] The first product of the relationship was *Basic Research and National Goals*, Report to the House Committee on Science and Astronautics by the National Academy of Sciences (1965).

[50] *Scientific and Technical Advice for Congress*, Government and Science No. 3, p. 86.

[51] The policy and organizational problems in oceanography led in 1966 to the establishment by statute of the National Council on Marine Resources and Engineering Development and the Commission on Marine Science, Engineering, and Resources. Federal officials make up the membership of the Council. Its responsibility is broad but it is principally concerned with the substance of a national program in marine sciences. The Commission is composed of private citizens and some government officials, appointed by the President. Its principal responsibility is to recommend an overall plan for the organization of a national oceanographic program. Both are temporary organizations.

The considerations which have played roles in the difficult problem of organizing an oceanographic program are analyzed in Don K. Price, *The Scientific Estate*, chap. 7. See also *Interagency Coordination in Research and Development*, H. Rept. 1939, 88 Cong. 2 sess. (1964), p. 49. More recent developments include a report by the President's Science Advisory Committee, *Effective Use of the Sea* (1966), which recommends establishing a new agency. See *Science*, vol. 153 (July 22, 1966), pp. 391–93.

Although the oceanography program has faced great difficulties, such problems can be met, and have been. More important is the criticism that there does not exist any point at which Congress can deal with science and technology as a whole. It is held that the process of authorizing programs and appropriating funds in the Congress does not provide any point at which the aggregate can be examined for its adequacy or inadequacy to the nation's needs. The Congress lacks any clear method of reacting to the overall program proposed by the administration and therefore makes few judgments among specialized fields.

Such criticism assumes the possibility of an overall federal R&D program in which the marginal contribution of each component and subcomponent is equal to its cost. The President's recommendations as they are received by the Congress represent judgments made on objectives, costs, and priorities. The recommendations, however, do not attempt to compare the value of the objectives sought in defense with those in health, atomic energy, or other dissimilar programs. Such weighting of objectives in one broad field as against others as has occurred has taken place in the formulation of agency proposals as they have interpreted target levels of expenditures, reviewed by the Office of Science and Technology, the Bureau of the Budget, and, ultimately, the President. The federal R&D budget is then a series of programs related only in that they are of a scientific, experimental, or technological character. The budget constitutes an aggregate program only in a statistical or accounting sense.

Application of the planning-programming-budgeting system instituted in 1965 should provide more precise information regarding a wider range of objectives including estimates of costs compared with estimated benefits.[52] These techniques may result in some sharpening of the evaluation process and of agency mission assignments but there are inherent limitations in these procedures as applied to development. Their usefulness to applied and basic research seems to be very slight. The government's R&D budget will continue to be a series of programs, submitted by the President to the Congress, and will emerge as such from the Congress, modified as congressional judgments on specific proposals may dif-

---

[52] That the process will yield many more and better proposals is clearly anticipated in the report of the House Committee on Government Operations, *Federal Research and Development Programs*, H. Rept. 1664.

fer from those of the executive. It is exceedingly doubtful that there exists such unity in science and technology or in the process of defining social objectives as to permit the development of broad overall criteria by which to compare the social utility of all areas of scientific and technical effort, and thereby identify optimum levels of expenditures together with appropriate allocations to each.

The government's programs do constitute a commitment to increasing knowledge and stimulating technical change across a broad frontier. There is a need for greater appreciation—on the part of the federal government, the executive agencies and the Congress, as well as the general public—of the progress that is or is not being made, of the obstacles encountered, of the problems generated by success, and of newly identified areas of opportunity in science and technology.

From time to time suggestions have been made that these needs could be met by an annual high-level, wide-ranging analytical review.[53] Such a mechanism now operates in the area of economic policy under the Employment Act of 1946. An annual report, differing from year to year in its emphasis, is submitted by the President to a special committee, the Joint Economic Committee. This body holds more or less extensive hearings on the President's report, accepting testimony (sometimes submitted by invitation) from a variety of experts and interested parties. The committee is not a legislative committee, but, in reviewing the President's report, it performs an important function in analyzing problems, identifying issues, and evaluating proposals for the further consideration of the public, the agencies concerned, and the congressional committees holding jurisdiction.

The Elliott committee recommended the establishment of a Joint Committee on Research Policy to "... offer Congress the opportunity for continuous review of the overall emphasis of its research and development programs and policies."[54] The executive

---

[53] Initially by William D. Carey, "A Proposal for a Yearly Presidential Report on Science," *Saturday Review*, Nov. 6, 1965, pp. 57–58, and again in Carey's "Equipping Congress To Deal with Science," in Harold Orlans (ed.), *Science Policy and the University* (The Brookings Institution, 1968); and by the House Committee on Government Operations, *Federal Research and Development Programs*, H. Rept. 1664, p. 41.

[54] *National Goals and Policies*, H. Rept. 1941, p. 56.

already has, in the Office of Science and Technology, the mechanism to permit substantial improvement in the methods by which the government could communicate on a systematic basis. The functions of the committee would include:

1. Evaluating agency functions and programs . . . to identify and advise on unnecessary gaps, duplications, and overlaps.

2. Assessing . . . the long- and short-term impacts of the total research and development program on board Government policy questions, on national research resources, and on specific important aspects of the private sector. . . .

3. Considering . . . the adequacy of non-mission-oriented basic research programs in relation to national goals of education and research excellence. . . .

4. Overseeing . . . the balance of the Government's total research and development program in terms of the specific Government objectives the program supports, the type of resarch performed, the limitations of scientific and technical resources, and long- and short-term national needs. . . .

5. Overseeing . . . the coordination of agency programs and policies to avoid conflicts damaging to Government purposes, to promote the efficient and effective allocation of total research and development resources, and to insure maximum useful exploitation of Government research and development results.[55]

The Elliott committee recommendations aroused little enthusiasm. There is some uneasiness among congressmen regarding the adequacy of congressional procedures in dealing with R&D programs. There are also well-established committees and hence interests in ongoing programs; there is also skepticism of the joint committee approach and doubt that new machinery will contribute very significantly to the solution of the problems that are important to the Congress.

In 1966 the Joint Committee on the Organization of Congress made two modest though significant recommendations relating to scientific and technical matters. The Joint Committee took the position that "Congress can best bring a greater order and efficiency to its supervision of the government's science and research programs by concentrating their review in as few standing committees as is practical." To accomplish this, it recommended that "the committee in each House that now most nearly approaches such

[55] *Ibid.*, pp. 55–56.

concentration have its present jurisdiction expanded to encompass the necessary coordination."[56] It was accordingly recommended that the Senate Aeronautical and Space Sciences Committee be redesignated as the Committee on Science and Astronautics, with its jurisdiction extended to include the National Science Foundation, the Bureau of Standards, and research involving the environmental sciences. It was further recommended that the jurisdiction of the House committee of the same name be expanded to include the environmental sciences. To meet the problem of conflicting action by appropriation subcommittees on interdepartmental programs, the Joint Committee recommended that "major, multi-agency program areas that cut across the jurisdictional lines of individual appropriation bills" be examined by the full appropriation committees or designated subcommittees.[57]

There can be no doubt that the complexities presented by science and technology require such specialized attention as the congressional committee system now provides. The organization of the Congress with regard to the development of technology will unquestionably continue to parallel agency responsibilities for mission-related functions. The support of science presents problems of a special nature since, although much science is supported as mission-related, the justification for federal programs in science rests upon grounds very different than those applying to technology. Congress tends to look upon science as requiring a more inclusive review than that applied to technology. In the House, the charter of the Committee on Science and Astronautics seems to be sufficiently broad to permit it to assume jurisdiction over federal scientific activities wherever they may be administered. The proposed changes in Senate organization would provide similar machinery.

At the same time, the demands made upon our scientific and technical capabilities, the fact that specialized congressional committees tend to become advocates of their particular interests and hence establish priorities within a limited frame of reference, and the sweeping impact of the changes generated in American life by technical developments together suggest the need for congressional consideration of the government's programs in a broader perspec-

[56] *Organization of Congress,* Final Report of the Joint Committee on the Organization of the Congress, S. Rept. 1414, 89 Cong. 2 sess. (1966), pp. 16, 17, 32.

[57] *Ibid.,* p. 32.

tive than has heretofore been undertaken.[58] It is significant that the Executive Office of the President has found centralized review an essential of the effective management of the wide-ranging structure of federal R&D. It has been suggested that the OST assume responsibility for submitting annual reports of the government R&D programs. If the nation is to control its technological destiny, as it is frequently admonished to do, there is need for some device within the Congress providing for periodic discussion and evaluation of the alternatives before us with regard to goals, emerging problems, manpower usage, and procedures. No doubt this need will be met in some measure since it appears to be true that some congressional committee can be found to take testimony on any problem not clearly within an established jurisdiction. The overall review of scientific and technical interests suggested here requires, however, clearer authorization since it necessarily involves consideration of matters now under clear assignment to established committees. These committees need not be joint; indeed committees in both houses might usefully experiment in dealing with the difficult problems involved. But the Joint Economic Committee constitutes a precedent that applied to R&D would accomplish increasingly important objectives for the Congress and the public. Evidence that Congress is recognizing the need to assume broader responsibilities than it has hitherto exercised may be found in the proposal of the Daddario subcommittee in the House that it should consider establishing a "technology assessment board" and the Muskie subcommittee in the Senate that there be established a Select Committee on Technology and the Human Environment.[59]

[58] The need for some such form of expanded communication was recognized by Elmer Staats, Deputy Director of the Bureau of the Budget, in suggesting in 1963 that the Congress could be kept more fully advised by reports from the Bureau and OST which would "explain the major trends and changes in research and development, indicate emerging research and development investment opportunities, comment on the balance among fields of supported research, and furnish measures of the impact of the research and development programs on our supply of manpower, our industries, and the universities," as well as "developing more adequate reports on agency research programs," and "making special studies and reports from time to time" (*Federal Research and Development Programs*, Hearings, pt. 1, pp. 567–68).

[59] House Committee on Science and Astronautics, *Inquiries, Legislation, Policy Studies Re: Science and Technology*, Second Progress Report, 89 Cong. 2 sess. (1966), pp. 27–28, and Senate Committee on Government Operations, *To Establish a Select Committee on Technology and the Human Environment*, 90 Cong. 1 sess. (1967).

The Informal Role of Congress

The role of legislators in the contractual R&D system is not, of course, limited to formal legislation, appropriations, and investigations. Congressmen and the staffs of congressional committees also have informal relations with the President, agency secretaries, and civil service personnel. Such contacts keep congressmen informed as they also keep the executive branch advised of legislative opinion. Depending upon the source, expressions of interest, approval, or disapproval may have considerable impact upon what an agency does and how it operates in anticipation of more formal contacts.

Of special importance are those relationships that affect the interaction of an agency and its research contractors. The protection of the public interest afforded by the automaticity of the low price bid on government procurement contracts is, in the present system, replaced by decisions made on the basis of the quality of a bid. While the competitive low bid procedure was not immune from the insertion of preferential pressures, the large element of judgment in the awarding of R&D contracts requires a far greater degree of trust and confidence on the part of the public.

Most senators and congressmen have, or have pressed upon them, at least a casual interest in assuring themselves and their constituents that they receive a reasonable share of government contracts. It is common for legislators to make their interests and the interests of their constituents known to the administrative officials of the executive agencies by various means. There is no doubt that congressmen frequently take steps to assure that a constituent's interests are considered fairly under established procedures.[60] This may, on occasion, produce action on a proposal that has been held overly long in the decision-making process.

[60] Congressman John Brademas (Indiana), after pointing out that "today's congressmen may often have to become a kind of lobbyist for bringing more defense business to his own district," continues: "We're often asked by newsmen, 'Are you suggesting that political influence has something to do with the allocation of these funds?' It's much more complicated than that. The fact that I am a Democrat during a Democratic administration doesn't mean that I always get the defense contracts for my district, because other congressmen are fighting for companies in their districts. I never know with complete assurance, when the contract is finally awarded, whether my effort made the difference or not. In any event, to be very candid about it, the effort has to be made because the public expects it" ("Technology and Social Change: A Congressman's View," in Aaron W. Warner *et al.* [eds.], *The Impact of Science on Technology*, pp. 146–47).

There is also no doubt that a congressman may be convinced that an R&D proposal of a firm in his district has not received proper consideration of its technical merits.[61] There are not infrequently contract awards that invite the inference that political pressures were determining.[62] There are also situations when the qualitative differences among proposals is so slight that making an award to a firm in a geographic area that is disadvantaged is a defensible course, and when an award on political grounds injures the public interest only in the possible discouragement of future bidders.

While the information available to the public is rarely adequate, in those cases that have attracted attention it is typically true that technical considerations have supported the disputed award. It is sometimes true that a contract award is challenged not on the issue of its technical quality but on other grounds, and the dispute is, in fact, one of broader policy. Charges of political favoritism may then be employed as a device to renew debate over matters other than those at issue in making an award. Concrete evidence that political pressures are applied with an intensity sufficient to override technical considerations is exceedingly difficult to find.[63]

[61] James R. Kerr, "Congress and Space: Overview or Oversight?" *Public Administration Review,* vol. 25 (September 1965), pp. 185–91.

[62] On the most highly publicized recent case, see Stanley E. Bryan, "TFX: A Case in Policy Level Decision-Making," *Academy of Management Journal,* vol. 7 (1964), pp. 54–57.

[63] Peck and Scherer conclude from their extensive study of weapons systems procurement that "in general . . . political considerations have not played a really major role in the choice of contractors for advanced weapons programs. Our research disclosed no instances in which firms were selected for which a nonpolitical justification could not be made—always there were at least some long-run considerations arguing for their choice. It is reasonable to conclude from the available evidence that political influences seldom lead to decisions which are seriously uneconomic from both short-run and long-run points of view.

"This conclusion will be greeted with skepticism by many veterans of the weapons industry. It could be that we have not penetrated sufficiently into the establishment to see fully the political influences at work. It is also possible that participants in the weapons business have been misled as to the importance of political influences. Clearly, considerable political activity accompanies the selection of contractors. One might well conclude that so much effort must have a corresponding effect.

"But much of this political activity has a ritualistic flavor. A congressman will inquire about a selection action at the request of an influential constituent, even when he doubts that it will make any difference. The service responds to the congressional inquiry with cordiality, but such inquiries may have little impact at the operating level where the source selection is usually made. The constituent, how-

It is obvious that all competitors in a bidding can seek to bring congressional pressures to bear, and equally obvious that, if the forces brought to bear are of approximately equal strength, neutralization occurs and the agency is free to make its own decisions, including a decision to postpone action. It is true that the chairmen of congressional committees and subcommittees have intimate knowledge of the programs of the agencies over which they have jurisdiction. Since they hold positions of power they are sometimes involved in the agency's administrative decisions, perhaps indirectly in that agency proposals and actions are inherently sensitive to the power exercised over them. Given the checks and balances which operate and congressional interest in defending the integrity of the system, very few congressmen have shown a disposition to assume the responsibilities that would go with drastic intervention. In any case, a true technical stalemate rarely exists in a complex development since it is very commonly true that advantages of one proposal are gained by making sacrifices elsewhere. Thus the agency decision must be made in terms of its appraisal of the trade-offs that exist in the proposals before it. If such considerations are not determining, there is some inferential evidence that decisions may reflect the interest of the agency in maintaining healthy competitive sources or in considering geographic distribution. On the former, no visible policy appears to exist; on the latter, congressional interest in geographic distribution is clear even though its influence is uncertain.

It is usual for a federal agency awarding an R&D contract to have the contract awards announced by the congressman of the majority party of the recipient district. This is a well-established procedure that reflects the need of congressmen to demonstrate that they are informed of federal actions affecting their constituents. The ritual unfortunately invites the interpretation that the congressman has played some significant part in contractor selection and on occasion invites the suspicion that he has successfully intervened in the administrative process.[64]

---

ever, leaves Washington convinced that dealing with the government is all a matter of politics" (Merton J. Peck and Frederic M. Scherer, *The Weapons Acquisition Process* [Harvard Graduate School of Business Administration, Division of Research, 1962], pp. 381–82).

[64] Robert E. Beach, President of the National Security Industrial Association, has criticized the practice of having congressmen announce defense contract awards:

It is a common practice for congressmen to make inquiries regarding the status of action on a project, usually at the behest of and as a service to a constituent. It is also true that congressmen sometimes take positions for or against some project and that projects are frequently identified with a contractor's proposal.

The interests of Congress are wide-ranging and its influence on R&D activities on occasion descend to the level of the contractual project. At a rough estimate, the federal agencies enter into some 60,000, to 80,000 contractual R&D relationships each year. The percentage of those which bear some imprint of congressional influence is not known but all the evidence suggests that it is very small. Although an occasional exception can be cited, the Congress has not overly infringed upon its delegation to the executive agencies in dealing with the choices that must be made between differing technical approaches to an objective.

"The folly of this practice is that it leads the public and other contractors to believe that the best, if not the only, way to obtain a defense contract is through political influence. I don't know of anyone in industry or in the military who endorses it or who would not like to see it discontinued. Protests have been filed by individual companies and by industry associations against the practice, which is apparently deplored by every one except the congressmen involved. Despite all this, the practice grows. It is probably a fact of life within the democratic process which is neither healthy nor defensible, but which nevertheless cannot be cured either by the military or industry" ("What Military-Industrial Complex?" [unpublished speech, April 23, 1964, at an NSIA meeting, Wright-Patterson Air Force Base, Ohio]).

It has been suggested that the public should have access to the facts and that the procedure of congressional announcement of awards might be supplemented by arrangements for fully disclosing to the public all communications between the Congress and the executive branch bearing on the award of a contract. A bill introduced by Senator Case would have required full disclosure of all contacts between members of Congress and the executive agencies which related to procurement, full disclosure by the agencies of the circumstances of contract awards, and establishment of a Joint Committee on Defense and Space Contracts to administer the program (*Congressional Record*, vol. 109, pt. 3, 88 Cong. 1 sess. (1963), pp. 3215–18, and also pt. 5, pp. 5903–4. In the House, Congressman Donald Rumsfeld has urged an end to the practice of having members of Congress announce awards of contracts to business firms and other types of institutions in their districts or states; see *Congressional Record*, daily ed., Aug. 3, 1966, p. 17344. For the types of news reports that cause concern, see "Politics in the Arms Business?" *U. S. News and World Report*, May 13, 1963, pp. 38–43.

CHAPTER VI

Business Firms as Contractual R&D Sources

American business firms have long been the major source of the technological change which has been such a significant factor in the nation's history. Until the 1920's, such contributions originated in the work of individual inventors who, with small staffs of assistants, sought to bring some idea to market acceptability. The federal government contributed directly to a few of those efforts as is illustrated by the contract between Congress and Eli Whitney to support the application of the idea of interchangeable parts to firearms. But such arrangements were unusual and the government relied upon the ability of private industry to place fully developed products on the market.

With the formation of such organizations as the General Electric and Bell Laboratories in the 1920's, business firms have increasingly undertaken organized R&D efforts to define objectives. Though the lone inventor remains a factor in American technical change, organized research and development effort has become the dominant source of technical advances.[1] The objectives sought are new applications of knowledge and the functions assumed are

---

[1] A listing of some important recent technological contributions by independent inventors and small organizations may be found in U. S. Department of Commerce, Panel on Invention and Innovation (Robert A. Charpie, Chairman), *Technological Innovation: Its Environment and Management* (Government Printing Office, 1967), p. 18. This report emphasizes the continuing important role of small enterprise in technical change.

those of linking new ideas, knowledge, and problems. The laboratories are the appliers of scientific knowledge as they are also in some measure the identifiers of problems for scientific research as well as contributors to the technology of science. It is this type of effort that stands at the core of the contractual relations of business and government in the R&D area.

This chapter will be devoted to the role of business firms in carrying out the technological objectives of government. Business firms, however, enter into contractual arrangements with the government to provide a wide variety of services that are not in themselves of an engineering nature though they frequently support the application of a new technology in a development program. The manuals relating to the use and maintenance of technical equipment are frequently prepared by the supplying contractor. Business firms also provide technical services in the installation, operation, and maintenance of highly sophisticated equipment. Such services are frequently provided by the supplier of the equipment but other firms may also be involved. Some firms have developed specialized competence in dealing with the problems of integrating new and complex mechanisms with more conventional equipment as, for example, on board ship.[2] An important group are specialized in the installation and use of computer services.

Any R&D contract calls for some management services in the course of its performance, but the government also contracts for management services as such. Management contracts are extensively utilized by the Atomic Energy Commission. Of a different nature is the contract between the Air Force and Pan-American Airways (with Radio Corporation of America as a major sub-contractor) providing for the operation of the Atlantic Missile range and a collaborative arrangement between NASA and the Air Force for the John F. Kennedy Space Center. The contractors have provided the necessary management, operation and maintenance services as well as the tracking and other instrumentation required by the agency programs.[3] Recently, the Navy has entered into a simi-

[2] For a description of the "systems engineering coordination" services of one such firm, Vitro, Inc., see House Committee on Government Operations, *Systems Development and Management*, 87 Cong. 2 sess. (1962), pp. 1554–62.

[3] The Pan American contract dates from 1953. See House Committee on Science and Astronautics, *Management and Operation of the Atlantic Missile Range*, 86 Cong. 2 sess. (1960).

lar contract with RCA for the management of its Atlantic Undersea Test and Evaluation Center.[4]

Business firms enter into a wide variety of other contractual relations. It has been estimated that government contracts for advisory services on its management problems amount to some $6 million annually. Business firms undertake analytical studies covering a very wide variety of problems of an economic nature.

At various times, agencies have sought to secure the services of particularly qualified technical groups employed by business firms as sources of advice on the development of a system and to provide technical direction. Such arrangements have led to conflict of interest problems and to difficulties in the relationships between the systems management/technical direction group and other business firms involved. Occasionally a firm has agreed not to bid on request for proposals so that it might serve as a source of objective, technical advice. Such arrangements tend to be unsatisfactory to both parties. One response is the transfer of the personnel involved and the contractual relationship to nonprofit corporations formed for the purpose. Another effort to solve the problems involved was made by NASA in seeking to secure the assistance of a small group of specialists employed by a business firm. NASA chose to encourage the firm to establish a profit-making subsidiary. The firm, the American Telephone and Telegraph Company, established Bellcomm, Incorporated, assigning to it a small group of its technical employees to provide the technical services desired under contract with NASA.[5]

R&D as a Function of Business Firms

Research and development is a specialized type of activity which is undertaken by only a small percentage of the nation's business firms. The National Science Foundation estimates that, in 1965, 13,400 business firms conducted R&D within their own organizations (Table 4). These firms, in 1965, expended $14.2 billion on

[4] *Aerospace Technology,* July 31, 1967, p. 122.

[5] *Systems Development and Management,* pp. 1751–76. For an account of the negotiations between NASA and AT&T leading to the formation of Bellcomm, see John A. Johnson, "The Expanding Role of Contract in the Administration of Research and Development Programs," *George Washington University Law Review,* vol. 31 (April 1963), pp. 747–67.

TABLE 4

Selected Data on Performance of Research and Development by Business Firms, 1964

Size of Firm by Number of Employees	Number of Firms Reporting R&D Performance			Numbers of Scientists and Engineers Employed[a]	Expenditures for R&D by Source of Funds (In Millions of Dollars)			Number of Firms Performing Federal R&D
	Total	Manufacturing	Nonmanufacturing		Total	Company Account[b]	Federal Government	
Less than 1,000	12,200	10,800	1,400	32,400	$734	$479	$255	n.a.
1,000–4,999	734	649	85	32,100	1,101	668	433	97
5,000 or more	433	397	36	279,100	12,362	5,291	7,071	179
All firms	13,400[c]	11,800[c]	1,500[c]	343,600	$14,197	$6,438	$7,759	n.a.

Source: National Science Foundation, *Basic Research, Applied Research, and Development in Industry, 1965* (1967). "n.a." = not available.
a. Full-time equivalents.
b. Does not include $165 million in company-financed R&D projects performed by nonindustrial organizations.
c. Totals rounded in source.

research and development compared with $3.6 billion in 1953. Of these amounts, $1.4 billion in 1953 and $7.8 billion in 1965 were on federal contracts (Chart 6). The R&D expenditures of business firms on their own account increased from $2.2 billion in 1953 to $6.4 billion in 1965. Performance of federal R&D by business firms, on the other hand, has increased from 26.9 percent of federal expenditures in 1954 to 65.1 percent in 1964.[6]

The R&D done by business firms is normally product-oriented and the bulk of the work done is of an engineering nature. New and improved products and services, or an improvement of the processes employed in production, are sought by the application of new knowledge. There are, however, a number of business firms, generally small, that sell R&D services to other firms. Business firms also utilize the services of universities and of independent nonprofit organizations. Such services may be sought to supplement a firm's own staff programs, or may constitute all of a firm's development efforts. However, in recent years business firms have increasingly undertaken basic and applied research.[7] Business firms now conduct more than a fourth of the nation's basic research, although this represents only 4 percent of business firms' expenditures for R&D. Federal funds account for 22 percent of industrial expenditures for the performance of basic research, or about 1 percent of federal funds expended by business firms.

It is a historic characteristic of development, but also of research, that in any given period of time, effort tends to concentrate upon a limited range of objectives. That being the case, the actual work of R&D is similarly concentrated in relatively few firms that

[6] Including the management of federal research centers by business firms. Expenditures on business-managed federal research centers amounted to 2.8 percent of federal R&D expenditures in 1964 (National Science Foundation, *Federal Funds for Research, Development, and Other Scientific Activities, Fiscal Years 1963, 1964, and 1965*, vol. 13 [1965], p. 37).

[7] Industry expenditures for R&D in 1962 of $11.5 billion were divided by purpose and source as shown below in percentages:

Purpose	Total Expenditures	Company Funds	Federal Funds
Basic research	4	7	2
Applied research	21	29	16
Development	75	65	82

Source: National Science Foundation, *Basic Research, Applied Research, and Development in Industry, 1962* (1965), pp. 145, 149.

CHART 6

Industrial Performance of Research and Development
by Source of Funds

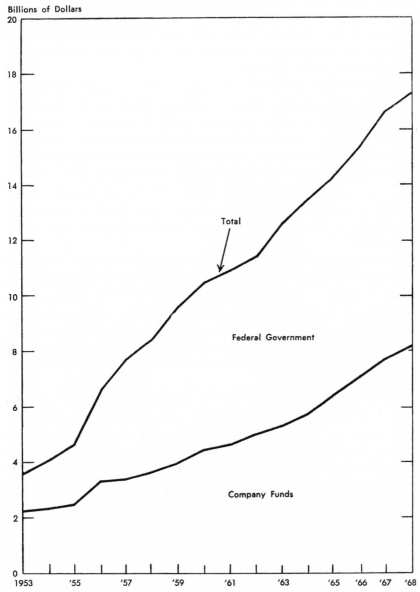

Billions of Dollars

Total

Federal Government

Company Funds

Sources: Figures for 1953–65 are from National Science Foundation, *Reviews of Data on Science Resources*, No. 10 (December 1966). Estimated figures for 1966–68 are from National Science Foundation, *National Patterns of R&D Resources: Funds and Manpower in the United States, 1953–68* (NSF 67–7), p. 23.

possess the funds, knowledge, and personnel relating to the areas of concentration. Two industrial areas, chemicals and allied products and electrical equipment and communication each account for a fifth of the R&D carried on by business firms for their own account. These, together with machinery, and motor vehicles and transportation equipment account for 58 percent of business-financed and -conducted R&D.

Federally financed R&D is focused upon a limited number of technical areas and is therefore concentrated in the industrial firms operating in those areas. In 1964, 61 percent of the R&D done by business for the federal government was devoted to aircraft and missiles, and another 21 percent to electrical equipment and communication. The third largest industry group carrying on R&D for the government was transportation equipment with 4 percent of federal expenditures. Small shares went to machinery, chemicals, professional and scientific instruments, and other industries.[8]

Of the 13,400 industrial firms doing research and development in 1964, most were small and conducted programs of modest size. Of these firms, 12,200, or 90 percent, had fewer than 1,000 employees. Such firms accounted for only 5 percent of private business performance of federal R&D. The 300 companies with the largest R&D expenditures, on the other hand, reported 91 percent of all expenditures on the performance of R&D by business firms. This group of 300 accounted for 97 percent of federally financed R&D done by business firms and for 82 percent financed by company funds.[9] Included are firms which in 1963 performed a volume of R&D work for the government that ranged from a high of $984 million down to approximately half a million dollars.[10] Many of these firms also held prime contracts with the government to sup-

[8] National Science Foundation, *Reviews of Data on Science Resources*, No. 7 (January 1966), p. 9.

[9] National Science Foundation, *Basic Research, Applied Research, and Development in Industry, 1964* (1966), p. 33.

[10] Data are for contractors of the three principal procuring agencies (DOD, NASA, and AEC). The consolidated list is in House Select Committee on Government Research, *Impact of Federal Research and Development Programs*, H. Rept. 1938, 88 Cong. 2 sess. (1964), pp. 63–71. The same report, pp. 147–265, provides considerable information on the principal fields of R&D activity for each of these companies (and subsidiaries), the role of R&D within the firms' operations, and the number (by type) of R&D personnel.

ply items which had moved from the development into the production stage.

Characteristics of R&D Contractors

The business firms that carry on R&D on government contracts are a highly diverse group in the size of their operations, the nature of their activities, the kind of services performed, and the degree of their involvement on government projects. They range from very large firms with scientific, technical, and managerial capabilities in a number of areas directed to very complex objectives down to very small firms engaged in some very specialized activity.

The number of firms doing R&D on prime contracts is strongly influenced by a given government agency's concept of the suitable unit of work. Prior to about 1950, the government generally entered into a prime contractor relationship with numerous component producers. The government's historic policy followed from the individual agency's desire or need to control its projects in great detail and to select from among competitive producers of components those judged best. At the same time, it was a response to the pressures from private business firms for direct participation in government procurement. Under fragmented procurement of numerous components from independent producers, final assembly was conducted by one of the contractors who received the components as government-furnished equipment for which he assumed no responsibility.

This procedure increased the number of prime contractors but left the government agency with the problems of assuring itself, as the development process proceeded, that the components supplied by each contractor were compatible in assembly and use, that each met reliability specifications, that they were made available on a coordinated schedule, and that the complete complex performed as intended. Such problems of coordination and synchronization are difficult to deal with in complex projects, and failures can be very expensive in time and money.

One of the significant responses of private industry to government programs—particularly in defense and space—has been the growth of firms capable of dealing effectively with very complex projects involving a variety of technologies and raising difficult questions of compatability and reliability.[11] These are systems managers to which the government has increasingly delegated responsibilities for assuring compatibility, reliability, and timeliness in complex developments, whether the components are produced by the contracting firm or supplied by subcontractors. The composition of a system is flexible, varying with the nature of the project.[12] Its most extreme form is the total package concept under which the contractor accepts a fixed-price-incentive contract and assumes responsibility not only for developing a product that meets performance specifications but also accepts responsibility for related equipment, spare parts at agreed prices and technical maintenance service over a period of time. The first application of total package procurement by the Air Force was for the very large

[11] Complexity may be measured in a variety of ways; one is that of the value per pound of the end product. For example, in the aerospace industry, "whereas during World War II days the value of the product was about $10 per pound, and in the 1950's about $100 per pound, its value today (in missile and space hardware) is running at more than $1,000 per pound" (*The Industry-Government Aerospace Relationship* [Stanford Research Institute, 1963], vol. 1, p. 41). Complexity may also be measured by the number of parts involved. The Lockheed C-141 Starlifter, for example, includes a quarter of a million parts and required some 20,000 engineering drawings in manufacture (*Sperryscope* [second quarter, 1963], p. 22). A space assembly of booster and capsule may contain some 300,000 parts as compared with the 3,000 which constitute an automobile. The Army's Nike-Hercules system "consists of approximately 1.5 million parts, ranging in weight from the smallest fraction of an ounce to hundreds of pounds. It contains one quarter of a million feet of wire, 2,000 vacuum tubes, 12,000 resistors, thousands of capacitors, relays and other devices, and in addition, a host of functional components such as gyroscopes, servomechanisms, and electronic computers. Approximately 80,000 Ordnance engineering drawings are required to depict the Nike-Hercules system on paper" (General John H. Hinrichs, in Senate Committee on Government Operations, *Pyramiding of Profits and Costs in the Missile Procurement Program*, 87 Cong. 2 sess. [1962], p. 517).

Accompanying increased complexity are increased problems in maintaining reliability in performance. "For an automobile driven continuously at 50 miles per hour for 1,000 hours, the average mean time between failures is 90 hours. For a modern fighter airplane now in operation the comparable time is 150 hours. In contrast to these, the Apollo command and service modules are being developed to a reliability measured in terms of 9,700 hours between failures" (Bernard D. Haber, "How Do the Changing Demands for Manpower and Technical Product Affect the Economy of Industry and the Community," in *NASA Conference on Space, Science, and Urban Life*, NASA SP-37 [1963], pp. 195–96).

[12] An invaluable study dealing in detail with twelve major system developments is Merton J. Peck and Frederic M. Scherer, *The Weapons Acquisition Process: An Economic Analysis* (Harvard Graduate School of Business Administration, 1962).

cargo plane, the C-5A, in 1965; a second is planned for the Navy's FDL (Fast Deployment Logistic) ship project.[13]

The government, it should be noted, usually has not turned over responsibility for an entire weapons system in its operational definition to a single contractor. Aircraft engines, for example, have normally been obtained under prime contractors separate from the contracts for airframes, as was the case in the C-5A development mentioned above. However, the contractor who is given responsibility for incorporating components assigned to others (i.e., government-furnished equipment) into the final assembly will also have responsibility for other components and will perform many if not all of the functions of manager of the system.[14] Theoretically, a contractual system manager accepts responsibility for delivering a device which will perform to established specifications and proceeds without interference from the buyer. In practice, few such relationships exist. Instead, the government agency contracts for what may be very large parts of a procurement but rarely all. In recent years extensive use has been made of the associate contractor approach to complex R&D procurements. Under this arrangement an agency contracts with one firm to assume responsibility for some components and for final assembly. Other firms supply subsystems and other components. The system-wide engineering and technical direction is supplied to all contractors

[13] Under the total package concept, "all terms and conditions of the contract, including price are agreed upon at the outset, immediately after the completion of contract definition, but before the selection of a source for the development production contract and while the matters still rest in a competitive environment." In the case of the C-5A, three aerospace firms competed for the airframe contract and two for the engine. Lockheed Aircraft Corporation won the system contract, and General Electric the engine subsystems. Contracts between the two firms detailed the responsibilities of each and the conditions under which they shared risks and rewards. In the case of the FDL, few of the nation's shipyards possessed the broad capabilities that were necessary and none entered the contract competition. Instead aerospace firms which had acquired some shipbuilding facilities were the respondents. (Major General Charles H. Terhune, "Total Package Concept," *Defense Industry Bulletin,* vol. 2 [February 1966], pp. 3–4; Rear Admiral Nathan Sonneshein, "The FDL Ship Project," *ibid.,* pp. 5–6, 42.)

[14] On the government's view of the system concept, see Robert F. S. Homann, "Weapons System Concepts and Their Pattern in Procurement," *Federal Bar Journal,* vol. 17 (1957), pp. 402–19; William F. Ballhaus, "Application of Weapon System Management Principles," in Senate Select Committee on Small Business, *Case Studies in Government Procurement,* 85 Cong. 1 sess. (1957), p. 177.

on the project by agency technical staff or by one of the agency's nonprofit technical organizations.

Moreover, the agency reserves the right to contribute technical advice, requires that it review and approve any deviation from the approved plans, and frequently maintains very close surveillance over all technical and financial aspects of the work.

What is involved in system management from the point of view of industry is the task of coping

with the vast amount of new technical data in a large variety of disciplines, and to coordinate the manifold efforts of a network of organizations, in order to develop a vehicle and all its related equipment to specified performance. . . .

As applied by the prime contractor, systems management includes consideration of alternative approaches in meeting the desired requirements, design of the system and subsystems at the frontiers of known technology, selection of subcontractors on a competitive basis, further design work in cooperation with these subcontractors in order to optimize the entire system, and supervision of the development work both within the prime contractor's organization and among the subcontractors.

The system contractor is responsible not only for achieving the desired performance levels, but also for controlling costs and meeting schedules. Systems management thus includes planning a series of milestones to be achieved, and clarifying their relationship to one another so as to expose potential problems in achieving performance, schedule, or cost goals. It includes establishing a process, with the aid of computers, for maintaining maximum visibility of progress and for shifting effort wherever needed to maintain the best balance of performance, schedule, and cost achievement. Finally, it includes establishing and operating many other controls over specifications, quality of workmanship, test standards, tolerance factors, and the cost effectiveness of hardware down to the smallest parts.[15]

[15] Jack J. Jones, North American Aviation, Inc., in *Federal Research and Development Programs: The Decision-making Process,* Hearings before the House Committee on Government Operations, 89 Cong. 2 sess. (1966), p. 79. Other views of business firms serving as system managers may be found in *Weapon Systems Management and the Team System Concept in Government Contracting,* Hearings before the House Armed Services Committee, 86 Cong. 1 sess. (1959); and Richard K. Waldo, "Technical Program Management," in *The Industry-Government Aerospace Relationship,* vol. 2, pp. 31–38.

Some businessmen believe that the government should retain the system management function, thereby avoiding problems of conflict of interest which may restrict the ability of a private system manager in securing access to the best avail-

A few companies are uniquely equipped for the very complex management and technological efforts systems management entails. But "no one single company could possess all the detailed scientific and technological skills required to bring into being" a system such as Titan I; ". . . not very many companies even could possess the technological and managerial skills to round up all the services required for a project of such magnitude." Hence, "the systems company . . . acts at once as a supplier to and an agent for the Government."[16]

A second group of contractors is concerned with major components and subcomponents. Some firms that maintain R&D operations in support of their normal product lines in such industries as chemicals, pharmaceuticals, or metals may direct a part of their capabilities to a government objective that is closely related to their commercial interests. In some cases, a firm might be reluctant to undertake work on its own account on a project believed feasible if a commercial application seemed to be remote. In others, the government's interest is in accelerating effort in some area in which a firm has specialized resources. In either case these would be firms characterized by some effort to maintain a balance between work done for the government and that done for their own account.[17] Some industrial firms, frequently large, which maintain

---

able thought on a given problem; see George L. Haller, vice-president of General Electric, in *Systems Development and Management,* Hearings before the House Committee on Government Operations, 87 Cong. 2 sess. (1962), pt. 5, p. 1729.

[16] Statement by W. B. Bergen, president of the Martin Company, in *Nation's Manpower Revolution,* Hearings before the Senate Committee on Labor and Public Welfare, 88 Cong. 1 sess. (1963), pt. 9, p. 3248.

[17] The effort to maintain a balance between commercial and government R&D work is characteristic of such industries as chemicals and pharmaceuticals, which have well-established commercial markets in which a succession of new products is of great importance. The American Cyanamid Company, for example, seeks government contracts "in certain areas but limited to those in which we have a commercial interest as well or to those in which we may be able to make an important contribution to national defense." Government contracts account for from 5 to 10 percent of the company's R&D budget. (Richard O. Roblin, "Research Organization: Centralized Versus Decentralized," *The Management of Scientific Talent* [American Management Association, 1963], p. 74.)

On the problems of planning and selection faced by companies in this category, see Herbert I. Fusfeld, "Effect of Government Expenditures on Long-Range Industrial Research," *Research Management,* vol. 7 (1964), pp. 107–27; and Charles D. Brown, "Product Planning in the Smaller Company," *Technical Planning in the Defense Industry* (American Management Association Bulletin 25 [1963]), p. 18.

R&D operations oriented to their normal product lines also have subsidiaries or corporate divisions which as prime or subcontractors are as specialized and as heavily involved in some particular aspect of government programs as are the systems managers.

The small firms which have developed a high level of competence in specialized areas constitute the third group. Some have established a product line for the commercial market but have been able to visualize more or less related products that might be developed for government objectives. In other cases, enterprising scientists or, more frequently, engineers employed by large firms, universities, or other institutions have formed their own firms and sought to convince a government agency or a larger firm that their proposals are worthy of exploration.[18] Some have been very successful and have moved out of the small business classification.[19] Many, after an initial success, have difficulties in expanding their technical competence as changing conditions require. Small firms may also have difficulties in dealing with the government.[20] In the

[18] William B. Farrington, "Squeezing Research Dollars," *International Science and Technology,* September 1963, p. 82; "Venture Capital Supports New Air Firms," *Aviation Week,* Dec. 31, 1956, pp. 67–74; Harry Schrage, "The R&D Entrepreneur: Profile of Success," *Harvard Business Review,* vol. 43 (November-December 1965), pp. 56–69; and "Ideas and Know-How Key to Small Business Success," *Defense Industry Bulletin,* vol. 2 (June 1966), pp. 5, 12.

[19] The Atlas program alone enabled eighty firms to grow beyond the small business category in a period of three years. *Weapons System Management . . . ,* Hearings, p. 326. See also "The Egghead Millionaires," *Fortune,* September 1960, p. 172.

[20] The Senate Select Committee on Small Business, after investigating the problems of two small business firms in dealing with the government, concluded that "it seems perfectly clear that the acceptance and performance of Government cost-type contracts involves many administrative details and burdens that could easily become pitfalls for the unwary. . . . Small firms are particularly vulnerable to these dangers by reason of their size alone. Several reports of the General Accounting Office, however, prove without question that larger businesses also experience considerable difficulty in performing the administrative details involved in such contracts" (*Case Problems in Government Contracting,* S. Rept. 1031, 86 Cong. 2 sess. [1961], p. 16). See also Earl G. Peacock, *Small Business Participation in NASA Research and Development Programs,* House Committee on Science and Astronautics, 87 Cong. 1 sess. (1961); House Select Committee on Small Business, *Proprietary Rights and Data,* H. Rept. 2230, 86 Cong. 2 sess. (1960); Peck and Scherer, *The Weapons Acquisition Process,* pp. 138–47, and Append. 7A; and G. B. Kefover, "Small Business in Government Sponsored Research and Development Programs," *Law and Contemporary Problems,* vol. 24 (Winter 1959), pp. 132–45, in which it is recommended that small firms pool their resources in dealing with the government. The characteristics and problems of the small firm based on technology are discussed in John H. Hoskins, "Designing a Technical Company," *International Science and Technology,*

R&D area, small firms receive a much smaller share of federal expenditures than they do in other types of procurement. In fiscal 1966, small business firms held 4.4 percent of all Defense Department R&D prime contracts whereas they held 21.8 percent of all forms of procurement.[21] Small business firms play a more important role in research (12 percent of DOD contracts) than in development (2 percent).[22]

This classification is of firms holding contracts directly with the government and does not include many firms which work on government projects as subcontractors to the prime contractor. The interest of the government in securing the best qualified producer of components and that of business firms not qualified as system managers in participating in government R&D programs is achieved by encouraging and, in fact, assuming that prime contractors will subcontract. In large development projects, a firm acting as a prime bidder will assemble a team of supporting subcontractors or will present in some detail its plans for use of subcontractors.

The volume of subcontracting is substantial. The large firms serving as prime contractors for the military agencies and for NASA subcontract from a third to half and more of the value of their contracts,[23] assuming the responsibility of securing competitive prices. The subcontractors are not necessarily small firms; some large part of the work subcontracted by the primes tends to be placed with very large firms. Problems are minimal if the object sought through a subcontract is clearly within the range of

---

April 1967, pp. 85 ff. William G. Colman, in "Small Business and Research and Development," *Federal Bar Journal*, vol. 17 (1957), pp. 285–97, supplies a historical account of the government's efforts to deal with small business problems.

[21] Office of the Secretary of Defense, *Defense Procurement from Small and Other Business Firms, July–November 1966.* See also testimony of Eugene P. Foley, administrator of the Small Business Administration, in *Impact of Federal Research and Development Policies on Scientific and Technical Manpower,* Hearings before the Senate Committee on Labor and Public Welfare, 89 Cong. 1 sess. (1965), p. 631.

[22] Office of the Secretary of Defense, *Military Prime Contract Awards and Subcontract Payments, July 1962–June 1963,* p. 23.

[23] While prime contractors sometimes subcontract as much as 50 percent of the value of a contract, a study of 60 major government contracts indicates that 75.7 percent of contract funds were retained by the prime contractor. It remains true, however, that most large contracts result in a very extensive network of tiers of subcontractors. "Prime Contractors Retain R&D Money," *Business Week,* No. 1835 (Oct. 31, 1964), p. 80.

validated knowledge and accepted techniques. However, if the subcontract requires R&D, the uncertainties may create difficulties. Moreover, the firm possessing the capabilities desired may object to the possibility that it may be required to confide proprietary information to a large firm that might become a competitive source. The legal position of the subcontractor may be a problem. In the past, subcontractors had no resource other than the federal courts against unfavorable action by a prime—such as rejection of its product—despite the fact that the unfavorable decision may have been made by a government representative.[24] A 1965 change in the Armed Services Procurement Regulations provides for arbitration procedures if the prime contractor chooses not to take the matter to the appropriate machinery for contract appeals. More difficult to evaluate are the problems that can arise from the practice of the prime contractors of looking upon subcontractors as a "capacity buffer" with the result that fluctuations in the volume of business are intensified for the smaller firms.[25]

The Roles of R&D Contracting Firms

Diversity is characteristic of R&D contracting firms but all of them are concerned with essentially the same types of problems. The discussion that follows applies to large as well as small firms, as direct or prime contractors with the government. Subcontractors have similar problems except that they negotiate with prime contractors as well as, or perhaps instead of, a government agency.

Within its areas of interest, the firm in effect deals with the development process as the government does, breaking the process up into the successive steps for which the Department of Defense uses the categories of research, exploratory development, advanced development, engineering development, and operational systems development. At a minimum, the firm must maintain its engineering abilities at advanced levels and be alert both to new needs and to new knowledge that may be relevant to the areas of its established interests or areas into which it might move. As the sys-

[24] See Geoffrey Creyke, Jr., and H. Randall Bixler, "Constructive Acceleration under Government Contractors," *Law and Contemporary Problems*, Winter 1964, pp. 145–46.

[25] Peck and Scherer, *The Weapons Acquisition Process*, p. 391.

tem has developed, the interested business firms have come to share with the government the task of evaluating new knowledge for its possible applications and new needs for possible solutions. Staffs capable of performing in exploratory engineering are being supplemented by research organizations in an increasing number of firms. In addition to conducting research, the organizations are also a means of anticipating developments elsewhere that may be of interest. Such anticipations may arise from analysis of probable developments, thereby identifying a possible requirement of the agency; they arise also from new knowledge arising from research which offers the possibility of yielding the solution to a felt problem or of providing a service for which a need is recognized only after it becomes available.

One characteristic of these firms is a high level of technical and managerial capabilities, reflected in the fact that about 45 percent of the employees in the aerospace firms are in salaried classifications, compared with 27 percent in all durable goods manufacturing firms.[26] All these firms have acquired staffs possessing specialized and advanced knowledge and skills and supplied with the necessary equipment and physical plant. Many firms have had long experience in organizing and managing R&D efforts. Their technical skills have been developed by experience, supplemented by recruitment and occasionally by the purchase of another firm which has acquired a high degree of competence in some specialized area. The proportion of technical to production personnel on the payrolls of these firms is about five times that of industry generally.[27] The task of internal management is no less important than in industry generally but is characterized by the special problems of dealing with large numbers of technical and professional personnel working on very complex problems and of conforming to such government requirements as reporting. These firms must also be ready to cope with sharp changes in their employment needs since the government in effect delegates to them the task of adjusting to

[26] Albert Shapero and Howard M. Wollmer, "Technical Profile of the Industry," *The Industry-Government Aerospace Relationship,* vol. 2. Append. H, p. 248.

[27] The proportion of aerospace industries employees classified as engineers and scientists in 1961 was 16.3 percent as compared with an all-industry average of 2.8 percent (*ibid.* p. 249). "Other salaried employees," which includes principally the managerial groups, constituted 29.3 percent of all employees.

new and frequently urgent programs, to completed programs, and to abrupt terminations.[28]

A second characteristic of coequal importance is a management that has acquired an understanding of and specialized skill in dealing with its customers, one or more government agencies.[29] Its critical problem is that of maintaining the competitive position of the firm as an effective contributor to the government's program not only in the execution of projects but also in their formulation. Management's prime responsibility is to ensure that it contributes to government objectives so that it receives a volume of contractual business adequate to employ its key personnel. Success in achieving that objective rests, in some intangible part, upon its reputation based on its performance record. However, the competitive proposal system operates to place heavy emphasis upon the quality of a firm's proposals that contribute to the current objectives of an agency.

A basic concern of the firm is to maintain an intimate knowledge of developments in its chosen areas of specialization and of the government's interest in those fields. The latter task involves knowledge of the thinking of the technical, the operational, and the administrative staff of the government agency directly involved, as well as other members of the government, not excluding members of Congress. The firm will recognize that, until a procurement decision is made, a government agency does not speak with a single voice and that frequently there will exist within an agency, within the various interested levels of government, including Congress, and in the technical community a considerable range of opinion as to what is needed and how it can or should be obtained. It is an important part of the contractual process that the firm's representatives participate in the informal discussions that long precede the establishment of requirements and in the debate as alternatives are narrowed. The firm may seek study and feasibility contracts, thereby contributing to, as well as being in-

[28] John S. Gilmore and Dean C. Coddington, "Diversification Guides for Defense Firms," Harvard Business Review, May-June 1966, pp. 144–50, which was based on Denver Research Institute, Defense Industry Diversification: An Analysis with 12 Case Studies (1966).

[29] The problems are well illustrated from the experience of the Martin Marietta Corporation (Martin Meyerson, "Price of Admission into the Defense Business," Harvard Business Review, vol. 45 [July-August 1967], pp. 111–23).

formed of, developments on concepts as they move toward the firmness that permits the issuance of the formal Request for Proposal (RFP). The firm that first becomes aware of an agency's interest in an area through the receipt of a Request for Proposal will normally find itself severely if not impossibly handicapped should it wish to submit a proposal.

A staff experienced in dealing with the government also offers the advantage of interpreting an agency's expression of a specific interest by considering it against a broad background.[30] Such a staff can be sensitive to changing directions in the interests of government agencies at early stages. Many of these changes will relate to improvements or changes in performance objectives in the items on which it has worked or is working. However, the firm must also be alert to the emergence of agency interests in other but related product and technological areas. Circumstances may lead a firm to decide that it should participate in one or more such fields utilizing such relevant capabilities as it already possesses and acquiring other skills it may need by selective hiring or by purchasing a firm which has already acquired some experience. The selection of the area of technology to which the firm will direct its efforts and seek to establish a strong position presents some difficult problems.

Except for areas of classified information, the general needs of each government agency, its technical interests, its program, and the funds that have been appropriated for new obligations are a

[30] A sales manager of a large defense contractor describes his activities in attempting to ascertain agency objectives and intentions, even when classified operations are involved, as follows: "We operate like good intelligence people. We read the newspapers and see who's hiring what kinds of talents. A well-written job description in the *L. A. Times* tells volumes about the work that's to be done. We also read all the aerospace publications in studied detail. We talk to our non-competing friends who make the other products which work with ours. Since the Defense industry is not, in the last analysis, a stable employment, most engineers have moved around a good bit. We salesmen, many of whom were working engineers ourselves, have wide personal friendships across the country, and we see people almost every day that are involved in all sorts of programs and who contribute bits of thread to the fabric. All these pieces of information build up into a pattern which eventually tells a tale. In the end, we get our information, but when we've gotten it, it has lost the tags of 'confidential' and 'secret' it originally bore. Now it comes as gossip which, fitted with other gossip, makes a picture" (Charles McIntosh, "As Salesmen See You," *Armed Forces Management,* vol. 11 [October 1964], p. 63).

matter of general public knowledge and considerable detailed information is available to those willing to make the effort to get it. Most agencies provide some guidance. However, the military agencies, in particular, are also interested in stimulating the imaginative contributions of their contractors and in avoiding the direction of industry thinking into narrow and specific channels. An Army spokesman, for example, has stressed "that the military departments can never do the R&D planning for industry. Alert companies or industrial associations must parallel the planning procedure of the Army. You must consider the threat beyond the way it is presently defined and speculate what deterrents are the best to meet the anticipated threat." He cautioned that "you then have a public responsibility to be honest with yourselves and the taxpayers."[31]

The precise nature of an anticipated R&D procurement remains uncertain until the agency issues a Request for Proposal. Important information can be gathered in advance as from agency criticism of existing devices and of ongoing development projects, from the nature of study projects supported, and from discussion of such subjects as possible uses of new materials, processes, and hoped-for performance. The typical RFP is the product of a long gestation period during which the agency has become increasingly specific in its statement of objectives and detailed in the methods to be followed. In this period the nature of the problem, the attainability of objectives, and the technical feasibility of alternative approaches have been discussed extensively among technical people in and outside the government. The firm's representatives may have participated in such discussions and in any case would have been aware of at least some of them. The same process applies to classified projects, except that the participants are limited to representatives of those firms that have been qualified by the agency as having a need-to-know.

Whatever its choice the firm will seek to augment its own resources by selective hiring, the systematic analysis of the relevant

[31] Major General C. W. Clark, director of Army Research, "Army R&D Expenditures, Industry Planning," *Army Research and Development Newsmagazine*, vol. 4 (May 1963), p. 32. See also General Clark, "Interrelations of Army R&D Expenditures and Industry Planning," in National Security Industry Association, *The Impact of Government Research and Development Expenditures on Industrial Growth* (NSIA, 1963), pp. 41–42.

literature,[32] close contacts with the conductors of basic research in appropriate areas, analysis of devices produced by competitors, and by acquiring advanced facilities and equipment of its own. In addition, a commanding position implies that the firm expends some of its own funds in projects ranging from basic research through the prototype stage as one business observer points out:

Company-sponsored projects will take several forms. There must, for instance, be a group of advanced theoretical thinkers to analyze long range defense requirements. The work of this group usually culminates in unsolicited proposals to the government for further study projects of a more detailed nature. Where solicited studies are precisely in the company's area of interest, the company must invest in these studies by "buying" them. It is always mandatory that the customer be informed of the fact that the bid is low for the amount of work that will be done in the study and that the remaining work will be supported by company funds. It is a practice of several of the defense organizations to initiate certain study programs where the costs are shared equally by themselves and the company doing the detailed study. Depending on the circumstances, this arrangement can potentially be a very wise investment for furthering the technical progress of the company.

Company-sponsored work which produces experimental hardware is surely one of the best schemes for demonstrating to the military a technical capability. To be able to back up proposals with working models of equipment and tangible proof that key specifications can be met is a powerful tool in placing a firm in a leading technical position. Investing money this way must be done judiciously and at best is very risky, but only by taking this risk can we hope to gain a leading position in the extremely competitive defense business.

. . . A rapidly rising wave of technological advances is underway with the defense industry riding on the crest. Any companies desiring to stay on this crest must plan their future to optimize their technical competence and ability to adapt to the rapidly changing technological requirements of the Defense Department.[33]

[32] In the case of military-related technology, the Armed Services Technical Information Agency (ASTIA) serves as an important source of information on new developments and current research activity. It is also useful in identifying problem areas. Among other government agencies, the Office of Technical Services of the Department of Commerce is an important source of unclassified information. The problems of information retrieval, however, are recognized as increasingly serious.

[33] Richard Hodgson, "The Importance of Planning," *Technical Planning in the Defense Industry* (American Management Association Bulletin 25 [1963]), pp. 5–6. See also numerous examples of company investment in developing capabilities to

It is common for firms to invest in a development project on the chance that it will be able at some point to interest the government in providing contractual support. The position of McDonnell Aircraft Corporation in its industry, for one example, is founded in large part on its pioneer work with jet propulsion, financed largely with company funds. That investment led to its first large development contract. McDonnell similarly invested its own funds in anticipation of the government's interest in space capsules, an investment permitting a response to a NASA Request for Proposal which resulted in the company's winning the award for Project Mercury capsules. More recently, a number of private firms have financed the development of submersibles, thereby pioneering in an increasingly important area. Such efforts made it possible for the Navy to secure the assistance of suitable submersibles for the recovery of a nuclear bomb lost in the sea off the coast of Spain.[34]

There have also been failures. A large investment in a four-engine turbojet transport by McDonnell, to use that firm again as an example, found no buyers.[35] Lockheed developed the small Jet-star in anticipation of an RFP which never appeared. The Martin Marietta Corporation has "$22 million invested in its nuclear division" on which it has "yet to realize a dime."[36]

Not infrequently a firm will continue work on a project after the government has terminated its support in the conviction that the objective is sound and that the government or perhaps a foreign customer will sooner or later find that it requires the product and will resume support of its development. An early example of a

compete for government projects cited in Herman O. Stekler, *The Structure and Performance of the Aerospace Industry* (University of California Press, 1965), chaps. 6–7; and E. B. Roberts, *The Dynamics of Research and Development* (Harper & Bros., 1964), pp. 84–85.

[34] See Flora Lewis, *One of Our H-Bombs Is Missing* (McGraw-Hill Book Co., 1967), and Tad Szulc, *The Bombs of Palomares* (Viking, 1967). For a listing of business activities in the building and, in some cases, operation of submersibles, see First Report of the President to the Congress on Marine Resources and Engineering Development, *Marine Science Affairs—a Year of Transition* (1967), pp. 130–32; and "Industry Investing Heavily in Oceanology," *Aerospace Technology*, vol. 21 (Sept. 25, 1967), pp. 44–84.

[35] Richard J. Whalen, "Banshee, Demon, Voodoo, Phantom—and Bingo!" *Fortune*, November 1964, pp. 136–39, 256–60.

[36] Statement of W. B. Bergen, in *Nation's Manpower Revolution*, Hearings, pt. 9, p. 3249.

firm continuing a development effort despite abandonment of the project by the government is the Douglas Aircraft Company's work on what became the DC-3. Convair continued work with its own funds on the MX-774 missile—what was to become the Atlas intercontinental ballistic missile—after the project was cancelled in 1947 until 1951 when the contract was reinstated.[37]

Sometimes a firm will complete a development without a contract or even the encouragement of the government agency. A recent example is the aluminum rifle developed as the AR-15 by Fairchild and rejected by the Army. Colt, the licensed producer, sold small numbers to the Air Force for use in survival kits. The weapon was so successful in Vietnam that the Army accepted it as the M-16 and has purchased large numbers.

Occasionally a firm that has lost a competition will undertake to establish a commercial market for its rejected design. Boeing, for example, although the loser in the competition for the C-5A contract has proceeded with a commercial version of its design, the 747. Similarly, although Fairchild-Hiller lost in the competition to develop a jet turbine-powered, light helicopter for the Army, it found a substantial commercial market for its FH-110, essentially the same design.

The historical record is clear that business firms, functioning as independent sources of initiative and using their own resources, have participated significantly in the technological development of the country. In providing pioneering services as well as a continuity of effort, they have contributed heavily to the nation's objectives.

Many of these firms have given attention to the possibility of reducing the impact upon them of the sharp fluctuations characteristic of government projects through diversification.[38] It is a reflec-

[37] General Nathan F. Twining writes: "The General Dynamics Corporation deserves a great deal of credit for whatever continuity this nation's ICBM development enjoyed historically in the late forties and early fifties. It was largely the General Dynamics research and development team and the company's own money which kept the ICBM effort alive" (*Neither Liberty nor Safety* [Holt, Rinehart, and Winston, 1966], pp. 301–2). See also Charles S. Ames, "The Atlas Program at General Dynamics-Astronautics," in Fremont E. Kast and James E. Rosenzweig (eds.), *Science, Technology, and Management* (McGraw-Hill Book Co., 1963), p. 199.

[38] A brief discussion of some of these adjustment problems and the techniques used to deal with them by Lockheed Aircraft Corporation is in *Nation's Manpower Revolution,* Hearings, pt. 9, pp. 3051–52. Cf. pp. 2895, 3248–51.

tion of the nature of these firms and of the environment in which they operate that they have made only limited efforts to develop products for civilian markets and that such efforts are frequently assigned to divisions or subsidiaries not involved in government contracts.[39] Instead, these firms have tended to seek diversification in some measure by acquiring control of firms operating in civilian markets. They have in greater degree applied their specialized skills to development projects in new fields of interest to the government, such as antisubmarine warfare, hydrofoils, and deep-sea exploration equipment.[40] The civilian applications of such projects are, however, not wholly neglected and some of these firms have also undertaken work in such novel and complex fields as sea farming, undersea mining, and pollution control. Some firms are working at the frontiers of broadening government interests and have made exploratory efforts to apply their management techniques to such diverse problems as information, fast surface transportation, advanced educational technology, housing, water and air pollution, and crime.[41]

A firm that has established relationships as a government contractor tends to continue such work; in fact, many are locked into the relationship to a large degree. The firm's dependence upon government work follows from the specialized nature of both its technical and management personnel and their preoccupation with large technological advances, as well as the high standards of quality and reliability that are characteristic of such work.

The transfer of R&D staff between government and commercial work within a firm is generally acknowledged to present difficul-

[39] For some examples, see *Industrial Research*, February 1966, pp. 77–78.

[40] Many of the large aerospace firms have or are doing some work with hydrofoils. The Maritime Commission's ocean-going hydrofoil ship, Denison, was built by Grumman together with General Electric and the Aluminum Company of America at a cost of $9 million, of which the government paid $2.5 million. The Westinghouse Electric Company has built a number of submersibles, which it offers for charter. A number of case studies are given in *Defense Industry Diversification*, A Report Prepared by John S. Gilmore and Dean C. Coddington, University of Denver Research Institute, for the U. S. Arms Control and Disarmament Agency (Government Printing Office, 1966), pp. 84–290.

[41] See *Convertibility of Space and Defense Resources to Civilian Needs*, Hearings before the Senate Committee on Labor and Public Welfare, 87 Cong. 1 sess. (1961); "Economics and Politics of Arms Reduction," *Bulletin of the Atomic Scientists*, April 1964, pp. 6–23; and T. R. Rowan, "Systems Analysis in Society," *Industrial Research*, August 1966, pp. 63–66.

ties. Over the past decade and more, it appears that few such transfers have taken place because of the vigorous growth of government programs. Transferring has been rare also because "apparently it is difficult to create a proper commercial orientation in that part of the staff which has spent its time fulfilling Government objectives unfettered by the realities of the market."[42] Moreover, the firm's resources tend to be preoccupied with existing and possible future contracts and projects. The characteristics of these firms are not easily shifted to effective operation in commercial markets. Moreover, while the applicability of the technical skills to civilian type products is uncertain, it is clear that under the circumstances that have existed, these skills are of greater importance and value to the government. The government, in turn, is dependent on the participating firms which have intimate knowledge of existing and potential technology related to the government's programs and which are sensitive to the government's problems and requirements.

A large firm that has committed itself extensively to government work may seek to forecast the level and specific nature of the government's probable needs some years in advance. Projections of growth in federal expenditures in an area serve such a purpose, however roughly.[43] The secrecy and uncertainty surrounding the nation's diplomatic and military strategies will lead some firms to make their own predictions of the nation's position and needs at some future time as a basis for forecasting the nature and magnitude of future requirements for technological developments.[44]

For reasons suggested, the bulk of new government contracts go

---

[42] Donald W. Collier, "A Civilian Looks at Government Sponsored Research and Development," *Congressional Record*, vol. 109, Append., 88 Cong. 1 sess. (1963), p. A 2083.

[43] A brief discussion of the problems facing the firm in evaluating trends of expenditures is George A. Steiner, "How To Forecast Defense Expenditures," in J. A. Stockfish (ed.), *Planning and Forecasting in the Defense Industries* (Wadsworth, 1962), pp. 243–68.

[44] For an example of corporate long-range planning based on possible strategic situations, see Harold A. Linstone, "An Approach to Long Range Planning: A Discussion of the Mirage 70 Study," in Stockfish (ed.), *Planning and Forecasting in the Defense Industries*, pp. 89–133. See also T. J. Rubin, *A Structure for Research and Development Planning* (General Electric Company, Technical Military Planning Operation, Temp. Rept. SP-164, 1962); and George L. Haller, "Industry Role in Defense Planning," *General Electric Defense Quarterly*, vol. 2 (October-December 1959), pp. 13–17.

to firms that have had earlier contracts. However, new firms appear in every annual listing of such contracts, as other firms are dropped.

A firm that has had no contracts with the government may consider attempting to secure a contract if it has acquired a technical competence which it believes to be related to the accomplishment of an agency objective. The firm may be attracted by publicity emanating from government agencies regarding their problems or their interests in new areas of technology. Outside the government there may be little or no market for the technical skills involved. The firm may hope that the development it believes feasible may lead to a production contract, or that it will develop skills and processes that may have application to commercial products. Less frequently, it may be hoped that the development will make possible a civilian-type product which might not be feasible unless some significant part of development costs were borne by a government project. The capability the firm possesses may have been developed through subcontracts, and the firm may believe that a prime contract would permit it tighter control over its special knowledge, providing a sounder financial relationship, possibly a broader and more diversified effort, and hence more rapid growth.[45]

In the early stages of government interest in a new area of science and technology, circumstances occasionally are such that one firm possesses unique ability to undertake the desired work. Initiative leading to a contract may come from either side. A govern-

---

[45] "There are several reasons why private industry does Government-connected research work. One is that it may be profitable—although not always so. There is a second advantage for industry in that having a research contract gives a claim and access to information that may otherwise be denied. A third reason is that sometimes the information produced by such research turns out to be valuable in commercial business. Finally, a fourth reason is that occasionally these research and development contracts lead to production work. If a company has been in on the ground floor, this obviously puts it in a much better position to go after and get the contract for production.

"With profits limited to 7 percent as the fee that we can get and with the allowance redetermination and red tape, such research really doesn't promise too much profit. However, the other three reasons, individually or in combination can be of quite some value"(Irven Travis and Charles L. Register, "Research Relationships between Industry and Government," *Technical Planning in the Defense Industry* [American Management Association Bulletin 25 (1963)], p. 10). The authors are executives of the Burroughs Corporation. For a brief but useful discussion of the incentives to entry upon government R&D and of the difficulties, see Peck and Scherer, *The Weapons Acquisition Process*, pp. 198–219.

ment agency's technical staff, particularly its applied scientists, may recommend that some new knowledge be applied in the search for solutions to one of its problems. A search then follows for the firm best prepared to undertake the work. Alternatively, a business firm may discuss its ideas with agency representatives and, if encouraged, follow through with a more formal, unsolicited proposal. Such a proposal may lead to an agency program or a project meeting one of its requirements. If the firm is judged to possess a capability which is, if not unique, nevertheless significantly superior to that of others, a negotiated contract follows. These patterns usually involve relatively small projects. However, a few have been very large, such as the series of Nike projects held by the Bell Laboratories under contract with the Army.

A firm with an ongoing research program which is related to its established areas of commercial interest but which covers some areas of interest to a government agency may be tempted to solicit government contracts. The firm may believe that little or relatively minor redirection of its research program will be sufficient to secure such a contract. If this maneuver is successful the firm can convert part of its R&D program from an operating cost yielding uncertain and, for some firms, apparently, diminishing returns to a self-financing operation yielding some net income.[46] The rapid rise in the costs of research which have resulted from the competition for R&D talent financed in large degree by government funds is an important consideration in making such a shift. Furthermore, the possibility exists that new products, materials, or processes may be uncovered, leading to production contracts with the government and, possibly, to products for civilian markets.

There are disadvantages, however, in converting even part of an R&D program supporting a firm's objectives to one which involves

---

[46] The possibility of the substitution of federal for private R&D funds was raised by David M. Blank and George J. Stigler, *The Demand and Supply of Scientific Personnel* (New York Bureau of Economic Resources, 1957), pp. 57–62. A more recent study, Guy Black in "Substitution of Public for Private Research and Development Expenditures" (working paper, Sloan School of Management, MIT 1964, #57–64), concludes that in the industries that are most heavily oriented toward R&D and receive the bulk of federal funds for R&D, an increase in federal funds seems to be associated with a modest decline in private funds, but in other industries, an increase in federal funds is associated with an increase of private funds. See also Collier, "A Civilian Looks at Government Sponsored Research and Development," *Congressional Record,* vol. 109, 88 Cong. 1 sess. (1968), p. A 2083.

selling the services of its R&D capability to the government. The redirection of effort required may be greater than anticipated. There is a possibility—considered by some a danger—that, over a period of time, work for the government will become dominant, weakening the firm's participation in technological change within its industry.[47] The government always acquires license to any patents that may result from R&D done under its auspices. Depending upon the purpose of the contractual work, the nature of the firm's commercial business and the statutory authority of the agency, the firm may not be able to retain exclusive commercial rights to inventions under the contract.[48] Judgments as to the significance of patents in the areas of R&D supported by the government vary widely. What does seem to be of basic importance is that the firm retain a position of leadership in its field, and it may believe that its position can be maintained by work on government projects.

There are other disadvantages that involve the firm's capacity and, from some points of view, its freedom to manage. Engineering practices required may be different under the federal aegis; certainly, standards of performance and reliability are in most cases far above those accepted or adequate for civilian use. Government accounting requirements differ from those normal in business and may be very involved. Agency auditors will ask not only for documentation of expenditures made but may ask also why

[47] From the point of view of some experienced businessmen, the ideal conditions for participation in government programs are as follows: the contracted effort should not exceed 15 to 20 percent of the firm's long-range research program; the work should be in fields of active company interest so that the staff can be absorbed in company work when the project terminates; and the proposal should be initiated by the company, avoiding the sales effort required in competitive bidding for government RFP. Such conditions may exist when a company enters the government contracting fields but are very difficult to maintain. See Herbert I. Fusfeld, "Effect of Government Expenditures on Long-Range Industrial Research," *Research Management*, vol. 7 (1964), p. 117.

[48] President Kennedy's memorandum and statement of federal patent policy (*Federal Register*, vol. 28 [1963], p. 10943) established a uniform patent policy for the allocation of rights in inventions made under federal contracts within the limitations of the statutory authorities of the various agencies. This policy provides for the allocation of rights in such inventions either at the time of contracting or after identification and reporting of an invention to the contracting agency, depending upon the type of contract and the contractor involved. Although the implementing procedures adopted by the agencies differ to some extent, the resulting rights allocations are now more uniform than in any previous time in recent history.

those expenses were incurred.[49] Audits must be expected on the completion of a contract but may be made at any time, particularly if the firm experiences significant difficulties in accomplishing its contractual objectives. Management of contracts can be made difficult by the fact that the government can be a capricious buyer. There may be long delays in securing a decision, whether on new proposals or on work in progress. There may be large fluctuations in the work ordered from time to time both on existing and new contracts. One result is a weakening of the ability of the firm to maintain its R&D staff intact and to keep its energies directed to productive efforts of its choice.

There are numerous other problems. Sale of the firm's research and development capabilities to the government may yield low returns compared with what might be possible if applied to commercial objectives. The hope of benefit to civilian lines of activity from government work has been disappointing in the large majority of instances.[50] Some experienced men argue that there exists a basic incompatibility between most government R&D work and

[49] One businessman writes: "The General Accounting Office was in my plant for nine months struggling to find something in error. By some incredible luck, they found nothing. And believe me, it was just as much luck as it was good management, because the complexity and the detail involved is such that you can hardly cope with it under our present system without a good deal of luck. This is a double-edged thing. Surely, government auditors are very useful and necessary. But when these government auditors and their congressional counterparts go into everything in such great detail, I only wish somebody would calculate the cost of all paperwork, all these auditors and all of these investigations. Our business organizations and procedures have had to be remodeled and modified to conform with government desires, even though efficiency has been lowered, and in many cases the cost increased" (Charles F. Horne, "The Impact on Business Firms," *Research Management*, vol. 5 [1962], p. 333).

[50] This is true even in the case of aircraft. The development of aircraft for military use has been fundamental to the development of civilian aircraft, but direct conversion of a military type to civilian uses is rarely possible. Only military cargo and refueling aircraft have potential for transfer to civilian use and then normally only after expensive changes. The Department of Defense has encouraged the development of planes which would be useful for both military and civilian purposes since it would then have a ready reserve fleet and costs might be reduced. However, only the Douglas C-54 cargo plane has been readily adapted to commercial airline use—as the DC-4 (*Business Week*, Dec. 25, 1965, p. 32). It should be noted that the C-141 aircraft was designed from inception to meet military requirements and to be certifiable by the FAA as a commercial air freighter. This is the first military aircraft so designed. See Senate Committee on Aeronautical and Space Sciences, *Policy Planning for Aeronautical Research and Development*, 89 Cong. 2 sess. (1966), pp. 242–43.

that connected with civilian pursuits and that the two should be operated as clearly separate units.[51] In any case, a firm doing contract R&D will find that its knowledge and skills will in time become increasingly specialized to government interests and more and more removed from the commercial area.

In the past, a firm possessing what it considered to be proprietary knowledge sometimes faced difficult problems since the government resisted claims that unpatented knowledge was proprietary in nature.[52] As a matter of policy, the government sought other sources if such claims were made. In practice, agencies must invite and deal with proposals including identified proprietary

[51] See Richard Hodgson, "The Importance of Planning," *Technical Planning in the Defense Industry*, p. 3. Hodgson writes: "When attempts have been made to modify for industrial application those very sophisticated, complex and extremely expensive devices designed for military use, unsatisfactory results have usually been obtained. It is often more efficient to start from the beginning in designing for the industrial application. We feel that industrial and defense work are largely incompatible" (p. 4). Hodgson is president of Fairchild Camera and Instrument Corporation. Cf. M. L. Weidenbaum, "Adjusting to the Defense Cutback: Public Policy Towards Business," *Quarterly Review of Economics and Business,* Spring 1964, pp. 7–14.

[52] Proprietary data is defined in the ASPR 9-201(b) as "data providing information concerning the details of a contractor's secrets of manufacture, such as may be contained in but not limited to his manufacturing methods or processes, treatment and chemical composition of materials, plant layout and tooling, to the extent that such information is not disclosed by inspection or analysis of the product itself and to the extent that the contractor has protected such information from unrestricted use by others." There can be no proprietary data as a result of work on a government contract since the government has paid for it and is clearly entitled to it, and it is necessary for purposes of reprocurement, maintenance, repair, standardization, and cataloging. The problems arise from data believed by the firm to be proprietary and held before a contract is entered into (*The Industry-Government Areospace Relationship*, vol. 2, pp. 73–75, and statement of Graeme C. Bannerman, in *Proprietary Rights and Data*, H. Rept. 2230, Append. 9, p. 206). See also A. R. Whale, "Government Rights to Technical Information Received under Contract," *George Washington Law Review*, vol. 25 (January 1957), p. 289; John P. Sutton, "Protecting Government Contractors' Proprietary Information," *Patent, Trademark, and Copyright Journal of Research and Education*, vol. 8 (Summer 1964), pp. 239–54; Albert C. Lazure and Joseph Church, "The Shadow and Substance of Intellectual Property in Department of Defense Research and Development Contracts," *Federal Bar Journal*, vol. 14 (October-December 1954), p. 300; John L. Nash, "The Concept of Property in Know-How as a Growing Area of Industrial Property," *Patent, Trademark, and Copyright Journal of Research and Education*, vol. 6 (Summer 1962), p. 289; G. F. Westernman, "Data Provisions in Defense Contracts," *Patent, Trademark, and Copyright Journal of Research and Education*, vol. 6 (Summer 1962), p. 261; Howard K. Forman, "Proprietary Rights and Research and Development Contracting —a Case Study," *Federal Bar Journal*, vol. 17 (1957), pp. 298–313.

knowledge. The General Accounting Office, "in the interest of preserving the integrity of the Government as a contractor," has ruled that the government has a duty not to disclose proprietary data.[53] The policy is to extend protection, but such protection is difficult to provide since the knowledge becomes a part of the thinking of the numerous agency employees who review the proposals.[54] Compensation for loss of such knowledge is possible. If a firm believes that an agency has improperly used proprietary information given to it in confidence, the firm may file suit in the Court of Claims for the breach of an express or implied contract.[55] If the agency invites bids or proposals from other firms based on the proprietary information, and a prompt protest is made to the Comptroller General, the agency may be ordered to withdraw the invitation or request and either to settle the matter with the firm or to enter into a contract with the firm.[56] On the other hand, if the firm's proposal includes proprietary knowledge which it has not identified as such, it runs the risk that it will be detected and become part of the common stock of knowledge without possibility of compensation.

The firm that wishes to participate in an area in which the government is pursuing an R&D objective will seek to have its name included on the appropriate list of sources maintained by the agency involved. Since agency contracting officers have the power to refuse to award contracts to firms that are judged "not responsible," the firm will discuss its capabilities with agency representatives and may be asked to submit to an agency survey intended to

[53] See 42 Comp. Gen. 346 (1963). The Armed Services Procurement Regulation (ASPR) providing for protection of proprietary information is 3-507.1.

[54] "The Government is at best a careless custodian of anything so fragile as property rights in know-how" (R. E. Beach, "The Government and Industrial Know-How," *American Bar Association Journal*, vol. 41, No. 1024 [1955]).

[55] *Padloc Co. v. United States*, 161 Ct. Cl. 369 (1963). ASPR 9-202(c) permits payment for such data if the government recognizes the claim, if it is necessary to a product or process, and if the contractor's claim is made during the negotiations preceding a contract. There are, however, numerous problems. For an industry view, see Beach, "The Government and Industrial Know-How," p. 203. On the general problem, see Richard J. Keegan, "Exchange of Technical Data in Government Research and Development Contracts," *Law and Contemporary Problems*, vol. 29 (Spring 1964), pp. 591–610.

[56] Theodore Kostos, "Unauthorized Use of Technical Data in Government Contracts: Remedies of the Data Owner," *Boston College Industrial and Commercial Law Review*, vol. 6 (1965), p. 753.

evaluate those capabilities. If the firm classifies as a small business, it will seek to secure a Certificate of Competence from the Small Business Administration to support its claim that it is "responsible" and merits consideration.[57] A small business firm may also consider pooling its resources with those of other small firms in order to submit a joint proposal. The authority of the Small Business Administration to approve such pools has, however, been little used.[58]

The presence of the firm's name on a source list assures receipt of some expressions of government interest, but the firm will also seek to expand its sources of information relating to technical developments as well as changes in agency objectives, programs, and funding. Much information of this type appears in the technical periodicals. Further information will be sought by representation at briefings, symposia, and other proceedings by which the agency communicates its interests to its suppliers. These sources support the firm's personnel in essential personal contacts with agency staff, particularly their technical personnel.

When a firm possesses interests in an area subject to security classification by one or more of the military agencies, the firm will seek to establish a "need-to-know." This may be accomplished by entering into a Policy or Project Agreement, an unfunded contractual agreement which permits the firm to receive information such as that included in the classified planning documents issued by each military service and to participate in a broader exchange of information relevant to the mutual interests of the firm and agency. It also involves the firm in an obligation to respond to agency expressions of interest with comment or proposals. Whether such contracts as emerge are awarded by selection of a sole source, by competitive negotiation or by competitive bidding, they will almost certainly be the product of discussions ex-

[57] Data on the number of certificates of competency issued and the value of contracts involved are in *The Role of Small Business in Government Procurement*, Hearings before the Senate Select Committee on Small Business, 87 Cong. 2 sess. (1962), p. 68. For an appraisal of the certification program, see Frederic T. Suss, "Set-Asides and Certificates of Competency—Positive Programs for Small Business in Government Procurement," *Law and Contemporary Problems*, vol. 29 (Spring 1964), pp. 431–37.

[58] *Ibid.*, p. 51.

tending over a considerable period of time between the agency and the representatives of one or more private firms.

The Contractual Relationship

The formulation of a project within an agency culminating in an objective formalized as an RFP is a process that is paralleled within the participating firms by a continuing effort to develop new knowledge, to identify problems and their solutions, and to define next-stage projects. The relationships between business firms and government agencies reflect the character of these successive steps in the R&D process, differing as the nature of the work requires. A firm's research activities may be partially supported by negotiated overhead costs charged to existing contracts. Research as well as exploratory development projects which the agency has found of special interest will be financed by study contracts. Some of these will evolve into studies of feasibility. When a project emerges as an advanced engineering objective, competition is more highly formalized. The firm's preparation of a formal proposal may be financed by charges to overhead costs of existing contracts or, occasionally, by a fixed-price contract. A proposal selected for execution will be financed by a variety of fixed-price or cost-reimbursement arrangements. A firm's actions in government R&D work will then normally have numerous contracts of a wide variety of objectives, dollar amounts, and durations.[59]

The relationships of the firm to the government are then of two types: as proposer of new work, and as performer of approved projects. While data distinguishing these two functions are not readily

[59] Distinctions in the average value and average duration of contracts for basic research, applied research, and development are difficult to make. Rough orders of magnitude are provided from a survey of Navy contracts in 1961 as follows:

Type of Contract	Average Duration of Contracts	Average Total Costs
Basic research	2–4 years	$60,000–$80,000
Applied research	1–4 years	$120,000–$2,300,000
Development	5–9 years	$2,500,000–$65,000,000

Source: *Federal Budgeting for Research and Development,* Hearings before the Senate Committee on Government Operations, 87 Cong. 1 sess. (1961), p. 85.

available, estimates have been made that as much as 18 percent of the professional R&D effort of firms in the aerospace industry is directed to the formulation of new projects and the preparation of proposals.[60]

Research by Business Firms

Since the establishment of the General Electric Laboratories, business firms have increasingly recognized that effective development programs rest upon the identification of problems and their solutions through the application of new knowledge or new combinations of knowledge. While there are a variety of ways in which new knowledge may be "coupled" to new technology, the tasks of interpreting new knowledge for its application potentials and of identifying specific research needs are increasingly performed by specialists, particularly the scientific staffs of industrial and government laboratories.[61] The success of industrial laboratories in such industries as electronics, chemicals, and pharmaceuticals is well known.

Since World War II, the government has recognized that it is important that firms participating in its R&D programs maintain research operations ranging beyond current development contracts and not necessarily related to them. It has been recognized also that the profits that such firms have received from allowable fees were insufficient to support the level of research activities that were desirable. Prior to 1960, the Department of Defense did not recognize costs of "general" research as allowable unless such research programs were specifically included in a cost-reimburse-

---

[60] C. F. Horne, "The Impact on Business Firms," *Research Management,* vol. 5 (September 1957), p. 331, cited in *The Industry-Government Aerospace Relationship,* vol. 1, p. 19. A rougher though not inconsistent estimate relating also to the aerospace industry places the annual cost of proposal preparation at $1 billion (L. A. Dragin, "Selling Your Proposals," *Data,* vol. 7 [January 1962], p. 29).

[61] J. E. Goldman writes: "You can have a lot of good science and you can have a lot of good technology, but if these are not in contact with each other, if these have no overlap, no relationship, no recognition of each other's problems, then science will never do the corporation any good, and development and technology will never tap the potential of a science. . . . It has to be done by people who are expert in this and who are trained and who learn the technique" (U. S. Air Force, Office of Scientific Research, *The Fundamental Research Activity in a Technology-Dependent Organization* [1965], p. 13). See also J. C. Fisher, "Basic Research in Industry," *Science,* vol. 129 (June 19, 1959), pp. 1653–57.

ment contract. Research costs were, however, recognized in the pricing of fixed-price, incentive, and price-redeterminable contracts.

In 1959, the Armed Services Procurement Regulations (ASPR) were amended to recognize that research was a necessary overhead cost of doing business if they were to contribute effectively to government programs.[62] It recognized also that the government had a need for information regarding industry's research activities.[63] Under provision made for "Independent Research and Development" (research not directly related to any one contract and financed by the firm), the government, upon request, reviews a firm's research operations and plans and analyzes their relationship to the government's interests. Then follows a determination of the share of the firm's independent research costs which DOD or NASA will allow to be charged to overhead.[64] The government's share of such proposed research costs may range up to 100 percent but averages slightly more than 50 percent. DOD reimbursements for Independent Research and Development totaled $227 million in 1966.[65] There are difficulties in distinguishing betweeen costs of research and the costs of preparing proposals that business firms

[62] The problems involved and the nature of the 1959 revisions of the Armed Services Procurement Regulations are discussed by Graeme C. Bannerman in *Federal Budgeting for Research and Development,* Hearings, pp. 93–96, 98: ". . . The problem was not one of whether we should allow it [independent research] or not allow it, but the question was one of trying to assure that we did not find ourselves supporting unreasonable programs by contractors who were predominantly governmental in nature and who, therefore, were not subject to normal, competitive restraints. . . . Such independent research is not limited to the extent that they relate to existing government programs but is intended to cover a fair share of the government's total cost."

[63] On the government's need to be informed on the research activities of its contractors, see W. O. Davis in *Proceedings of the Fifteenth National Conference on the Administration of Research* (Denver Research Institute, 1961), p. 70.

[64] By Armed Services Procurement Regulations, the costs of a contractor's independent research "not sponsored by the contract" is allowable "to the extent that they are related to the products for which the government has contracts" provided the costs are "reasonable" and are allocated as indirect costs to all work of the contract on such product lines (ASPR 15.205.35[e]). This policy is followed by NASA, but the Atomic Energy Commission allows such costs only when specifically provided for in the contract (AECPR 9–7.5006–10[e(20)] and 9–15.5010–12).

[65] Based on a survey of all defense contractors having an auditable government-contract workload in excess of $10 million (House Committee on Appropriations, *Department of Defense Appropriations for 1968,* 90 Cong. 1 sess. [1967], pt. 3, pp. 64–65).

may charge to overhead costs on contracts. It is estimated that the contribution of the Department of Defense to the research, proposal writing and bid-preparation costs of firms holding R&D contracts approximates $1 billion per year. The National Aeronautics and Space Administration also supports independent research through negotiated advance agreements.

Study and Feasibility Contracts

New knowledge, new needs, the emergence of problems soluble by the application of existing techniques, and ideas that have emerged from a firm's development activities but which are aside from the mainstream of an ongoing development project are some of the sources that suggest the desirability of exploring a possible course of action. An important contribution by business firms to the government's programs and to the competitive position of each firm is the submission of unsolicited proposals to the agency with a general interest in the area of technology involved.

The agency may provide full or partial support for further work by means of a study contract. While such contracts are usually relatively small in dollar value, they are numerous. They may extend over a succession of contracts. Many will be dropped as unpromising but others will contribute to the definition of an agency requirement and hence to larger development projects. By submitting unsolicited proposals, and undertaking more detailed study of subjects in which the agency is interested, a firm can establish an advantageous position for itself, serving its self-interest further by contributing to the formulation of requirements that its own facilities may be best able to satisfy.

The Advanced Development Contract

The work of business firms may lead one or more of them to make specific proposals for development projects. The accumulation of information from those study projects, from the work of an agency's technical staff, and possibly from other sources evaluated by the agency in terms of its operational needs from time to time results in the decision that an effort be made to produce a particular device. The agency's first step in this direction will probably be more detailed analysis of the feasibility of the project, accomplished through studies which it will invite a number of firms to undertake. Such studies will usually be made under fixed-price contracts and are intended to insure that the unknowns are identified before large-scale development is undertaken. Since the possibility of an advanced development contract now exists, firms that are particularly anxious to secure the contract may decide to apply an effort beyond that possible with the contract funds available, investing their own funds in the hope that their competitive position will thereby be enhanced.

Completion of one or more feasibility study steps may lead to dropping a project, to its postponement or to the formulation of a formal requirement and, ultimately, to the issue by the government of a Request for Proposal. This process may involve a device that is significantly different from any other but that also includes the successive steps within the advanced development classification by which a device moves from relatively primitive to highly sophisticated characteristics.

In the development process, a product is very rarely brought directly from the first prototype to full consumer acceptability and production in a single uninterrupted step. New knowledge or more frequently the application of known materials, processes, or components to a new use typically yield results which fall short of the performance desired or believed attainable. Even when the governmental customer finds that the device has some desired performance characteristics, he or the producer or both will recognize that it falls short of theoretical possibilities in one or more ways and that it may be technically obsolete.

Until a specific development has been brought to a level that fully satisfies the consumer, the development process yields ideas for a device superior in at least some respects to that which will be delivered. Though some such ideas will have been incorporated in the development project at hand, these will tend to be minor deviations from the plans established. New ideas that differ from the preconceived development plan may be incorporated if they do not interfere with satisfactory work already done and do not delay the completion of the project. Other ideas will not be incorporated in the device under development. The time schedule and the budget may prohibit the work required to put them into immediate effect; they may not be suitable for the specific device under development, or some sweeping and expensive change in components already completed may be required. Serious consideration of such ideas will be postponed until the device has been tested and its operational characteristics analyzed. Such ideas, with perhaps the addition of others obtained from the firm's own research, constitute the core of another proposal.

The development process therefore has a regenerative effect: current work gives birth to new proposals. This characteristic of the development process is recognized in Department of Defense contracts by a highly important financial provision. The cost of preparing proposals for new projects of possible interest to the Department will normally be reimbursed by the government as overhead chargeable to work involved upon contracts having some relationship to the new proposal.[66]

As has been pointed out, many of the ideas that promise to contribute to the development of a device are generated during the work on a project in hand. The accumulation of such concepts, an essential of the R&D process, confronts the firm with the task of selecting those that seem most promising and relevant. To these must be added new knowledge emerging from outside sources. All these ideas must be evaluated by the firm not only in purely technical terms but also in the light of the probable interest of the customer.

From the government's point of view, successive development efforts eventually reach a point where the fact that a technically more sophisticated product has become possible may be of uncertain significance depending on the costs involved to secure the higher performance. Accurate appraisal requires testing by application to its intended uses before a decision can be made. The further technical sophistication possible may or may not be desirable. In time, other criteria such as simplicity, durability, or economy of operation will be introduced. The product, as it moves to standardization, represents a blend of numerous values interrelated in complex ways that cannot be wholly anticipated but which determine the interest in purely technical optimization.

[66] A General Accounting Office study estimated that advance agreements with 59 firms in 1963 involved a DOD commitment of $294 million (House Committee on Science and Astronautics, *Government and Science*, 88 Cong. 2 sess. (1964), pp. 277–78.

The Formal Request for Proposal

In an area of active government interest, each of the firms on an agency's source list may receive invitations to submit proposals on many if not all the projects which represent the government's interest in the technology; alternatively, in the case of very large projects, the government may limit its invitations to a selected list of firms, thereby reducing the costs of competitive proposal preparation. Other firms will be advised to seek roles as subcontractors. Occasionally, a firm not invited to bid does so on its own initiative and at its own cost. If the government's interest in the area is a growing one there may be many more RFP's than any one firm can deal with.[67] For a business firm a critical problem is to select those government invitations to which it will respond. Conversely, if the development of the technology appears to have reached a plateau and the government's interest is declining, the flow of RFP's may represent a volume well below the aggregate capacity of the interested firms.

The decision to submit a proposal at whatever level of a development cycle involves very complex considerations. One observer points out that

in responding to customer requirements, the nature of the response required by a contractor is heavily dependent upon how far the requirement has progressed in the *Requirement Cycle*. Is it a newly *Conceived Requirement*? If so, was it conceived by the customer or by the contractor? If conceived by a contractor, was it ourselves or a competitor? Perhaps things have progressed to the point where the customer is taking positive action to formalize a requirement, in which case the customer has assumed most of the initiative and we are dealing with an *Anticipated Requirement*. Or have things progressed far enough for the customer to plan for or actually release an inquiry to industry? If so, we must be prepared to respond to a *Firm Requirement*. Still, the cus-

[67] The problem of selection may be particularly difficult for the small firm which may receive very numerous RFP's for relatively small projects and may have little opportunity to estimate the probable actions of other firms. A useful discussion of the problem is in Johan Bjorksten, "How Are Research and Development Procedures Advantageously Modified by Location in a Research Park?" *Proceedings of the Eighteenth National Conference on the Administration of Research* (Denver Research Institute, 1964).

tomer may see the time has come to phase out this requirement in favor of a new one, in which case we are responding to a *Retired Requirement* and this latest procurement may be the last. In all cases, knowledge of the status of the requirement guides the action to be taken.[68]

√ There are other considerations, such as the volume of work the firm has on hand, and its relationships with the originating agency. A probable decline in workload by the time the contract can be expected to become effective will accentuate the firm's interests. A probable heavy workload is not likely to discourage a decision to submit a proposal if confidence in securing the contract is high. The growth of the firm and, with it, higher profits and higher executive salaries rests upon expansion of the number and size of contracts in hand. Moreover, a significant percentage of R&D contracts are terminated before completion, and some operate at expenditure levels below those anticipated. Terminations may follow from inability to solve problems inherent in R&D work as quickly as necessary or with the effort available. They may also stem from an agency decision that the project is no longer required because of the superiority of competitive development projects, reappraisals of probable costs, or other factors. The possibility of a termination is, therefore, an important consideration.

√ For firms active in a given field, arrival of an RFP signals the formalization of an agency's objectives, to which the firms have contributed. Most RFP's will constitute logical extensions of earlier efforts by a firm or its competitors, efforts in which the firm's technical staff has cultivated an active and detailed interest. In many cases, the firm's decision to submit a bid has been made, at least tentatively, before the RFP is received.

Selection of the RFP's on which the firm will bid is of critical importance and is the point of maximum risk assumption by firms selling R&D to the government. It is often said that a firm conducting R&D for the government assumes no risk since such work is usually done on cost-reimbursement contracts. The observation is substantially correct but also of little significance. As in private

<hr/>

[68] The author continues: ". . . There is no substitute for familiarity with the requirement, the customer, the contractor, the market environment, the political environment, and the nature of the response required in attempting to produce quality program valuation data" (William C. Walter, "Program Valuation," *Data*, vol. 7 [January 1962], p. 25).

business, so in government contracting, a firm which experiences a succession of failures to secure contracts faces a crisis which threatens its survival and usually results in a substantial change in the character of the firm.[69] This is true not only because of the financial costs involved (if the firm has contracts with the Defense Department, the costs are reimbursable) but because of the fact that the preparation of a proposal requires considerable effort by the ablest members of the firm's technical staff. In the aerospace industries characterized by relatively few but large firms and by government procedures which limit the number of invited bidders, about 75 percent of the proposals submitted are unsuccessful.[70] However, the experience of contractors with bids for NASA contracts over the 1961–65 period was that one out of nine bids was successful.[71]

An excessively high rate of failures means that the firm's most important resources—its ablest technicians—are failing to contribute to the firm's growth or to maintaining its relative position in its industry. An unsuccessful proposal may mean on occasion that some of the firm's ideas and, possibly, knowledge it considers proprietary are incorporated by the government in the work statement supplied the successful bidder. The firm's survival may be jeopardized or its competitive strength seriously weakened. Though the unsuccessful firm may have charged the costs of proposal preparation to overhead allowable on other contracts, and therefore suffered no direct financial loss, the compensation it has received contributes little to its ability to compete and survive. In the case of some proposals, the firm which feels that it must win the contract can increase its probability of success by making a greater effort, thereby hoping to submit more mature and detailed proposals than those of its competitors.[72]

[69] Frederick T. Moore, "Efficiency and Public Policy in Defense Procurement," *Law and Contemporary Problems,* vol. 29 (Winter 1964), pp. 3–18.

[70] *The Industry-Government Aerospace Relationship,* vol. 1, p. 19.

[71] A NASA study dealing with 49 prime contract procurements over the 1961–65 period shows that business firms requested 3,504 RFP's. Four hundred and fifty bids were submitted in response, and fifty-four awards were made (*Impact of Federal Research and Development Policies on Scientific and Technical Manpower,* Hearings before the Senate Committee on Labor and Public Welfare, 89 Cong. 1 sess. [1965], p. 877).

[72] The problem of selecting the RFP for action and the further problem of deciding on the level of effort to be made has generated a significant literature. Among others, see B. V. Dean and R. H. Culhan, "Contract Research Proposal Preparation Strategies," *Management Science,* vol. 11 (June 1965), pp. 187–99;

The specificity of the work statement will vary over a very wide range.[73] Least detailed and precise will be the description of the work called for in a project in the earlier stages of development, involving the application of knowledge recently derived from research, and including unknowns in one or more areas. The specifications in the RFP are likely to be broad, and the firm is free to consider novel features; indeed, it may be expected to include such features in its proposals. Under such circumstances, unusually imaginative attacks on the objective are likely to attract special attention. Work done on the project will relate to the feasibility of further work, and one or more possible approaches to the unknowns. There will follow one or a series of projects in the intermediate stages in which primitive components will be developed to successively higher levels of performance. This stage terminates when reasonably precise specifications for all components have become available and reasonably precise performance goals for the total system can be established. Toward the end of the spectrum will be projects involving nothing that has not been done before, but requiring further perfection of components and their combination in a manner that will achieve a prototype better capable of meeting such goals as higher performance or greater reliability. At the fringe will be projects calling for further, but now relatively minor, changes in the device to enhance its performance or reduce its costs, and perhaps including such changes as are necessary to secure quantity production of a device previously produced only as custom-built prototypes. If the RFP relates to latter stages in the development process, the firm will normally be confronted with considerable specificity in the RFP statement. In such a situation a high degree of responsiveness to the specifications is critical.

Peck and Scherer, *The Weapons Acquisition Process,* chap. 15; Herbert K. Weiss, "The Relation of Proposal Effort to Sales," in Burton V. Dean (ed.), *Operations Research in Research and Development,* Proceedings of a Conference at Case Institute of Technology (John Wiley & Sons, Inc., 1963), pp. 212–38; Johan Bjorksten, "Bidding Strategy," in Walter L. Johnson (ed.), *The Management of Aerospace Programs* (AAS Science and Technology Series, vol. 12 [American Astronautical Society, 1967]), pp. 133-42.

[73] Hyman Lazeroff, "The 'Scope of the Work' Provision in Government Contracts," *Federal Bar Journal,* vol. 12 (May 1952), p. 310; Ernest W. Brackett, "New Concepts in Procurement Techniques," *The Armed Forces Comptroller,* vol. 9 (1964), pp. 23-26.

√ The decision to submit a bid must then be made in the light of the firm's confidence in its technical capabilities as contrasted with those of its competitors. It must assume that some of those competitors can meet the specifications as well as it can and that variations in the overall quality of the proposals submitted may be very small. Differences will exist, but superiority in one area will tend to be offset by inferiorities in others, a result that may follow from choices made regarding technical incompatibilities (trade-offs).

Cost estimates are included in some detail in all proposals. While the CPFF contract continues to be used for the earlier stage development contracts, policies pursued with regard to it as well as the nature of the CPFF contract require that a firm give close attention to its cost estimates, item by item. Prior to about 1962 such estimates were frequently not made with great precision nor did the sponsoring agency attempt detailed verification since technical considerations were overriding. Since that time, the agencies have given cost estimates careful consideration to assure that they were complete and accurate. While technical considerations remain of primary importance, accuracy of cost estimates are necessary to agency evaluation of alternatives as well as to the agency's control over its operations. In the past, heavy cost overruns created a situation where in some years a quarter to a third of Defense Department funds were committed to meeting underestimated costs of contractual projects.[74] The firm can expect that its cost estimates will be studied and that it will be called upon to defend questioned items.

√ Increasing attention to costs has also been required by changes in the type of contracts being offered. Since 1961 the Department of Defense and since 1962 NASA have sought to employ cost-reimbursement plus incentive-fee (CPIF) or incentive award contracts whenever possible.[75]

[74] "Heat on R&D Costs," *Business Week*, Nov. 10, 1962, p. 122.

[75] One of the earliest CPIF contracts was between the Air Force Space System Division and the Thompson Ramo-Wooldridge Space Technology Laboratories (STL) for the Vela Nuclear Detection Satellite Program. In this case STL responded to the RFP with a proposal for a cost-plus-fixed-fee contract of $13.9 million and a target fee of $1 million. The contract was negotiated as a CPIF of $13.9 million and a target fee of $1 million with incentives of plus or minus $1 million. The incentive was weighted 32.5 percent applying to cost and 67.5 percent applying to reliability, early demonstration, and lifetime in orbit. The Space Technology Laboratories failed to meet the cost target but did achieve the other objectives. The contract was characterized by relatively few changes in the work statement. The fifteen

The low level and downward drift of the profits that could be derived from the fees offered under CPFF contracts prompted vigorous industry complaints.[76] On its part the DOD recognized that the CPFF emphasized technical advances with minimal regard to costs. The emphasis on maximizing technical advances resulted in numerous changes in the work statement as the work proceeded— changes originating with the technical personnel involved on a given project, whether employed by the government or by industry. Efficiency was measured by the magnitude of technical accomplishment and not by relating the cost to the effectiveness of the changes made.

Since 1961 the government has directed greater efforts to controlling costs, in part by utilizing profit incentives. The goal is sought by requiring more deliberate and detailed consideration of proposals on the part of both industry and government so that once a contract is let, changes in the work statement can be held to a minimum. With more detailed specifications, industry can estimate more accurately its costs and can also be given an incentive to reduce those costs as the work proceeds. Instead of a fixed fee, the government can then offer a fee which varies with the accomplishment of fixed goals relating to costs, reliability of the product, and timeliness of delivery. With regard to each goal established, the fee earned may vary upward from zero without the 15 percent maximum that applies to CPFF contracts. The firm may be asked to suggest appropriate targets and fees in its proposal. The presence of incentive fees in the contract requires that the firm possess a high degree of confidence in its proposal. An incentive fee relating to costs requires also that both the firm and the agency have assured themselves regarding the accuracy of the cost estimate, the former that the estimates are not too low and the latter that they are not too high. A high fee earned as a percentage of incentive cost always invites the criticism that the agency accepted unnecessarily high cost estimates.

If the RFP was concerned with an advanced development, ac-

---

changes that were made were all at the government's initiative and cost about $1 million. See C. W. Borklund, "Why One Incentive Fee Contract Is Paying Off," *Armed Forces Management* (October 1964), pp. 38–42.

[76] See *The Industry-Government Aerospace Relationship,* vol. 1, pp. 46–52; and vol. 2, Append. G.

ceptance of its proposal means that the firm can expect an offer of a cost-plus incentive contract that will include a fee which varies with its performance regarding costs, the reliability of its product, and performance on schedule. In its simpler form, the contract will provide for such variable fees on the end result. It may, however, be offered a contract in which such fees are provided for each of numerous steps of the development as the firm has identified them in its proposal. Under such conditions a heavy premium is placed upon the accuracy and the detail with which the firm has planned its operations.

If the project relates to a late stage development in which a number of firms have participated over some time, any one of the firms may recognize that its best efforts cannot yield a proposal that will differ in clearly significant and distinguishable ways from those that will be submitted by one or more of its competitors. Attention will be given to the form of presentation and special efforts may be made to comply with the nontechnical policies of the agency that are subject to the control of the firm such as subcontracting. Anticipation of such situations invites the firm to mobilize other sources of support.

The employment by the firm of former agency officials, particularly retired military officers, may occur for a variety of reasons, including the possibility that such men may increase the firm's understanding of military needs and attitudes and hence contribute to the firm's responsiveness to agency requirements. Given the decentralized nature of decision-making in the agencies and the inhibiting force of congressional disapproval, such employees may contribute to a firm's responsiveness in preparing proposals but are unlikely to have influence which would assure acceptance of a proposal that was technically inferior.[77] Business firms have also

[77] *Employment of Retired Commissioned Officers by Defense Department Contractors*, Report of the Subcommittee for Special Investigations to the House Committee on Armed Services, 86 Cong. 1 sess. (1959). The report led to full committee consideration of proposed legislation (H.R. 10959) subsequently passed by the House. The Senate Armed Services Committee held hearings (*Conflict of Interest of Retired Officers*, 86 Cong. 2 sess. [1960]) on H.R. 10959 but took no action.

One industrialist warned against the use of retired military officers as salesmen: "Military requirements today are so bizarre, the technology so advanced, the standards so tight that few men can bridge the gap between the vast defense market and the manufacturing capacity that must supply it. Industrial organizations that use their retired generals to bridge that gap, instead of to sell, are in the lead. Their

tried to better their chances of winning R&D contracts by the submission of unnecessarily elaborate brochures, as well as the entertainment of agency officials. Both gambits have met with unfavorable congressional and agency reactions.[78] Some firms have sought public support for their proposals, as through advertisements in the public press, and have provoked congressional criticism for doing so.[79] Other means of promoting a given position as in the technical and professional journals are, no doubt, useful. A firm may keep congressmen representing the districts in which it has plants informed and may assume their interest if for no other reason than that the jobs of constituents may be at stake.[80] But although all these devices may be brought into play and the firm has

---

staffs become professional enough to evolve plausible weapons or other systems to do things never attempted before. At the same time they are commercially knowledgeable enough about their own organizations that they don't risk their companies' shirts on a project" (Theodore K. Steele, executive vice president of Bulova Research and Development Laboratories, "How To Get Government Contracts," *Industrial Research,* December 1961, p. 18).

[78] The overly elaborate presentation has been met by admonition. Thus the Commander, Air Force System Command, wrote in 1962 to Air Force procurement officers, presumably for transmission to contractors, that "proposals submitted in response to our requirements need only be prepared simply and economically, providing a straightforward concise delineation of the proposing contractor's capabilities to satisfactorily perform the contract being sought. Proposals, therefore, should be practical, legible, clear and coherent. The use of elaborate formats and binders, color where black and white would suffice, and expensive exhibits are neither required nor desired" (in Ralph C. Nash, "Pricing Policies in Government Contracts," *Law and Contemporary Problems,* vol. 29 [1964], p. 378). Some proposals are exceedingly detailed—the cost submittal of one competitor in the C-5 competition ran to 7,000 pages. The Air Force is experimenting with limiting the number of pages allowable in initial submissions (see House Committee on Appropriations, *Department of Defense Appropriations for 1968,* pt. 4, pp. 473–74).

The problem of entertainment was dealt with by the House Committee on Armed Services in *Employment of Retired Military and Civilian Personnel by Defense Industries: Supplemental Hearings Released from Executive Session Relating to Entertainment Furnished by the Martin Company of Baltimore, Maryland of U. S. Government Officers,* 86 Cong. 1 sess. (1959). These hearings were one source of efforts to restate principles relating to conflicts of interest relating to federal employees. A specific result was a DOD regulation, issued in 1964, prohibiting its employees from accepting any gifts, including luncheons, from contractor representatives.

[79] In *Employment of Retired Commissioned Officers by Defense Department Contractors,* the House Armed Services Committee expressed the opinion that "such advertising is detrimental to the defense effort. It provokes controversy and promotes dissension and introduces biased, narrow, and prejudicial considerations in purely military decisions" (p. 15).

[80] The subject of congressional influence is discussed in chapter V.

made strenuous efforts to impress on the agency its abilities and advantages, the firm must operate on the assumption that its proposal will be considered primarily if not solely on its technical merits as such merits are judged by the agency.

Negotiating the Contract

The acceptance of its proposal brings a firm into negotiating the details of the contract with the sponsoring agency's representatives. The details of the work statement and such related matters as costs, delivery date, and staffing are the principal parts of the contract which are subject to negotiation between the agency and the firm. There may also be special provisions relating to capital or equipment to be furnished by the government,[81] management controls relating to scheduling and progress reporting (such as PERT [program evaluation and review technique]), and plans for subcontracting. If the agency has accepted the firm's proposed work statement and the accompanying cost estimates there are few if any matters which require lengthy discussion. If, however, the agency wishes to make additions or changes in the work to be done, or to introduce ideas contributed by its professional staff or drawn from information and ideas contained in the proposals of other firms, negotiations may become lengthy. If the agency offers a cost-plus-incentive-fee contract, there will be detailed negotiations on the estimated costs, and the incentives relating to costs, reliability of performance, and delivery which the firm can accept.

Both parties will enter negotiations aware of the interests of the other and of the constraints that operate. The experienced firm will recognize the limitations under which the agency's contracting officer must operate and the fact that both the firm and the agency wish to avoid agreements that the agency will find difficult or awkward to defend, should higher authority investigate.

On his part, the contracting officer has the responsibility of arriving at an agreement to secure the performance of work which

[81] The government assumes that the firm has or can obtain the financial resources necessary to the performance required by the contract. However, a firm otherwise deemed competent and responsible has available a variety of sources of government assistance in financing a contractual operation. See E. K. Gubin, "Financing Defense Contracts," *Law and Contemporary Problems*, vol. 29 (Spring 1964), pp. 438–52.

the agency has decided it wants by the organization which its selection process has identified. While the contracting officer has the responsibility of enforcing regulations and in general establishing a defensible relationship, he is also under pressure from the agency's technical and operational personnel to interpret those regulations in such manner as may be necessary to accomplish their ends. If agreement cannot be reached within the limited range of options available to him, the contracting officer may report the existence of a stalemate and recommend that another source be found. It is reasonable to assume that firms which are the sole or very superior source for a procurement may be able to secure more advantageous terms than firms in more highly competitive situations, but there is little evidence that such terms are markedly more attractive. In any case, as has been pointed out, the government's policies with regard to utilizing multiple sources serve as an important restraint on the demands of contracting firms.

It is also frequently the case that until a device is standardized, agency representatives prefer to retain such control over a development project as will permit them to make changes in the work statement as the work progresses. The agency may judge the situation to be one in which it wishes to maintain close surveillance and perhaps contribute to the firm's work; it will therefore insert a clause providing for the agency's "technical direction." Such a provision permits a pooling of knowledge and skills of the technical personnel of the agency and the firm and gives greater emphasis to the attainment of technical objectives than to adherence to cost estimates. Such arrangements anticipate that changes, possibly numerous and substantial, will be made in the work statement. Changes are readily made in a cost-plus-fixed-fee contract which normally makes provisions for change orders. Under other types of contracts, changes in the work to be done require more difficult and time-consuming negotiations, with the firm holding an advantageous bargaining position.

This is why the standard federal R&D contract has in the past provided for reimbursement of actual direct costs incurred, plus an agreed overhead rate and a negotiated fixed fee. The contracting firm's proposal includes a detailed estimate of the costs. While the technical quality of its proposal was the basic consideration leading the agency to make its award, costs are also important not so much as a measure of efficiency—given the nature of development projects—but because they indicate how the firm proposes to do the work and also because of the agency's need to control its program budgets. The firm will be called upon to defend its estimates. The agency will seek to determine on the one hand that costs were not clearly underestimated since such underestimating may force it to divert funds from other programs. On the other hand, the agency will seek to identify proposed expenditures it considers unnecessary or too high. The embarrassment of some agencies, particularly the military, caused by the numerous and large underestimates of costs during the 1950's plus congressional prodding has led them to enhance their ability to estimate costs independently for the purpose of evaluating long-range programs as well as specific proposals.[82] More effective cost control is also sought by two methods which place the burden of securing more accurate estimates upon the contractor. One is the statutory requirement that the firm certify its cost estimates as current, complete, and accurate—such certification including subcontract costs.[83] If such certification proves to have been inaccurate, the firm runs the risk of disallowances of such costs. Ultimate costs may also vary from estimates not because the estimates were wrong but because the contractor failed to exercise adequate cost controls. The other method is to make greater use of contracts which provide a profit or loss incentive to greater efficiency with respect

[82] During the 1950's virtually all large military contracts reflected an acceptance by the military agencies of contractor estimates which proved highly optimistic. Such contracts ultimately involved costs in excess of original contractual estimates of from 300 to 700 percent while slippages in delivery dates were of similar magnitude.

[83] The Hébert Act (P.L. 87–653, Sept. 10, 1962) amended the ASPA of 1947 (U.S. Code, Title 10) by adding a subsection to section 2306 providing that, with certain exceptions, a prime contractor shall be required to submit cost or pricing data prior to the award of any negotiated prime contract where the price is expected to exceed $100,000 and that he shall be required to certify that, to the best of his knowledge and belief, the cost or pricing data submitted are accurate, complete, and current. It provided also that any contract under which such a certificate is required shall contain a provision that the price to the government, including profit or fee, shall be adjusted to exclude any significant sums by which such price is increased because the contractor-furnished cost or pricing data are inaccurate, incomplete, or noncurrent.

For a discussion of DOD policies in implementation of this act, see William W. Thybony, "Changing Defense Procurement Procedures," *The Federal Accountant*, vol. 12 (March 1964), pp. 47–62; and Walter F. Pettit, "The Defective Pricing Law and Implementing Regulations—a Year and a Half Later," *Law and Contemporary Problems*, vol. 29 (Spring 1964), pp. 552–64.

to costs as well as such other objectives as performance, reliability, or timely completion.

The fee provides funds for expenses which relate to the contract but which are not otherwise allowable under statute or agency regulations.[84] That part of the fee not so absorbed provides the firm's net income on the contract. In cost-plus-fixed-fee contracts the fee is a negotiated fixed amount frequently expressed as a percentage of total estimated costs. The fee suggested by the agency's contracting officer is usually based upon historic practice and recent trends, averaging somewhat less than 7 percent of the total estimated costs, well below the statutory ceiling of 15 percent, and varying within a narrow range with the nature of the work to be done. The fee is subjected to a limited amount of bargaining depending upon the agency's interest in having one firm rather than another undertake the project.[85]

The firm can consider a cost-plus-incentive-fee contract only if the work statement describes the performance required with a higher degree of specificity than characterized most CPFF contracts in the past, if it has had or has observed experience with similar projects, if it has estimated costs with care, if it has a high

[84] Nonallowable costs include some which are inescapable costs of business such as interest and other financing costs. Other costs subject to ruling as nonallowable are more or less discretionary, such as recruitment, advertising, entertainment or donations, employees travel allowances, and executive salaries (ASPR and FPR, sec. 15, pt. 2). Disallowances constitute a substantial charge against the fee, running from 2 to 4 percent of total costs (Graeme C. Bannerman in *Systems Development and Management,* Hearings, p. 553). The effect of disallowances is to reduce the fee available as profit by from a quarter to a third (Stanley M. Sjoston, comptroller of Melpar, Inc., "Cost Disallowances," *Research and Development Contracting* [George Washington University, Federal Publications, Inc. (1963)], pp. 143–51).

[85] Fees on cost-reimbursement contracts in recent years have averaged from 5 to 7 percent on estimated costs and from 8.5 to 10 percent on fixed price incentive contracts. Such fees have apparently been established by relying on historical profit levels with relatively little variation according to the circumstances of specific contracts such as quality of past performance, assumption of risks, and similar factors. A marked downward trend for earnings of the defense industry—from 6.3 percent on sales in 1956 to 3.1 percent in 1962—has aroused considerable attention (Logistics Management Institute, *Study of Profit and Fee Policy* [1963], pp. 47–48). Cf. Ralph C. Nash, "Pricing Policies in Government Contracts," *Law and Contemporary Problems,* vol. 29 (1964), pp. 370–72; and H. W. Hannum, "The Need for Profit," *Research and Development Contracting,* pp. 155–58.

The Department of Defense in 1963 promulgated new regulations (ASPR 3-808) which supply a formula for profit determination based on the stated policy of "utilizing profit to stimulate efficient contractor performance."

degree of confidence in its ability to perform, and if the incentives are provided for technical performance, costs, and delivery, independent of each other. There will be some uncertainty as to the effort required, but it will have been determined that the unknowns involved in the project are minimal. The firm must have assurance that changes in the work statement will be restricted, and it will have identified in advance the technical services that will be available to it from the government or from subcontractors. While incentive-fee contracts have not been in extensive use long enough to provide a body of experience that can be analyzed, the incentive feature seems to have been welcomed by business firms.

The contract also will include numerous provisions required by statute, presidential order or agency regulation, establishing requirements relating to employment conditions, nondiscriminatory employment, small business preference in subcontracting, compliance with the Buy America Act, exemption from state and local taxes, liability for damages, operational and terminal audits, and others.[86] These are all contractual requirements. Many of the Armed Services Procurement Regulations provide the contracting office with the flexibility necessary to permit tailoring a contract to specific circumstances and are thus open to proposals from contracting firms. A firm is wise in questioning the application of all ASPR's, including both those that appear in the contract by statement or reference as well as those not so mentioned which may be made applicable by judicial interpretation. It is possible for a firm to secure exemptions from some nonstatutory agency requirements, but this is time-consuming since action is normally required at the agency's highest administrative levels. Most contracts will also provide for conformity of the product to such established hardware specifications as are applicable. The experienced firm will have prepared its proposal with such regulations in mind but

---

[86] On some of the difficulties raised by these requirements, see Paul H. Gantt and William H. Speck, "Domestic vs. Foreign Trade Problems in Federal Government Contracting: Buy America Act and Executive Order," *Journal of Public Law*, vol. 7 (1958), pp. 378–409; Robert S. Pasley, "The Non-Discrimination Clause in Government Contracts," *Virginia Law Review*, vol. 43 (1957), pp. 837–71; Robert O. Shreve, "Impact of Statutes, Regulations, and Policies on Individual Companies," Append. E, pp. 61–78; and Robert O. Shreve and Herbert A. Bricker, "Burdens on the Procurement Process," Append. D, pp. 41–58, in *The Industry-Government Aerospace Relationship,* vol. 2.

the new entrant may find its operations seriously affected by the unanticipated effect of such requirements. While the cost of meeting all contractual requirements is reimbursable, failure to operate in conformance exposes the firm to disallowances of costs that will erode its profit and may produce losses. The firm will also recognize that there will be areas open to conflicting interpretations between the agency representative and the firm and that such conflicts may produce some erosion of the profit element of the fee.

Because of the contract provisions cited, it is sometimes pointed out that the private firm and the government agency do not meet as equals in negotiating contracts, and that to a large degree the firm must accept unilaterally issued regulations if it wishes to contract.[87] The basic terms of the contract are established by statute. The bulk of the ASPR's have evolved as the result of a continuous appraisal of the government's purpose of providing terms that permit effective contractual relationships but are protective of the public interest.

Furthermore, the ASPR's have evolved with considerable input from industry as the armed forces have sought to solve problems in a way that would conform to statutory requirements, protect the government's interest, and permit effective contractual relationships. If the individual firms have limited opportunity to question contractual terms when they sit down at the negotiating table, industry groups have acted in advisory capacities to express industry interests. Industry trade associations such as the Aerospace Industries Association, the Electronic Industries and the Atomic Industrial Forum have been active spokesmen for their membership. The National Security Industrial Association, formed with the encouragement of the first Secretary of Defense, James Forrestal, directs its efforts to a wide variety of problems in government-industry relationships, not limited to defense. Its 1,258-man advisory committee on procurement problems provides an impressive basis

[87] Arthur S. Miller writes, "The government is largely in control of the chief attribute of traditional liberty of contract: the terms and conditions of the contract itself," and observes that "the government is under no restraint as to many of the terms and conditions of its contracts and may impose those conditions it deems necessary" ("Administrative Discretion in the Award of Federal Contracts," *Michigan Law Review* [April 1955], p. 783). See also Paul F. Hannah, "Government by Procurement," *The Business Lawyer*, July 1963, pp. 997–1016.

for communicating contractor views.[88] The associations mentioned along with others in 1964 formed a Council of Defense and Space Industry Associations that provides a means whereby they can act in concert to coordinate and communicate industry views. On its side, the Department of Defense has a quasi-official organization in the Defense Industry Advisory Committee. Membership of DIAC includes representatives of both the Department of Defense and industry, appointed by the Secretary of Defense.

Although there is much truth in the assertion that the contract is one of adhesion to terms established by the government, it is also true that the government pays the costs of the required conditions and that such provisions are generally uniform for all contracts. While the terms offered may have inhibited some firms from undertaking government R&D, evidence of reluctance to enter into competition for government contracts is difficult to uncover. The possibility does exist that the government has established conditions which reduce the efficiency of the system, and that the costs of some contractual requirements exceed the benefits derived.[89]

[88] Elmer J. Stone, chief counsel for a large government contractor, observes that "the Department of Defense has been generally faithful in coordinating its proposed ASPR regulations with industry and bar groups and permitting them to comment on the proposals and to discuss them with the [ASPR] committee" ("Contract by Regulation," *Law and Contemporary Problems,* vol. 29 [Winter 1964], p. 34). Important instances of nonconsultation have, however, occurred; and in addition, some large procuring agencies such as NASA have no arrangements to consult with industry. In any case, consultation is primarily a source of information to the agency and is a form of bargaining only in a very informal sense.

[89] It is difficult to evaluate the cost-benefits of regulatory controls. Calculation of the costs of controls are occasionally made, though not in relation to the benefits to be gained. The judgment of the business community is clearly that the costs of regulations have become unreasonable. One businessman expressed his opinion that "the net result is an overall loss to the government and the taxpayer. . . . [The fact that the vigorous competition for government contracts exists] and that there are companies willing to work under existing conditions does not make the situation right. . . . With nearly every congressional inquiry or investigation into procurement practices, a new regulation is born and a new pyramid of paperwork is generated. . . . The money spent trying to control every possible circumstance or combination of circumstances which has or might develop has become a game of permutations and combinations reaching astronomical proportions."

He concludes: "Rules and regulations are required in all facets of our society and government contracting is no exception. However, a reasonable, sane, restrained policy would be better understood, more easily policed and much cheaper in the

Managing the Contractual Project

√ A business firm's arrangements for doing work agreed to is strongly affected by the contractual relationship. The effort has been sold to the government and must conform not only in end product but also in the process of performance to the numerous requirements of the relevant procurement regulations. At a minimum the project is isolated for accounting purposes since the firm must be able to assure the agency of its compliance with the financial requirements of the contract. In addition, an audit by the General Accounting Office within three years after termination is to be anticipated. More thorough physical isolation will be sought if the firm has reason to believe that close contact between the performing team and other operations of the firm will raise questions as to its rights to information it considers proprietary and possibly also with regard to patents.[90]

The need for specific financial accounting does not necessarily prevent the firm from managing its contractual projects much as it would handle R&D conducted on its own account. Normally, however, only small projects and early stage studies which are, in effect, best-effort arrangements would be so handled. A project director will in any case be appointed, his status in the organization determined by the size of the effort and the importance that the firm attaches to it.[91]

---

long run. Under current practices by the government, the defense and space industry is becoming a public service segment of the economy in a regulated situation. The announced policy is to procure most of the defense and space needs from 'private industry,' but legislation indicates that the government intends to convert such contractors into an industry as fully regulated as any public utility with an even greater restriction on profit. I contend that, if the government would take advantage of the benefits of a truly free enterprise system, with limited controls, the taxpayer would be amazed at how much more he would receive for his defense dollar" (Harry Benoit, Jr., "Can You Have Government Contracts and Free Enterprise?" *Financial Executive*, vol. 31 [September 1963], p. 48). See also note 49.

[90] This problem of segregating commercial and government efforts is recognized in President Kennedy's statement on federal patent policy cited in note 48. See also Federal Council on Science and Technology, *Annual Report on Government Patent Policy* (1965), p. 20.

[91] On the functions of the project manager in business firms, see Paul O. Geddes, "The Project Manager," *Harvard Business Review*, May-June 1959, pp. 89–97.

If the project is of the study type and the contract is fixed-price, the firm will normally be left to its own devices. Such a contract is an agreement to provide the best effort possible. The firm also has an incentive to maximize its effort since such a contract may be a step toward a larger program. The stated value of the contract is then an estimate subject to change and the work statement is similarly subject to revisions; moreover, it is probable that the end product will differ more or less substantially from that planned. Frequently, however, the contract will contain a "technical direction" clause. To this end government technical personnel will work closely with the contractor's engineers. The project then makes use of the technical know-how of government specialists—and perhaps of the staff of one of the nonprofit research centers. Changes will be made at the initiative of the government's technical people or as the firm recommends. Such changes may number in the thousands on a large contract. Each requires approval as to design, and if an increased cost is involved, approval of that is also necessary. The relationship is, as is frequently pointed out, a cooperative one in which many contribute to the objective of obtaining a desirable if not optimum technical goal.

The cost-plus-fixed-fee contract provides no effective control over the tendency of business firms as well as agency interests to evaluate project costs in sanguine fashion. The technical direction inserted by the government optimizes technical progress but usually means also an escalation of costs. The agencies have become very much aware that a CPFF contract emphasizes technical objectives but does not provide for cost restraints. While business firms can, of course, point to numerous successes in contractual development, the government has terminated some projects prior to completion as not warranting further expenditures and some of these must be considered as failures of the contracting firm to perform as proposed. There have been many more instances of failure to complete a project on schedule and/or at or near the estimated costs.[92]

The great importance of most contracted programs to agency objectives, the need for timely completion as basic to agency planning, and the fact that large cost overruns are not only disruptive

[92] Peck and Scherer, *The Weapons Acquisition Process*, chap. 16.

of agency budgets but are also antithetical to good planning have resulted in the establishment of agency controls over CPFF contracts which are unknown in other types of procurement.

Such controls rest upon detailed reporting programs and these are an essential part of CPFF contracting. If such reports suggest that progress is falling behind schedules or that costs are mounting disproportionately to the rate of progress, the firm can expect the agency to investigate. Its investigation may delve into virtually any aspect of the firm's procedures or organization. There may be examination of the controls exercised by management over operating units, of cost control procedures, make-or-buy decisions, procedures used for component procurement, manpower utilization, controls over engineer design and design integration, the adequacy of reliability and quality procedures, and the adequacy of management of facilities.[93]

While some observers consider such agency investigations as interference with private business,[94] the circumstances of many development projects, their size and importance, the nature of the cost-plus contract, the overly optimistic proposals and plans of some business firms, and the absence of market constraints combine to require their application in the best interests of all concerned.

Conclusion

Business firms have been employed to attain the technical objectives of the federal government since its earliest days. As has been pointed out in earlier chapters the nature of the relationship between government and private industry has varied with time. Over most of the nation's history the government's efforts have been concentrated on adapting to its special needs the knowledge or the products already developed by private institutions—principally industry. In seeking such adaptations, government personnel determined the changes necessary in devices available from private firms so that government requirements were met (a process consid-

[93] For a catalog of management functions in which a government agency may take a critical interest, see USAF Systems Command, *A Summary of Lessons Learned from Air Force Management Surveys* (AFSCP 375-2 [1963]).

[94] See Paul F. Hannah, "Government by Procurement," pp. 997-1016; and Elmer J. Stone, "Contract by Regulation," p. 38.

erably accelerated during periods of war). The specifications so established were then supplied to business firms which engaged in price competition to supply the products.

The government's reliance upon the market not only continues but has been greatly increased though changed in character. The government is no longer a passive participant in technological change but pursues objectives that go far beyond the products that firms may offer to the civilian markets. In numerous and important areas, the government has assumed the initiative in identifying objectives believed to be attainable. It relies heavily upon private firms to accomplish those goals. Much military technology is now distinct from, and more advanced than, that employed by industry in producing civilian products; since 1945 we have been conscious of the need to explore in more deliberate fashion the application of military (and space) technological achievements to civilian uses. The government has achieved the present status of military (and space) technology by entering into relationships with industry to develop and produce new devices unique to government needs with new performance characteristics attainable only through development efforts. Through the contract the government can mobilize not only industry's capacity to produce but also its creative capabilities.

The bulk of federal R&D funds go to firms which specialize in work for the government. As a group, these firms make up what is generally described as the defense or the aerospace industry. Included among these firms are both independents and subsidiaries of other firms frequently substantially autonomous. The specialization in government work follows from the nature of the government's R&D programs, and the advantages that follow from special competence in dealing with the government. It follows also such considerations as the incompatibility of differing standards of quality and reliability, of differing compensation practices, and of difficulties relating to the ownership of knowledge including patent policies. In effect, that part of the business world which is heavily committed to government R&D programs is specialized to that purpose.

The fact that a number of firms are heavily dependent upon government R&D contracts is sometimes taken to mean that such firms have a special character; that is, that they are of a quasi-public nature.[95] As an aggregate, the firms which have organized R&D capabilities in areas of the government's interest are vital to its objectives. It does not follow that any single firm is or need be characterized by the importance that must be accorded the aggregate. Agency policies strongly encourage the existence of two or more sources of any given technical capability and similarly encourage competition between them. It is rare, in fact, that any one firm possesses or long retains unique capabilities; what can be done by the staff of one firm can normally be done by others if the necessary incentives exist.

It is true that a high degree of continuity of contractual relationships between a firm and government agencies is common. Such continuity follows from periodic re-examination of the relationship and repeated decisions that it is to the advantage of the agency to renew the relationship. It rests concomitantly upon the firm's success in anticipating changes in the interest of the government and in readiness to submit proposals that merit new contractual arrangements.[96] The existence of a long sequence of contracts

[95] David Bell, in testimony supporting the *Report to the President on Government Contracting for Research and Development,* raised a question about the special character of the business firm which does a very large percentage of its business with the government: "Well, is it a public agency or is it a private agency?" He suggested that "it is organized as a private corporation and I personally would say that philosophically it should be regarded as part of the private sector, but it obviously has a different relationship to governmental decisions and the Government's budget and all the rest of it than was the case when General Motors or the United States Steel Corporation sold perhaps 2 or 5 percent of their annual output to Government bodies" (*Systems Development and Management,* Hearings, pt. 1, p. 52).

In contrast the aerospace industry sees itself not as "a captive industry nor is it a tamed one, if these terms convey any idea of relinquishment of managerial or fiscal responsibility. Nor is this industry an element of any sinister military-industrial cabal. It is merely that segment of American private industry which, because its experience made it an obvious choice to be the keystone of the nation's defense and space program, has had to learn to live in a close working relationship with government. As such, it has been something of an industrial guinea pig over the past fifteen or twenty years. And the experiences it has undergone in that capacity have broad implications for all American industry.

"The great significance of the experiment involving the aerospace industry, viewed at this moment of time, is in pointing up the philosophical crossroads at which this nation, as well as its major regions, stands in terms of the future relationship between government and industry as they both approach the problems and opportunities that will now face us to a greater extent in the future" (Karl G. Harr, Jr., "Experiment in Tomorrow," *Aerospace,* Fall 1965, p. 11).

[96] The continuity of contractual relationships does not mean that firms maintain

does not violate the basic principle that the relationship between the government and any one firm is not of the character of a franchise but is established anew by each individual contract.[97] Variations in success in this process and shifts in the kinds of competence required by government programs have resulted, over time, in substantial changes in the list of firms engaged on government R&D projects.

Continuance and strengthening of the contractual relationship depends upon the effectiveness with which the government manages its programs and its ability to make use of industry's responsiveness to the profit motive. The experience which both industry and the government have acquired over the past two decades are encouraging a clearer definition of the contractual relationships and a sharper delineation of the roles of the government and of business firms. In these changes the government holds the initia-

---

their relative positions indefinitely. Relative standings can change rapidly—firms that held leading positions at one time have dropped to low contractual levels; some have moved from prime to subcontracting roles. Frederick T. Moore points out that "22 of the firms on the list of 100 largest defense contractors in 1961 had not been on the list a year earlier in 1960. This kind of rapid entry to and exit from the 'industry' is unique." Over a longer period Moore notes the twenty-year shift of prime defense contracts from automobile, steel, and chemical firms to aircraft, missile, and electronic firms. "Eight of the firms listed in 1961 do not appear on the list of the 20 largest in World War II. This is a remarkable change in the composition of the 'giants' in an industry and is unmatched by any other major American industry of which the writer is aware" (*Military Procurement and Contracting: An Economic Analysis* [RAND Corporation, 1962], p. 109).

Frederic M. Scherer concludes from an examination of the "demise of defense contractors" that "competitive survival in the face of a rapidly changing technology demands that contractor management give first priority not to achieving good performance in ongoing programs but to moving into promising new fields and thereby developing company capabilities for winning programs of the future" (*Weapons System Acquisition Process: Economic Incentives* [Harvard University, Graduate School of Business Administration, 1964], p. 80). See also William L. Baldwin, *The Structure of the Defense Market* (Duke University Press, 1967), chap. 8.

[97] A report of the House Committee on Government Operations, for example, observes that "it is axiomatic in Government contracting law that each contract must stand by itself and that the profit must be completely independent of other contracts. Without this wise ruling, the relationships between the Government and the contractor would amount to little more than a subsidization of the company if it could offset losses on one contract by recouping them on future contracts" (*Pyramiding of Profits and Costs in the Missile Procurement Program*, H. Rept. 970, 88 Cong. 2 sess. [1964], p. 119). The government, however, does not always follow this axiom. The Renegotiation Board, for example, does consider returns from all government contracts in applying its allowable profits criteria.

tive and future government-industry relationships depend upon the government's policies and the manner in which they are applied.

The most significant trend in the past few years has been the recognition that the uncertainty as to objective and procedure inherent in all development projects can be minimized by recurring appraisals at responsible decision-making levels. The development process is increasingly viewed as a series of discrete steps which need not be held internal to a bureaucratic structure, whether within government or within a business firm. The feasibility of an objective and the precise steps to be taken are identified in successively more specific stages, each typically involving interaction between the agency and the business firms involved. The contracts which support those steps begin with the fixed-price—frequently cost-sharing—type, move through the cost-plus-fixed-fee stage and on to cost-plus-incentive contracts which terminate the development process. Minimizing the role of the cost-plus-fixed-fee contract permits the agency to make greater use of the profit motivation of business firms to determine in advance what the problems are and how they may best be solved. It also permits greater control over technical personnel, whether within the government or a basic firm, and minimizes the need for government to intervene in the internal management of business firms. It requires of the government that it have personnel qualified to make technical judgments at each step of the process and also that it make decisions on the alternatives which the contractors have identified. It requires of the business firms greater and more precise efforts to identify the work to be done and the costs.

The government continues to experiment in its search for procedures and will necessarily have to engage in more and more careful evaluations of industry reactions. The necessity for doing so stems from the very great advantages that inhere in the contractual relationship. In utilizing industry the government can enlist for its purposes both existing organized capabilities and those that can be developed. It does so with a high degree of flexibility that rests on its avoidance of long-range commitments to any one organization, commitments that tend to introduce considerations other than those of the immediate objective and the means of accomplishment.

CHAPTER VII

The University as a Research Center

The contributions made by the university-associated scientists and engineers to the military technology and medical practices of World War II provided the stimulus for the postwar interest of the federal government in maintaining academic research at high levels and in directing it to public objectives. The wartime contribution revealed capabilities that had been hitherto unappreciated in many quarters. These capabilities originated in a volume of university research that was comparatively small, though sufficient in scope and sophistication to include an appreciative familiarity with advanced European thinking and the ability to utilize the services of the significant number of eminent European scientists who came to this country. It was the pool of knowledge and skills provided by this combination which the Office of Scientific Research and Development organized and directed to war needs with such success.

Evolution of Research as a University Function

The wartime role which university-based research personnel were able to play was the product of a long period in which research activities of university faculty members increased very slowly. While it is not possible to evaluate here the contributions of university-based research to the nation's rapid technological development in the century before World War II, it seems clear that the university's educational and training functions were widely considered to be more important than faculty contributions to new knowledge. To this broad generalization the field of agriculture was the most marked exception. Although the application of machinery to agricultural tasks was a function discharged by private industry, increasing the effectiveness of agricultural materials and methods presented a host of questions that defied authoritative analysis by private means. The concept of publicly financed agricultural experiment stations was a solution borrowed from Europe, but attaching those stations to the agricultural schools of the land-grant universities was an American arrangement.[1] The work of the experiment stations constituted the larger part of budgeted research conducted by American universities before World War II. Though they functioned with increasing effectiveness they served as a precedent for organizing research efforts in other areas only in that some of the land-grant universities also established engineering experiment stations which operated on a modest scale.

Lacking the public identification of goals that were not being met by private industry and government laboratories, research activities at the universities, aside from agriculture, grew but slowly. American colleges and universities originated as institutions wholly devoted to teaching and most so remained. Some propensity to engage in research and writing has been a characteristic of some members of college and university faculties as long as these institutions have existed. However, throughout the earlier history of American universities and colleges, faculty research activities were viewed as conflicting with teaching and, at best, tolerated.[2]

Moreover, the normal financial support of most colleges and universities—whether public or private—was directed principally, and often solely, to their teaching function. It followed that the teaching loads were heavy and the time that faculty members could devote to research was very limited.

[1] Research was not quickly or easily accepted as a function of the land-grant colleges and their agricultural experiment stations. On the difficulties and the eventual establishment of a project system with central review and approval machinery, see H. C. Knoblauch, E. M. Law, and W. P. Meyer, *State Agricultural Experiment Stations: A History of Research Policy and Procedure*, U.S.D.A. Misc. Pub. No. 904 (1962), chaps. 3–6, and 9.

[2] Herbert E. Longenecker, *University Faculty Compensation Policies and Practices in the United States* (University of Illinois Press, 1956).

The establishment of research as a proper, and then as a characteristic, function of all university faculty members emerged with
the establishment of graduate schools modeled on the German pattern, as with the founding of Johns Hopkins and the University of
Chicago, and the evolution of such institutions as Harvard University and the University of Michigan.[3] Since the terminal degree of
the graduate school is the Ph.D.—a research degree—it followed
that a research-oriented faculty was essential to proper support and
administration. Policies encouraging research in such institutions
included the recruitment of research-minded faculty members,
promotions based on research accomplishments, the reduction of
teaching loads, and the provision of necessary facilities. Such policies provided the environment for effective teaching of graduate
students. As such, research was not distinguishable from the institution's teaching functions but an integral part of it which was so
budgeted and administered.

The emphasis on research in such institutions gradually extended in varying degrees to other faculties such as medicine, technology, and engineering. The Ph.D.'s were the best qualified men
available for faculty appointments, and colleges joined the universities in seeking to maximize the number of Ph.D.'s on their faculties and in giving preferred recognition to scholarly publications.
Though this evolution was slow, research productivity had been established as a basic consideration in faculty appointments and promotions in a few institutions as early as 1900.[4] Almost simultaneously, concern was expressed that the growing emphasis upon
training and research interests of college and university faculties
might affect the quality of teaching unfavorably.[5]

[3] On the observations made in this and the following paragraphs, see John S.
Brubacher and Willis Rudy, *Higher Education in Transition: An American
History: 1636–1956* (Harper & Bros., 1958), pp. 171–95; Abraham Flexner, *Universities, American, English, German* (Oxford University Press, 1930), pp. 181–82; Richard Hofstadter and C. DeWitt Hardy, *The Development and Scope of Higher Education in the United States* (Columbia University Press, 1952); Merle Curti (ed.),
American Scholarship in the 20th Century (Harvard University Press, 1953).

[4] Brubacher and Rudy credit President William R. Harper of the University of
Chicago with first establishing publicly a "publish or perish" policy with regard
to faculty promotion (*Higher Education in Transition*, p. 85).

[5] William James, "The Ph.D. Octopus," *Educational Review*, vol. 55 (February
1918), pp. 149–57; Andrew F. West, *Short Papers on American Liberal Education*
(Scribners Sons, 1907), pp. 52–56; and more recently, Jacques Barzun, *Teacher in
America* (Little, Brown & Co., 1945), chap. 14.

Although the prestige of research and the role of research as a proper function of college and university faculties were being well established, research activities continued to be carried out on a relatively small scale. Such activities were confined principally to the wealthier universities. Although trained in research a large proportion of Ph.D.'s who served as faculty members were fully occupied with teaching responsibilities.[6] The financial support necessary to release time for research was available from the normal sources supporting educational institutions only in very limited amounts; in many institutions, it was not available at all.

Financial support for expansion of faculty research efforts came primarily from sources outside the university. By the 1930's the interests of the philanthropic foundations were turning from general support of higher education to an increasing emphasis on the support of research projects. Industrial firms also supplied funds, almost always to support specific projects. Funds from these sources occasionally were used to permit a faculty member to devote his full time to a project. Normally, however, such funds permitted faculty members to devote part of their time to supervision of the activities of graduate students and full-time technical assistants. These activities were sufficiently extensive prior to World War I that affiliated research organizations had come into existence at a number of universities. The affiliated research institutions provided a method of administering research projects of substantial size, a way of employing nonteaching personnel, and a formal pattern for financially and administratively segregating research sponsored by outside sources from the universities' teaching functions.[7]

In the late 1930's there were in the United States some 1,450 institutions of higher education employing approximately 100,000 faculty members and expending about $420 million annually. It has been roughly estimated that 15 percent of all faculty members engaged in some research. Almost all of them were associated with some 200 institutions which encouraged research in some measure.

[6] Less than 25 percent of the holders of Ph.D.'s in the 1920's produced significant research after their dissertations. Brubacher and Rudy, *Higher Education in Transition*, p. 190; National Resources Committee, *Research—A National Resource*, vol. 1: *Relation of the Federal Government to Research* (Government Printing Office, 1938), p. 17.

[7] Ernest V. Hollis, *Philanthropic Foundations and Higher Education* (Columbia University Press, 1938).

A small number were faculty members of independent liberal arts colleges. The large majority were associated with the 86 institutions maintaining graduate schools offering the Ph.D. degree, and associated professional schools as in medicine, engineering, and agriculture.

Wide differences existed in the effort devoted to research activities in these institutions. By no means all professional schools cultivated research activities while graduate schools varied widely in the number of fields in which they offered advanced degrees and in the research activities of the faculty of such departments. Contemporary estimates identify from ten to twenty institutions which selected faculty members of all departments with a view to research ability and which provided time and facilities for such work. This concentration of research interests is reflected in the number of Ph.D.'s conferred. In the late 1930's, eleven institutions conferred 50 percent and fourteen others accounted for another 25 percent of all Ph.D.'s.

The field of agriculture remained, prior to World War II, the best-financed and most highly organized field of university research. The $16 million annually spent by the agricultural experiment stations represented some 60 percent of all funds specifically budgeted by all universities provided for research. Grants and gifts to universities provided by philanthropic foundations and industrial firms for all other research totaled about $12 million annually. It is more difficult to estimate the expenditures by universities for research from their own funds since such expenditures frequently if not normally take the form of faculty time released from teaching, or the purchase of equipment used both in teaching and research. A contemporary estimate placed the annual value of such nonspecifically budgeted research in the late 1930's at about $24 million or about 10 percent of the expenditures of research-minded institutions.[8]

The War Period

Large-scale federal financing of research—other than in agriculture —conducted by university faculties began in 1940–41 with expenditures by the National Defense Research Committee of about $4

[8] The data in this and the preceding two paragraphs are from National Resources Committee, *Research—a National Resource*, pp. 170–75.

million. Under OSRD, these expenditures mounted rapidly. The participation of other agencies also increased, partly by direct contract, partly by the assumption of responsibility for projects started by OSRD. In fiscal 1945, federal expenditures for research at nonprofit institutions are estimated at $225 million.[9]

The concentration of research activities within relatively few institutions was reflected in the relations of OSRD with the universities at the beginning and during the war. While OSRD sought the assistance of scientists wherever they might be located, the effect of the agency's operations was a heavy concentration of contractual expenditures in a small number of institutions. Three factors were determining. One was the existing concentration of research capabilities at relatively few institutions. A second was the ability of some institutions to respond quickly to OSRD's requests while others, for lack of interest or because of statutory impediments, were very slow to do so. A third was OSRD's objectives of rapidly accelerated development and application, which in many cases required scientists to work closely in large laboratories dedicated to specific programs.[10] As a result, of the $518 million obligated by OSRD over the war period, 23 percent went to one institution and 16 percent to another. These plus eight other institutions accounted for 59 percent of OSRD's total expenditures, with much of the remainder going to industrial firms.[11]

The Immediate Postwar Period

As was pointed out in Chapter II, attitudes favorable towards a continuation of federal-university research relationships required some time to emerge as effective policies. Both types of OSRD pro-

---

[9] National Science Foundation, *Federal Funds for Science: Federal Funds for Scientific Research and Development at Nonprofit Institutions, 1950–51 and 1951–52*, vol. 1 (1953), p. 46.

[10] John E. Burchard (ed.), *Rockets, Guns, and Targets* (Little, Brown & Co., 1948), p. 307.

[11] The institutions were, in order of the dollar cost of their efforts, Massachusetts Institute of Technology, California Institute of Technology, Harvard University, Columbia University, University of California, Johns Hopkins University, University of Chicago, George Washington University, Princeton University and the University of Pennsylvania. Nine other institutions held wartime contracts exceeding $1 million. All but one of the first ten were private institutions, as were five of the remaining nine. The data are from James Phinney Baxter III, *Scientists against Time* (Little, Brown & Co., 1946), pp. 456–57.

grams—the research centers managed by universities under contract, and project research arrangements with faculty scientists—were sharply curtailed in the latter half of 1945. Much the same was true for the operations of the Manhattan Project. Though policies looked toward maintenance of these relationships, the federal agencies required time to develop postwar programs, secure budgets, develop procedures, and select projects for support. The result was a sharp decline in federal expenditures for university-related research. All of the contractual research centers suffered severe losses of personnel. Some collapsed before interested federal agencies had the opportunity to consider their continuation. A few were converted into government operated installations. The majority, however, remained in operation with skeleton staffs and, with varying delays, renewed their operations under Army, Navy, or AEC contracts with the managing institution. Meanwhile, the sharp rise in enrollments at educational institutions together with some increase in research activities by business firms resulted in a few years of severe shortages of research personnel.

The research centers for some years accounted for the larger part of federal funds expended for research by the universities (Chart 7). The centers were distinct entities, to a considerable extent separated from other university activities and affecting traditional university functions in varying degrees. The characteristics of these centers are discussed in Chapter IX.

Contractual project research suffered a partial hiatus as OSRD liquidated its operations. Leadership in establishing a clear policy of seeking out the assistance of university scientists on a project basis was supplied by the new Office of Naval Research. Inaugurated in 1946, ONR within a year had entered into appropriate contracts with some 150 educational institutions covering approximately 500 research projects and entailing obligations of $20 million.[12] The Army's technical services—Signal Corps, Ordnance, Engineers, and Chemical—assumed a number of OSRD projects, particularly those which offered prospect of early application. The Army's operations were decentralized in the technical services and through its regional procurement operations. The application of normal procurement procedures was to create difficulties between

[12] *Department of the Navy Appropriation Bill for 1949*, Hearings before the House Committee on Appropriations, 80 Cong. 2 sess. (1948), pp. 964–67.

CHART 7
Sources of Research Funds Expended
by Colleges and Universities

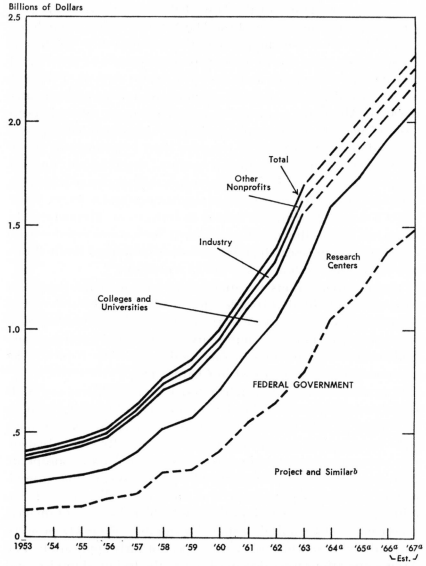

Sources: for 1953–63: National Science Foundation, *Reviews of Data on Science Resources,* vol. 1 (May 1965), p. 6; for 1964–67: National Science Foundation, *Federal Funds for Research, Development, and Other Scientific Activities,* vols. 14 (1965) and 15 (1966).

a. Projected from National Science Foundation estimates of federal R&D obligations to educational institutions.

b. "Similar" is primarily expenditures of the Cooperative State Research Service for Agricultural Experiment Stations.

the Army and the universities. It also made for difficulties in identifying the size or nature of the Army contractual research programs. The Air Force followed procedures similar to those of the Army. The National Institutes of Health meanwhile had assumed responsibility for many of OSRD's contracts in the medical field, employing its grant authority to make arrangements with the researchers and their universities. In the atomic energy field, the transfer of research projects sponsored by the Manhattan Project to the Atomic Energy Commission resulted in reduced activities for a number of years as programs were reviewed and projects transferred. A few other agencies established new programs in the period prior to 1950—as in the Department of Agriculture.

It should be observed here that there was at the time little or no consideration of procedures that might be alternative to those which had been followed by OSRD and which in turn had as precedents the practices of private industry and the foundations in providing funds for the carrying out of specific projects by designated individuals. The possibility of emulating the agricultural experiment station approach was suggested but met vigorous opposition and was not seriously explored.

Continuation of the OSRD type of relationship based on direct contact with a faculty member and subsequent contractual involvement of his institution permitted the bypassing of numerous potentially thorny issues in the relationship of the federal government to institutions of higher education. The OSRD did deal with university administrations when the use of university facilities was required and when it was necessary to arrange for leaves of absence for faculty members. Both ONR and the Army also dealt with administrations seeking their cooperation in accepting contracts involving faculty members. By dealing directly with faculty members and appealing to their research interests, the agencies were able, with a minimum of effort or controversy, to establish within the universities a higher priority for research activities by their faculties than had existed before. Furthermore, they were able to do this without entering into discussions with university administrations on broad policy questions, without developing criteria for selecting institutions, without giving consideration to the internal problems of the institutions that might be created, and without making long-range commitments to any single source of research effort.[13] It was possible to push aside questions of such nature because the sums that were, or seemed likely to be, available for university project research were relatively small. Discussion at the time was in terms of sums which, while substantially higher than those available before World War II, were thought of as falling well short of estimates of the capacity of university faculty to utilize research funds.[14]

Research in the Nation's Institutions of Higher Education

In seeking to increase the volume of research by college and university faculty members, federal programs affect directly or indirectly the entire structure of higher education. As Table 5 shows, since 1950 the nation's colleges and universities have grown markedly in number of institutions and in number of faculty members, this growth representing primarily a response to the increasing demand for college and postgraduate education. The number of institutions which maintain graduate schools and which offer the Ph.D. in one or more fields increased from 88 in 1950 to 228 in 1964. The funds available for research purposes increased between 1953 and 1966 about five times. As Chart 7 indicates, the sixfold increase in federal funds for university research dominates this growth.

It was pointed out earlier in this chapter that American institutions of higher education have differed and continue to differ

[13] See John Walsh, "Research and Graduate Education," *White House Conference on Education: A Milestone for Educational Progress*, Printed for the Senate Committee on Labor and Public Welfare, 89 Cong. 1 sess. (August 1965), pp. 143–49.

[14] Vannevar Bush, visualizing a National Research Foundation as the sole source of federal support for basic research, recommended a budget of $33.5 million rising to $122.5 million in five years. Until about 1953–54, most of the discussion of budgets for university research was related to estimates of existing research capabilities. While the methods used in arriving at these figures are not indicated, they appear to be estimates of the amounts that could be spent "effectively" with given manpower supplemented by additions to the nation's scientific strength which would follow from the proposed training and educational programs. In the case of basic medical research, for example, the report estimated that $5 million could be spent effectively the first year. "After a program is underway perhaps 20 million dollars a year can be spent effectively." (*Science—the Endless Frontier* [Government Printing Office, July 1945, reprinted by the National Science Foundation, July 1960], pp. xxiv, 16).

TABLE 5
Institutions of Higher Education: Background Data

Kinds of Data	1949–50	1963–64	1965–66
Number of institutions	1,851	2,132	2,230
Faculty (by number of persons) and other professional staff[a]	246,722	494,514	586,000[b]
Student enrollment (degree credit)	2,659,021	4,234,092	5,526,325
Current income	$2.4 billion	$9.6 billion[b]	n.a.
Current expenditures	$2.2 billion	$9.2 billion[b]	$11.4 billion[c]

Sources: U. S. Office of Education, *Digest of Educational Statistics 1966* and *Projections of Educational Statistics to 1975–76* (1966). "n.a." = not available.

a. Includes professional staff engaged specifically to conduct organized research and instructional staff. Of the total figures, faculty for resident instruction in degree-credit courses comprised 191,396 in 1949–50, 358,153 in 1963–64, and 432,000 in 1965–66.

b. Estimates for United States and outlying areas (Guam, Puerto Rico, Canal Zone, and Virgin Islands).

c. Estimate.

widely in the provisions they make for research activities on the part of their faculties. Some research is conducted by faculty members of the four-year colleges, but those institutions have in the aggregate a relatively small proportion of all faculty members and carry on an even smaller proportion of research. Research is a function associated with the faculties of the graduate schools of universities and some of their professional schools, particularly those of engineering, medicine, and agriculture.

Federal research programs which enlist the services of university personnel are concentrated in the physical and life sciences and in engineering. It follows that data relating to college and university personnel in those areas will indicate the functions performed by different types of institutions and their relationship to federal programs. Chart 8 summarizes a National Science Foundation survey which identifies the employment status and the functions performed by 140,000 (full-time equivalents) scientists and engineers associated in 1961 with 1,712 institutions of higher education. Included in the 1,712 institutions are 844 which granted the baccalaureate but no higher degrees and 562 schools which offered two-year programs. These institutions employed 19 percent of the 140,000 scientists and engineers but 32 percent of scientists and engineers engaged in teaching. Research was not an important activity in these institutions; they employed less than 1 percent of scientists and engineers engaged in research.

Also included among the 1,712 institutions are 306 which maintained programs offering graduate degrees in one or more scientific or engineering fields. These 306 institutions accounted for 72 percent of the scientific and engineering faculty members, all of the graduate students, and with associated agricultural experiment stations and contract research centers, virtually all other professional scientific and engineering personnel. (See Chart 9 for a detailed breakdown of employment at graduate institutions.)

CHART 8

Employment and Utilization of Scientists and Engineers by Institutions of Higher Education in 1961
(Full-Time Equivalents)

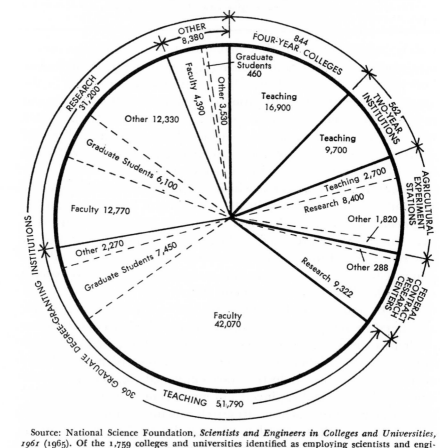

Source: National Science Foundation, *Scientists and Engineers in Colleges and Universities, 1961* (1965). Of the 1,759 colleges and universities identified as employing scientists and engineers that were surveyed, 1,712 responded. The 47 that did not respond are estimated to employ 9,400 scientists and engineers.

CHART 9

Employment and Utilization of Scientists and Engineers at
306 Institutions Granting Graduate Degrees
(Full-Time Equivalents)

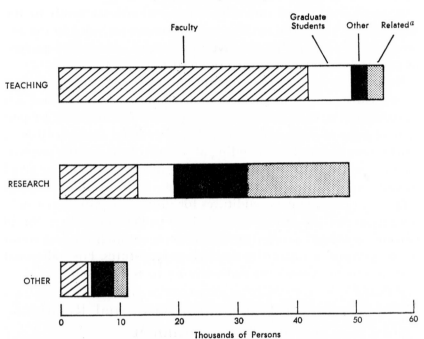

Source: National Science Foundation, *Scientists and Engineers in Colleges and Universities,*
1961 (1965), pp. 15, 18–19.
a. Agricultural experiment stations and federal contract research centers.

The 306 institutions which offer graduate degrees in one or
more scientific and technical fields differ greatly in size and in the
functions they perform. Included are independent technical and
medical schools. Most are universities but these vary greatly. Some
maintain schools or departments with graduate programs in most
if not all of the recognized fields. Others offer graduate degrees in
only one or a few scientific areas. These institutions differ also in
their participation in federal project research programs, depending upon the emphasis placed upon graduate education; the size,
interests and quality of the faculty; the opportunity given faculty
members to prepare research project proposals of competitive quality; and the institution's interest in accepting federal contracts.

The differences among institutions are reflected in their participation in federally financed research. In 1951 the NSF, using generous criteria, estimated that 687 out of a total of 1,871 colleges and universities possessed "a present or immediate potential capacity for conducting scientific research and development."[15] In that year 203 colleges and universities received federal funds in the aggregate of $253 million. The 86 universities included in the 203 received 77 percent. Twenty-five universities received 67 percent of the funds and the largest ten received 43 percent.[16]

In 1963 the number of institutions receiving federal project funds had increased to 450.[17] Included were some 186 liberal arts colleges and 55 state colleges but they accounted for only 1.1 percent of federal obligations.[18] On the other hand 100 institutions, chiefly universities but including also some of the 11 independent medical and 22 of the independent engineering schools, received $1 million or more each. This group of 100 institutions received 90 percent of federal expenditures for university project research. Twenty-five of the group accounted for 59 percent and ten for 38 percent of federal project funds.[19] Federal research funds account for 65 percent of university research expenditures. For individual institutions the range was wide—from 7 to 100 percent.[20]

The Variety of University Contractual Relations to the Government

The discussion that follows in this chapter is concerned principally with the organization, operation, and impact of the project research system directed principally to work in the physical and biological sciences, engineering, and, to a lesser extent, the social

---

[15] National Science Foundation, *Federal Funds for Science*, vol. 1, p. 26.

[16] *Ibid.*, p. 29.

[17] In 1963 federal agencies awarded approximately 20,000 project grants with an aggregate face value of $631 million and an average value of $31,500 (*Statistical Review of Research and Development*, Study Paper No. 9, House Select Committee on Government Research, H. Rept. 1940, 88 Cong. 2 sess. [1964], p. 171).

[18] U. S. Office of Education, *A Survey of Federal Programs in Higher Education* (1962), p. 7.

[19] *The Federal Government and Education*, H. Doc. 159, 88 Cong. 1 sess. (1963), pp. 49–50.

[20] *Statistical Review of Research and Development*, H. Rept. 1940, pp. 174–76. Much of the data presented in this report is from Victor J. Danilov, "Trends in University Research," *Industrial Research*, April 1964, p. 30.

sciences. The project approach involves government agency approval and funding of research proposals submitted by faculty members with the approval of their institutions. This method of organizing and administering university research has become the most important type in terms of funding involved as well in its impact upon university organization and functions.

Universities also engage in programmatic contractual research under which the research area is broadly defined with the tasks of selecting projects and tasks delegated to the university-appointed administrator of the program. Most important of the program arrangements is that which involves the university, or a group of universities organized as a consortium, in the management of a research center. The physical facilities of the center are usually provided by the government and its operating costs are met under a full-cost reimbursement contract. These organizations are sometimes integrated with the university as regards location and teaching functions. At the same time, they may be virtually separate organizations with little relationship to normal university activities. This type of arrangement is discussed in Chapter IX. In recent years there has been a significant growth of another type of contractual arrangement that seeks to overcome the limitations of project research; it resembles the program-oriented operations of the formally designated research centers. These programs are broadly defined and place responsibilities for both project selection and performance with the contractor. Such arrangements may provide for facilities on a scale not possible under project grants, since they can direct efforts to broad objectives without seeking to identify detailed activities, permit greater continuity of effort, and place upon the contractor a high degree of independence and responsibility. Example of such arrangements are the materials research program and the joint electronics research program, both of the Department of Defense, the primate research centers of the National Institutes of Health, and the research centers of the Office of Education.

The government's materials research program had its origin with the Materials Coordinating Committee of the Federal Council for Science and Technology which found shortages of trained personnel, laboratories and laboratory equipment devoted to research in materials. The FCST recommended in 1959 that selected universities be given financial support and assistance in furthering an interdisciplinary laboratory program for the purposes of increasing the number of Ph.D.'s in the fields of interest, stimulating research, and providing equipment and facilities, all with long-term financial support. The major part of the program (Project Pontus) was assigned to the Advanced Research Projects Agency (ARPA) of the Department of Defense with AEC and NASA also contributing.

In 1959 NASA established the Interdisciplinary Materials Science program at Rice University. The ARPA in 1960 entered into four-year contracts with three universities. These have been renewed and others have followed. More recently the program has been expanded by three-year contracts with industrial firms, each involving a subcontract with a university. For example, the Martin Company's Denver Division contract includes a subcontract with the University of Denver; Union Carbide Corporation has subcontracts with the Case Institute and Bell Aerospace Corporation; and Monsanto Research Corporation has a subcontract with Washington University in St. Louis.[21]

Somewhat similar in organization is the Joint Services Electronics Program, which was established through long-term contracts with MIT's Research Laboratory of Electronics, Columbia's Radiation Laboratory and Harvard's Radio Research Laboratory. In addition JSEP sponsors electronics research at Stanford University, Polytechnic Institute of Brooklyn, University of Illinois, University of California, University of Southern California, and University of Texas. These programs are supported on a "level of effort" basis with stable funding over an extended period of time. General guidelines are given these laboratories with specific project selection and direction left to the discretion of the university laboratory directors.[22]

[21] The National Research Council Committee on Scope and Conduct of Materials Research report, *More Effective Organization and Administration of Materials Research and Development for National Security: A Report to Detlev W. Bronk* (NAS-NRC Pub. 718 [1960]), contributed to the establishment of the program. On the organization of the program, see *Tenth Annual Report of Activities of the Joint Committee on Defense Production, 1960,* S. Rept. 1, 87 Cong. 1 sess. (1961), pp. 13–15; and *Army Research and Development Newsmagazine,* April 1965, p. 21.

[22] Lieutenant Colonel R. D. Lambourne, "The Joint Services Electronics Program," *Army Research and Development Newsmagazine,* May 1965, pp. 6–7, 18–19.

Beginning in 1960 under the leadership of the National Heart Institute, the government has supported centers for wide-ranging research on the primates. Seven such centers are now in operation, all administered by universities, for the purpose of "providing the best possible environment in which resident and visiting scientists of many disciplines can advance knowledge of the biological characteristics of the primate as it relates to the health of man."[23] Each center was financed by NIH by means of a nonmatching construction grant and an operation grant that committed funds at an established level for seven years in advance, subject to review in the fourth or fifth year. The research activities in these centers are not directed. They reflect a pragmatic approach, in terms of which the center's staff of scientists works around a central theme. The facilities are available to visiting scientists interested in a specific project, and resident or "core" staff collaborate with other scientists on specific problems.

The most recent programmatic center approach to university research is that of the Office of Education. With the Higher Education Act and the Elementary and Secondary Education Act, both of 1965, the Office of Education received authority and funds to launch a vastly increased program of research and development in education, supplementing its activities in project research. Nine university-based research and development centers were quickly established, each broadly specialized.[24] In addition, some twenty regional educational laboratories dealing with the technology of education have been or are in process of formation as are also several centers concerned with educational policy. Most are administered by universities, singly or in consortia.

A third type of relationship has emerged as such agencies as the National Science Foundation, the National Institutes of Health,

[23] Willard H. Eyestone, "Scientific and Administrative Concepts behind the establishment of Primate Centers," *Journal of American Veterinary Medical Association*, Dec. 15, 1965. See also *Federal Foreign Research Spending and the Dollar Drain*, Hearings before the House Committee on Government Operations, 89 Cong. 2 sess. (1966), pp. 53–57.

[24] See U. S. Department of Health, Education and Welfare, Office of Education, *Support for Research and Related Activity* (1965), pp. 18–21, and C. Ray Carpenter, "Reflections on Research on Higher Education: Strategies and Tactics," *College & University Bulletin* [of the Association for Higher Education], Nov. 1, 1965, reprinted by the Joint Economic Committee, in *Technology in Education*, 89 Cong. 2 sess. (1966), pp. 262–69.

and National Aeronautics and Space Administration have sought to strengthen the research capabilities of selected universities. These agencies have made a limited number of "institutional" grants designed to permit the university to expand and strengthen its capabilities in designated programmatic areas without attempting precise designations. In practice these grants have been made by inviting universities to submit plans for developing their capabilities in areas of agency interest. The agency then selects for financial support those plans that appear to offer the greatest promise with some attention given to such considerations as geographic location. The university may be expected to provide a large percentage of the necessary funds from nonfederal sources.

Because some agencies do not distinguish this type of program from project research, it is possible to provide only rough estimates on the magnitude of these arrangements. The National Science Foundation in 1966 expended about $11 million in "institutional" support.[25] The National Institutes of Health are permitted by statute to expend up to 15 percent of their research appropriations for institutional support and actually expend about 10 percent.

Institutional research capabilities may also be fostered by formally recognizing the historical experience that research support frequently has permitted staff expansion and enhanced strength. Selection for support is then made of research capabilities that may not be competitive in the project system but which provide a promising foundation for expansion to effective levels. This approach was undertaken by 1967 by the Department of Defense with its Project Themis budgeted at $20 million. Project Themis is directed to universities not heavily involved in government programs.[26] Such institutions are invited to submit programmatic research proposals in scientific and technical areas relevant to the Department's mission. It is expected that the proposals would involve a minimum of eight to ten faculty members and sixteen to twenty students, not necessarily available at the time of submis-

[25] See National Science Foundation, *Federal Support for Academic Science and Other Educational Activities in Universities and Colleges in Fiscal Year 1965*, NSF 66–30 (1966), p. 4.
[26] Office of the Director of Defense Research and Engineering, *Project Themis, a Program to Strengthen the Nation's Academic Institutions* (January 1967).

sion. Interdisciplinary approaches are encouraged with planning and selection of specific tasks delegated to the program manager. Funding of accepted proposals is by full cost-reimbursement contracts.

Research in the physical, biological and social sciences and in engineering dominates in the contractual relationships between the universities and the government. The universities also provide a variety of services other than those of conventional degree training. Among these, the most important involvement of universities in terms of dollar value and personnel involved is the technical aid projects of the Agency for International Development. Almost from its beginnings in 1950, the Technical Cooperation Administration sought the assistance of universities in providing and managing teams of qualified personnel for the execution of overseas assistance projects. Utilization of university resources was much accelerated by the Foreign Assistance Organization about 1955 and has since remained at high levels. In 1965 AID had contracts with 70 colleges and universities representing obligations of about $170 million and providing the professional and technical personnel for 143 projects in 39 countries. The contractual technical assistance projects have presented a variety of problems relating to the contractual relationships and the ability of the universities to staff and manage their operations, problems which cannot be discussed here.[27]

From its beginnings the Peace Corps has called upon the universities to provide its volunteers with special training during the summer period preceding their assignment overseas. In 1966 some sixty-five colleges and universities provided such training for Peace Corps contracts. The Peace Corps is also experimenting with a special training center unrelated to any university and employing returned volunteers as instructors.

In addition to providing training, the Peace Corps has also sought to enlist universities to provide "full administration" or "professional support" for its volunteer groups overseas. A small number of universities do undertake the management of projects overseas, but the Peace Corps has come to rely upon contractual

[27] A recent, important addition to an extensive literature is John W. Gardner, *A.I.D. and the Universities: A Report to the Administrator of the Agency for International Development* (Government Printing Office, 1964).

arrangements with other types of nonprofit organizations.[28] As the Peace Corps has accumulated experience it has increased its efforts to evaluate its programs through research. Most such projects have been contracted to university groups[29] and would be included in the research expenditures cited.

The Office of Economic Opportunity also calls upon private sources, including universities, for contractual research. A few of the urban programs—the Job Corps Conservation programs—are conducted by universities under contract but the majority are operated by business firms, sometimes with a university playing a supporting role as a subcontractor.[30]

The Organization of University Project Research

The federal policies established in the period 1945–50 sought to stimulate and direct to agency interests a greater volume of research activity by university faculty members within the existing institutions without providing for changes in their organization or policies. It was believed that the objective could be attained by supplying what it was assumed had been lacking in the past—funds that would permit faculty members to carry out research projects supplementing their teaching responsibilities. Such funds would be supplied by the federal agency and would be made available for the use of selected faculty members. University officials participated in the discussion of the proposed policies but did so primarily as representatives of the scientific community. Though university faculty were to do the work desired, no serious thought was given to entrusting university administrators with decision-making roles relating to the content of scientific and technical research funded as projects by federal agencies.

To operate the system, a complex four-part structure characterized by diffused participation and responsibilities was quickly devised. The formal elements are (1) the sponsoring federal agencies; (2) the faculty members who as principal investigators pro-

[28] *To Amend Further the Peace Corps Act,* Hearings before the House Committee on Foreign Affairs, 89 Cong. 1 sess. (1965), p. 184.

[29] For the 1962–66 list, see *To Amend the Peace Corps Act,* Hearings before the Senate Committee on Foreign Relations, 89 Cong. 1 sess. (1965), p. 81.

[30] *Examination of the War on Poverty Program,* Hearings before the House Committee on Education and Labor, 89 Cong. 1 sess. (1965), pp. 36–40, 187.

pose projects (or agree to proposals made to them) and conduct or supervise the work; (3) the membership and particularly the leadership of the scientific area within which a project falls; and (4) university administration.

The Sponsoring Agencies

Chart 10 indicates the nine federal agencies maintaining major programs offering grant or contract support to research proposals of the type that might be performed by faculty members. In addition, a larger number of other agencies operate smaller, typically narrowly specialized programs. In no case are the funds earmarked by statute for use by university personnel, although it is frequently understood that such use is intended. The limitation on allowable overhead costs in the past and the current application of cost sharing assure that funds appropriate for grant purposes do gravitate to university faculties.

Each agency pursues objectives within certain identified areas of interest. Such interests may be limited to those which support the agency's basic mission or may reflect its responsibility for generally promoting research in a defined field. While each agency pursues specialized interests and a few have an exclusive jurisdiction over a field, it is typical that an agency's interest is in some specific part of a broad field in which other agencies also have research programs. Thus, the National Institutes of Health, representing all fields of medicine, is the principal source of project funds for medical research. However, each of the other eight principal agencies shown in Chart 10 and several not identified also support research in some aspect of medicine which may overlap in some degree but which does not therefore necessarily duplicate the NIH program.[31]

The agency functions include those of delineating its program, securing funds, determining the procedure by which its objectives may best be attained, establishing and publicizing the subject areas in which it is interested in receiving proposals, providing procedures for selection of proposals and awarding funds, maintaining contacts with its research performers as well as with other

[31] See *Department of Health, Education, and Welfare Budget for Fiscal 1963*, Hearings before the House Committee on Appropriations, 87 Cong. 2 sess. (1962), pt. 2, p. 46. Such overlap of interest on the part of the agencies is a characteristic of virtually all the large scientific areas.

CHART 10

Federal Agency Obligations to Educational Institutions for Project Research and Development

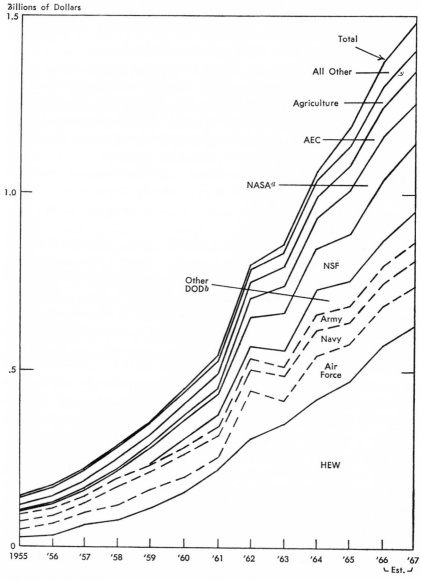

Billions of Dollars

Total

All Other

Agriculture

AEC

NASA[a]

NSF

Other DOD[b]

Army

Navy

Air Force

HEW

Source: National Science Foundation, *Federal Funds for Research, Development, and Other Scientific Activities,* vols. 5–15.

a. National Advisory Committee on Aeronautics (NACA) from 1955 to 1957.

b. Other DOD funds include the Advanced Research Projects Agency and department-wide funds.

scientists in the areas of its interests, and receiving reports. In addition, there are numerous other activities such as arranging for audits of financial accounts, property inventories, approving certain types of purchases and travel, and patent problems. In administering their programs the agencies in varying degrees must deal with the interests of individual private and professional groups. Some agencies invite private individuals to participate or advise in program development. Agencies with mission-oriented objectives make some use of advisory committees to advise on programs under consideration and, possibly, to stimulate interest and participation in their areas of interest. These administrative operations have been discussed at greater length in Chapter IV.

The University Faculty

Initiative in preparing a research proposal with a request for support rests with a faculty member, frequently a senior man who has acquired a reputation in a field and who designates himself as the principal investigator who will guide if not actually do the work required. A research proposal may be an expression of interest on the part of a faculty member in applying more time and effort to a research problem than is possible under the conditions of a normal teaching load and limited institutional resources. It is, under present conditions, more likely to be an expression of interest in continuing a research project which has been pursued on a substantial scale for some time and which has, step by step, opened up new areas inviting exploration. The researcher may also be motivated to submit a proposal by the expectation of his institution that he do so, since all or part of the salaries of his junior colleagues, full-time assistants, and graduate students, and perhaps even his own, are dependent upon such funds.

The probability that a properly prepared proposal will be accepted will vary with the funds available for the scientific area involved and the programmed interests of the agency to which it is submitted.[32] Broadly speaking, the chances of acceptance are good

[32] In 1964, the Division of Research Grants of the National Institutes of Health approved 17,300 of the 21,400 research grant applications received (including noncompeting continuations) (*Handbook of Programs of the U. S. Department of Health, Education, and Welfare* [1964–65 ed.], pt. 2, pp. ii–203). The rejection of research proposals on scientific grounds alone is most readily measured in a situation where the availability of funds was clearly not a restriction. In the case of NIH programs

—although probabilities vary widely—if the proposed research is judged to have scientific merit in promising to develop new knowledge in an area of interest to the agency; if it reveals a knowledge of related recent and current research; presents a method of procedure which seems feasible and likely to produce significant results; and if the requested funds for salaries and equipment are within the agency's resources and are deemed likely to accomplish the objective.[33] The probabilities are increased if the proposal calls for a continuation of a research program previously supported with results satisfactory to the agency, particularly if interim results have attracted some professional attention. The chances for acceptance are popularly believed to be enhanced if the principal investigator has an established reputation for effective research by the standards of his discipline or if he has been associated with an established researcher who will vouch for his ability. Some agencies, however, give special consideration to proposals submitted by younger men who have not yet acquired professional reputations.

The effects of the system upon research performers have been very favorable. Men who have proven their competence as researchers in areas selected for agency support have acquired a high degree of independence as well as of responsibility.[34] They have also enjoyed the benefits that follow from a rapid rise in the demand for scarce services. Salaries have increased markedly, employment opportunities are numerous, advancement may be rapid, and opportunities to choose between full-time research and some mix-

---

in 1962 and 1963, some 30 percent of all proposals were rejected although the agency failed to use all the grant funds available to it during those years.

[33] Ernest M. Allen, "Why Are Research Grant Applications Disapproved?" *Science*, vol. 132 (Nov. 25, 1960), pp. 1532–34.

[34] "The significance of the research contract for the professional scientist is profound because it establishes a relationship that cuts across the normal lines of hierarchical authority in a bureaucratic organization. The scientist, as principal investigator, becomes responsible for the quality of his work and for meeting various research requirements of the project monitor, or official representative of the sponsoring group or agency, rather than to his immediate administrative supervisor in the employing organization. Under such conditions, the employer comes to provide service functions to the principal investigator, rather than exercising direct supervisory responsibilities over the research" (Howard M. Vollmer, "The Social Organization of Science and Technology" [mimeographed; Stanford Research Institute, 1964]). See also Donald F. Hornig. "The Evolving Federal Role," in Boyd R. Keenan (ed.), *Science and the University* (Columbia University Press, 1966), p. 51.

ture of research and teaching are frequent. For those who choose a university post, opportunities to secure income from research during summer and other vacation periods are abundant as are also opportunities for advisory and consultant activities outside the university.

Along with such gains has come a marked rise in the prestige of scientists. The fact that research contracts are awarded in a national competition confers upon the winner a status that is understandable to the nonscientist and is hence in part independent of the nature of the research project. Some scientists also enjoy opportunities to participate in determining public policy relating to research as in advising in the selection of project proposals and perhaps in contributing to agency program formulation. Some have substantial influence on broad policy. Such influence is expressed formally through membership on advisory committees and panels of such agencies as PSAC and indirectly the NAS, through appearances before congressional committees, and in numerous less formal ways.

This is not to say that there are not problems for those who conduct research. There is inevitably an area of conflict between the government's interest in the development of new knowledge that has some probability of application to a felt need and the scientist's interest in a problem he has identified that may yield new knowledge in an area in which the government agency interest has not been established.[35] There exist, then, pressures to prepare project proposals with an eye to their chance of acceptance. Furthermore, such proposals must be prepared with a specificity not required under other circumstances.[36] There will be uncertainty and

[35] E. R. Piore noted in 1953 that "one can say without reservation that the underlying motivation of the Government in science is the utilization of science" ("The Aims of Government in the Conduct and Support of Research," *Proceedings of the Conference on the Administration of Research* [1953], p. 11). Leland J. Haworth, director of the National Science Foundation, observed that "so for the present our best drawing card for financial support by the public is the ultimate usefulness of science. I do not defend the fact that this is so; I simply state it as a fact" ("Some Problem Areas in the Relationships between Government and Universities," NAS-NRC *News Report*, vol. 14 [November-December 1964], p. 92). All available evidence reflects a dominant utilitarian interest on the part of Congress and therefore of federal programs in science.

[36] For advice on proposal writing, see Raymond Ewell *et al.*, "Developing Effective Proposals for Submission by Institutions and Individual Faculty Members," in Harrison Sasscer (ed.), *New Prospects for Achievement: Federal Programs for*

there may be long delays in actions on such proposals. Grant-type contracts may be awarded in amounts less than requested, sometimes without acknowledgement of the effect of a reduced level of effort upon the project's objectives. Work under a grant involves a commitment to a prescribed course of action even though redirection of the effort as may be suggested by the work in process is possible. The investigator is, however, under pressure to produce results which can support a request for renewal or extension.

There are also difficulties in the sponsor relationship, reflecting confusion as to the nature of the grant form of contract. With time it has become increasingly clear that the grant is in no sense a gift, but for all practical purposes a purchase of work; work that is to be done as described in the proposal and in the approved budget and within the regulations of the sponsoring agency.[37] The familiar, informal, and unobtrusive controls of the university are supplemented by another set of controls applied by the sponsoring agency, frequently through the university. Though abuses apparently have been few, the interest of the Congress in assuring itself that funds are used solely for approved research has resulted in increasing controls. The research worker is affected by limitations on his authority to deviate from his approved budget and by the requirement that he furnish periodic reports accounting for the effort applied as well as terminal reports. Such accounting, while minimal, has not been customary within the university, and it has aroused some resentment, generating interest in revising the grant concept with a view to returning to the simple relationships.

Scientific and Technical Peer Groups

Virtually all scientists and engineers are affiliated not only with some institution but also with one or more groups formally organized as a learned or technical society.[38] Some of these are organiza-

Colleges and Universities (American Council on Education, 1964), pp. 35–45. National Academy of Sciences, *Federal Support of Basic Research in Institutions of Higher Learning* (1964), pp. 3, 81–82, emphasizes the point that proposals can be written so as to retain a high degree of flexibility in directing the course of a research project.

[37] National Institutes of Health, *The Public Health Service and the Fountain Committee* (March 15, 1963).

[38] National Academy of Sciences, *Scientific and Technical Societies in the United States and Canada* (1961), lists 1,597 scientific and technical societies. Historical and analytical accounts of some 60 societies of national scope may be found in Joseph

tions that represent all branches of science, such as the American Association for the Advancement of Science; others relate to a single large field such as the American Chemical Society; and still others are further sub- or sub-subgroupings concerned with highly specialized interests within the broader field. Some are regional, most are national, and a few are international. Membership in some is open to any person willing to pay the dues. Others maintain formal procedures of nomination and election that sometimes involve criteria which operate in more or less exclusive fashion. Still others are less formal, though invitation in some form is essential to participating membership.

Of special importance is the National Academy of Sciences-National Research Council, dealt with more fully in Chapter VIII. The NAS is a highly prestigious organization with sharply limited, self-perpetuating membership that has become very influential in the promotion of scientific interests. Although it has no formal ties to the universities, the NAS-NRC has properly been described as "born of the university and bearing the marks of its parentage,"[39] and university-affiliated scientists dominate its membership.[40]

Such organizations and groupings have existed as long as there has been scientific activity, linking men in common interests, joining in common enthusiasms, furthering knowledge by sharing observations, establishing standards, tendering recognition, and generally establishing and upholding the values to which scientists respond.[41] The role played by each member within these organiza-

---

C. Kiger, *American Learned Societies* (Public Affairs Press, 1963). The 88 professional scientific societies in existence in 1920 grew to 176 in 1959. Membership in the 65 societies for which information is available increased from 134,178 in 1937 to 524,494 in 1959 (National Science Foundation, *Dues and Membership in Scientific Societies* [1960]).

[39] Hugh L. Dryden, "The University and the Exploration of Space," *Science*, vol. 150 (Nov. 26, 1965), p. 1133.

[40] Of the National Academy of Sciences' 695 American members in 1964, 561 were affiliated with universities, 65 with nonprofit organizations, 34 with government, and 24 with industry (*Impact of Federal Research Development Policies on Scientific and Technical Manpower*, Hearings before the Senate Committee on Labor and Public Welfare, 89 Cong. 1 sess. [1965], p. 487).

[41] An important study of the nature of the organization of scientists is given in Warren O. Hagstrom, *The Scientific Community* (Basic Books, Inc., 1965). The relationship of scientific communities to the scientific process is dealt with perceptively in Thomas S. Kuhn, *The Structure of Scientific Revolutions* (University of Chicago Press, 1962). See also Norman W. Storer, *The Social System of Science* (Holt, Rinehart & Winston, 1966).

tions stems in large part from his professional reputation, which is a reflection of his peers' judgment on the quality of his research contribution to the field.[42] An important function performed by virtually all the formal organizations is the publication of one or more journals in which are published the reports of research in the scientific area of interest to them.[43] The editors and editorial boards of these organizations exercise great influence in judging the importance of research reports.

There exist also numerous informal groups, more or less loosely organized around common specialized interests. Some circulate their research plans and research results among their members. Such exchanges are highly important in evaluating and coordinating the direction of scientific effort.[44]

[42] Analysis of the citations of a man's work appearing in professional journals has, for example, become an important technique. See Irving H. Sher and Eugene Garfield, "New Tools for Improving and Evaluating the Effectiveness of Research," in M. C. Yovits *et al.* (eds.), *Research Program Effectiveness* (Gordon & Breach, 1966), pp. 137–46.

[43] Such journals have proliferated with increasing scientific and technical activity. While most journals are financed from dues and subscriptions, to some degree the federal government bears part of their publication costs since page charges, applied to authors of published papers, are an allowable charge against grants and contracts. While page charges are by no means universal, the Federal Council for Science and Technology in 1961 recommended that all agencies accept them, and the practice of levying page charges has been increasing (National Science Foundation, *Characteristics of Scientific Journals, 1949–1959* [1964], pp. 10–11).

[44] Derek J. de Solla Price terms these informal groupings "invisible colleges" and writes of them: "Starting originally as a reaction to the communication difficulty brought about by the flood of literature, and flourishing mightily under the team-work conditions induced by World War II, their whole raison d'être was to substitute personal contact for formal communication among those who were really getting on with the job, making serious advances in their fields. In many of these fields it is now hardly worth while embarking upon serious work unless you happen to be within the group, accepted and invited to the annual and informal conferences, commuting between the two Cambridges, and vacationing in one of the residential and work centers that are part of the international chain. The processes of access and egress from the groups have become difficult to understand, and the apportioning of credit for the work to any one member of his sub-team has already made it more meaningless than before to award such honors as the Nobel Prize. Are these 'power groups' dangerously exclusive? Probably not, but in many ways they may turn out to be not wholly pleasant necessities of the scientific life in its new state of saturation" (*Science since Babylon* [Yale University Press, 1961], p. 99).

A related type of organization is illustrated by the Information Exchange Groups established by NIH as an experiment. IEG No. 1, for example, operated to exchange information on research in the fields of electron transfer and oxidative phosphoryl-

Members of these groups play other significant roles as well. Some, selected because of the reputations they have acquired, are drawn into the process of administering the government's R&D programs. Whether as regular staff members, members of advisory panels of the PSAC, the NAS, or some other agency, or as formal or informal consultants, they participate in the formulation of federal programs. Some participate in the evaluation of the completed and proposed work of others. Such evaluations strongly influence, if they do not determine, whether a research proposal will receive financial support. Members of these groups not only contribute judgments which command attention and thereby influence reputations but, in some cases, also have power to enforce their judgments by influencing decisions allocating the funds available for research within a field.[45] As groups or subgroups,

---

ation. "At least 90 percent of the important papers published anywhere in the world . . . are submitted to the IEG and these reach the membership three to twelve months before the same papers can be read in the usual journals" (*Science*, vol. 148 [June 18, 1965], p. 1543). Though these groups were judged highly successful, NIH discontinued its sponsorship of them in 1966 because of administrative problems accentuated by an increasing pressure to form more and, it is charged, pressure from the editors of established journals (David Green, "Death of an Experiment," *International Science and Technology*, May 1967, pp. 82–88).

[45] As members of the system, relatively few scientists have been critical of its operation. However, one scientist writes, "Never has so much money been spent with so little return. The men on the committees or panels which allocate the funds are on the whole sincere and honest. But they are human and often enough they give large sums to their friends or to each other. I could cite many instances in which many thousands of dollars have been allocated to workers who, instead of advancing science, have published erroneous results that have retarded progress" (L. V. Heilbrunn, "The Waste of Scientists," *The Nation* [1957], p. 426).

On the alleged excessive power of scientists, particularly in situations where secrecy is imposed, see Hans J. Morgenthau, "Modern Science and Political Power," *Columbia Law Review*, December 1964. The role of scientists in decision-making on science-related issues has attracted much attention. See, for example, Robert Gilpin and Christopher Wright (eds.), *Scientists and National Policy-Making: The Rise of an Apolitical Elite in Science and National Policy Making* (Columbia University Press, 1964).

The Elliott committee gave some consideration to complaints it had heard regarding "the degree of influence exerted by advisory panels" and the fact that the faculties of the major sponsored research institutions "supplied an exceptionally large number of advisory panelists, and that this might in turn lead to a showing of favoritism." The committee found that the ten universities receiving 38 percent of federal research funds did supply 36.8 percent of the membership of federal review panels. It also found that these universities conferred 31.5 percent of all doctorates in the years 1960–63 and that 54.2 percent of that part of the membership

both formal and informal, they also exercise influence upon the agencies in determining the funds that will be allocated to programs or that will be sought for such purposes.[46]

It follows that the nature of a researcher's membership in such groups may be as, if not more, important to him than his institutional affiliation. This is particularly true for university faculty though such membership is also of significance for scientists and engineers employed by business firms and other types of organizations. Membership in these groups is not necessarily related to the nature of the individual's employing institution although the reputation of the employing institution may be a significant factor. The members of these groups, by the prestige accorded them for their recognized achievements, serve to enforce the standards by which a scientific community operates. They are highly influential in identifying as promising or not the work of younger men, helping to evaluate the proposals they submit and the work they accomplish. The observation is frequently made that the project research system has reduced the loyalty of the university scientist to his institution.[47] If, and to the extent that, this is true, it is to these informal peer groups that the scientists have turned.

---

of the NAS associated with universities were faculty members of these ten institutions (*Statistical Review of Research and Development,* H. Rept. 1940, p. 172). The House Government Operations Committee also reviewed the relationship between grants awarded by NIH and institutional affiliation of study section members (*Health Research and Training,* H. Rept. 321, 87 Cong. 1 sess. [1961], pp. 29–30).

[46] See, for one example, the criticism by the members of a National Science Foundation advisory panel on chemistry of the inadequate support given to research in chemistry by NSF as well as other agencies. The panel estimated that federal support of basic chemical research amounted to $37 million in 1963. In contrast it estimated a minimum need for $88 million without allowing for salaries which in other fields would be charged to research contracts ("Federal Support of Basic Chemistry," An Independent Report Prepared by Members of the Advisory Panel in Chemistry of the National Science Foundation, printed in *Government and Science,* Hearings before the House Committee on Science and Astronautics, 88 Cong. 2 sess. [1964], pp. 823–30). The panel's report was followed by a survey by a committee of the more prestigious National Academy of Sciences–National Research Council entitled *Chemistry: Opportunities and Needs* (1965).

[47] For example, Dael Wolfle's observation that the project-grant system "undoubtedly weakens the scientist's ties with his own university. The scientist prefers to entrust his proposals to his colleagues on a Washington review panel rather than the uninformed or biased decisions of his own dean or president" (*Scientific American,* vol. 213 [July, 1965], p. 24).

Research and the University Administration

An institution's capacity to participate in sponsored research programs is determined by its policies with regard to the recruitment and retention of faculty, the opportunity given faculty to do such research as may be a necessary preliminary to the submission of research proposals of competitive quality, and the institution's willingness to employ without faculty status professional personnel for research functions. The institution may encourage the faculty to prepare research proposals and endorse them uncritically; it may insist upon certain financial provisions; it may be selective of the areas in which it wishes to seek research support; it may establish criteria as to the employment provisions that may be made. The institution may visualize contractual research as a source of institutional growth, or it may restrict such research in defense of its concepts of its proper size and functions.

Application of policies of the nature cited results in sharp differentiation between institutions of higher education. Competence and interest in research are characteristics on which high values are placed in the recruitment and promotion of faculty members by most institutions maintaining programs leading to the Ph.D. degree. However, while personnel qualified by training to undertake research are scattered among all educational institutions, those with outstanding interest and ability in conducting research tend to be recruited by those institutions which place a high value on research accomplishment. Once such institutions have established reputations for research accomplishment, they have superior opportunities for recruiting the qualified personnel necessary to staff research activities. While other institutions may welcome research-minded faculty, their interest lies first in teaching services and their appeal is to men whose preference is for classroom work. Such institutions also characteristically request faculty members to carry teaching loads which seriously limit, if they do not prohibit, research activities.

The administrative officers of universities are involved in faculty project research financed by an outside sponsor in three main ways. All federal agencies require that the principal investigator secure the assent of his institution to the submission of a proposal. In giving its consent the university agrees to the use of its facilities for the research, and it may be necessary that it adjust its programs to shifts in availability of faculty and facilities. The university assumes no formal responsibility for the results of the research. It does administer the regulations of the sponsoring agency and thereby accepts an increased burden on its managerial staff. Among the many services required of it, the university agrees to receive the funds involved, assumes responsibility for utilizing the funds in accordance with the terms of the grant or contract and the regulations of the agency, agrees to maintain records and accounts suitable for government auditing, arranges for the installation, maintenance, and safety of such special equipment as may be provided for, and deals with patent problems according to its own and agency policies.[48]

Impact on the University

The increasing prestige of research supported by rapidly increasing funds and the interest of many faculty members in giving their research more or perhaps all of their time while remaining on the campus have forced research-minded universities to move toward new arrangements in administrative provisions for research, in the work load assigned to faculty members, and in compensation arrangements.

In some institutions, sponsored research remains wholly a matter of the unregulated initiative of the faculty member without special administrative procedures other than some arrangements with the business office to handle funds and to meet auditing requirements. In other institutions, arrangements exist to review faculty proposals before they are endorsed by the university. At its simplest, such review is conducted by a faculty committee. It can,

[48] The university's need to deal with patents received by faculty members has paralleled the growth of sponsored research as a university activity. In the 1920's only 3 institutions had established policies regarding ownership and management of faculty patents. Eighteen more established such policies in the 1930's and 52 in the 1940's. A 1962 survey found 147 institutions with formalized policies. A large number of universities assign management of their patents to the Research Corporation, a nonprofit organization founded in 1912; others have agreements with the Battelle Development Corporation. Archie M. Palmer, *University Research and Patent Policies, Practices, and Procedures* (NAS-NRC Publication No. 999 [1962]).

on the other hand, involve an administrative officer such as a vice-president for, or coordinator of, research.[49] Such officers have varied functions; some are limited to handling the business side of such sponsored research as faculty members may enter into, including conducting negotiations with government agencies. Others serve to apply institutional policies to facilitate and encourage faculty participation in sponsored research. Such organizations are in many universities the only point at which information regarding the institution's research activities is available.[50]

These arrangements are supplemented in many institutions by organizations affiliated with the university which have the function of dealing with external sponsors of research. Such organizations may seek to provide uniformity in sponsor-faculty relationships, to relieve the researcher of administrative problems, and to provide the administration with information regarding the sponsored research activities of the faculty. Organizations of this nature had come into being in the 1920's with the formation of a Division of Sponsored Research by the Massachusetts Institute of Technology in 1920, the Office of Research Administration at the University of Michigan at the same time, and the Lehigh University Institute of Research in 1924. Many were formed during World War II to deal with government programs of research; many have been founded since. Some are integral parts of the university, operating as conventional departments. The number of this type has increased rapidly. There are now perhaps 3,000 such organizations, 50 or 60 of them within large universities.[51] Others have been established as separately incorporated nonprofit organizations; the

[49] William C. Wheadon, "Organizing University Research," *Industrial Research*, April 1964, reprinted in *The Role and Effect of Technology in the Nation's Economy*, Hearings before the Senate Select Committee on Small Business, 88 Cong. 1 sess. (1963), pp. 727–32. A brief analysis of university organization for research administration based on a Public Health Service study is summarized in *Government and Science*, Hearings before the House Committee on Science and Astronautics, 88 Cong. 2 sess. (1964), p. 135.

[50] One of the more elaborate efforts to make information available is Michigan State University, Office of Research Development and the Graduate School, *Sponsored Research* (1961). More comprehensive but less detailed is Frederick Sudermann, *Federal Programs Affecting Higher Education: An Administrative Reference Manual* (State University of Iowa, Division of Special Services, 1962), distributed by the American Council on Education.

[51] Archie M. Palmer and Anthony T. Kruzas (eds.), *Research Center Directory* (2d ed.; Gale Research Co., 1965).

first of this type was the Purdue Research Foundation organized in 1930.[52] Some of these organizations confine their activities to the business aspects of contractual research. Many, however, administer the research itself, sometimes with their own full-time personnel; others use the part-time services of regular faculty members. In the case of state institutions, some of the affiliated organizations were formed to overcome the constraints of statutes which restricted the universities' ability to enter into contractual arrangements. Some, on the other hand, appear to be little more than a device to solve the perennial faculty problem of securing the services of a full-time secretary.[53]

Adjustments in University Administration

Whatever organizations exist at any given institution to deal with the problems and opportunities of sponsored research, the university's fundamental problem is that of responding to the growth of research as it affects the nature of faculty obligations and faculty compensation. Before World War II, a faculty member of an institution with some commitment to research taught from nine to twelve credit hours per week (three or four courses depending upon the term or semester system).[54] In many institutions the work load was heavier. The twelve hours in the classroom—more if laboratories were involved—the necessary preparation for such teaching, the numerous nonteaching duties required of many faculty members, and the general need to keep up with the professional literature, represented a demanding work load to which research was added as the time, energies, and interest of the faculty member permitted. For his services the faculty member was normally paid his salary over a nine- or ten-month period. The summer months were unpaid vacations in which the faculty member

[52] Archie M. Palmer, *University Research and Patent Policies, Practices, and Procedures.*

[53] A useful analysis of the origins and nature of university institutes and their relationship to the departmental structure is Gilbert Shapiro, "Social Science Research and the American University," *The American Behavioral Scientist* (October 1964), pp. 29–35.

[54] A review of the available data is supplied by W. Hugh Stickler, "Working Material and Bibliography on Faculty Load," in Kevin Bunnell (ed.), *Faculty Work Load: A Conference Report* (American Council on Education, 1960), pp. 80–97. See also Harold Orlans, *The Effects of Federal Programs on Higher Education* (Brookings Institution, 1962), chaps. 3 and 7.

could do what he liked. Many, impelled by low salaries, taught in summer sessions or found other sources of income. In addition, the practice of permitting faculty members to accept remunerative work related to their professional interests during the teaching year on a part-time basis was widely accepted. It was rationalized on the twin grounds that the income received was a desirable supplement to inadequate salaries and that such activities contributed to the faculty members' knowledge and effectiveness.

For many years the acceptance by faculty members of remunerative professional assignments on a part-time basis during the school year presented university administrators with difficult problems.[55] On the one hand, administrators had good reason to insist that a full-time faculty appointment required full-time effort. On the other hand, such outside work supplemented salaries that were rarely competitive with alternative employment opportunities. Furthermore, such outside work and contacts, depending on their nature, might be expected to enrich the faculty member's knowledge and experience and hence his effectiveness as a teacher. Most universities had therefore developed policies, whether formal or informal, that permitted a limited amount of such supplementary work and income. In the postwar period, however, the number and magnitude of federally sponsored projects have constituted a special case. The universities have been forced to adopt policies relating to sponsored research which more clearly define the conditions of faculty employment.

There are two different policies currently in vogue. One policy calls for the support of the research interests of the faculty member as a supplement to the resources made available by his university. Under this concept, federal grant funds provide special equipment and compensation to assistants (generally, graduate students). Such funds also provide income to the faculty member, but only during periods like summer vacations when his time is not obligated to his institution. The income so provided relieves the researcher from the possible necessity of engaging in other income-producing activities and assures that his time will be spent on his research.

[55] Policies currently in effect are surveyed in National Science Foundation, *Faculty Consulting: College and University Policies, Practices, and Problems,* NSF No. 8 (February 1966).

This view of the nature and purpose of project grants was frequently expressed during the discussion of the establishment of the NSF. Until 1960 that agency adhered to it.[56] Federal funds, in this view, are not intended to support faculty researchers for that part of their research time which constitutes their obligation to their institution. To the degree that this view has prevailed, few problems have been presented to the faculty member's institution since there is no competition between sponsored research and teaching. At the same time, it means that the volume of university-based research is limited to the university's ability to release faculty from teaching duties and to periods when no teaching is required.

The other and now dominant policy places no such restrictions on the use of funds. Mission-oriented agencies concerned with maximizing research efforts in their areas of interest have left to the investigator and his institution the decisions regarding the magnitude of the effort and the relationship of project time to university obligations. Given the nature of research, proposals involving all or substantial fractions of the faculty member's time soon appeared. Such agencies as ONR and NIH from an early date accepted project budgets which provided that time spent by faculty

[56] The National Science Foundation in 1958 established a formal policy prohibiting what it termed "overload" research (*Government-University Relationships in Federally Sponsored Scientific Research and Development* [1958], p. 24). The current NSF position states that the Foundation "assumes that research is one of the normal functions of faculty members of institutions of higher education. Time spent on research within the term of appointment is deemed to be included within the regular institutional salary of the faculty member. Research is not an 'extra' function for which additional compensation or compensation at a higher rate may be requested. Grant funds may NOT be used to augment the total salary or rate of salary of faculty members of the institution receiving the grant during the period of time covered by the term of faculty appointment" (*Grants for Scientific Research* [1963], p. 9).

The NSF action was greeted in some quarters as an unwarranted interference by the Foundation with the freedom of the universities to determine their own policies. There was, however, little expressed agreement with the charge that "if this first step succeeds, it may prove to be but the beginning of a series which would eventually destroy the university's freedom to determine its own policies" (Harold K. Work, "Where Are We Going in Research—for Education?" *Proceedings of the Twelfth National Conference on the Administration of Research* [University of Denver, 1959], p. 20). For another dissent, see W. A. Koehler, "Faculty Compensation for Sponsored Research: Good or Bad?" *Journal of Engineering Education*, vol. 50 (1960), pp. 569–71.

members on project research during the teaching year be charged against the contract funds.

Under such conditions the nature of the faculty member's employment becomes a critical question. Some institutions have always permitted the investigator to supplement his university salary from project funds. With the upsurge of defense-related research stimulated by the Korean War, a substantial number of prominent institutions endorsed that practice for projects requiring secrecy on the grounds that inability to publish research results prohibited the normal processes of professional recognition for research efforts.[57]

Few if any institutions continue the practice of permitting a faculty member to supplement his basic university salary during the academic year from project funds.[58] One consideration has been the growth of disapproval by the sponsoring agencies and the emergence of government-wide regulations which encouraged the universities to consolidate control over federal funds and eventually prohibited the application of project funds to the augmentation of faculty income.[59] Of importance also was the fact that the

[57] By agreement between a number of major universities under what has since become known as the Harrell formula; see Longenecker, *University Faculty Compensation Policies . . .* , pp. 108–9.

[58] Little information regarding university policies is available. Extra or supplemental income from grants during the academic year is permitted as a matter of policy at a few institutions, is contrary to policy but permitted at some, and is prohibited at others. Normally this is a matter of negotiation between the faculty member and the administration. Extra compensation appears to be common when the faculty member must sacrifice income received from outside consulting in order to conduct a research project financed by a grant or contract. It exists also when faculty salaries are relatively low and the university takes the position that the individual's obligation to his institution is not of a full-time nature. See Fred R. Cagle, *Federal Research Projects and the Southern University* (Southern Regional Education Board, 1962), pp. 45–47; Harold Orlans, *The Effects of Federal Programs on Higher Education*, pp. 119–20; and Longenecker, *University Faculty Compensation Policies . . .* , p. 108.

[59] Thus, representatives of the Defense Department are quoted in 1954 as stating that "it is our policy not to consciously enter into a contract wherein contract money is paid to a faculty member during the academic year as a supplement to his basic salary. However, there is no objection to a faculty member's total income being raised by summer work on a contract for time not otherwise paid for by the university" (L. R. Lunden, "Fiscal Implications of Federally Supported Research," *Educational Record*, vol. 35 [April 1954], p. 91). Agency practice is now governed by Bureau of the Budget Circular A-21, which prohibits augmentation of

practice of permitting federal funds to be used to supplement faculty incomes constituted a surrender by the university of the principle that the faculty member who had time to do research during the teaching year did so as one of his obligations to his institution, for which his regular salary was compensation. The severe lag in faculty salaries following World War II presented all universities with exceedingly difficult problems. While project funds represented opportunities for adjustments in the cases of those holding grants or contracts, such individual solutions generated serious inequities within faculties. Moreover, the university was identified with the researcher, its facilities were used, its students frequently employed as assistants, and it was responsible to the sponsoring agency for the disbursing of funds. Over the past decade, heavily involved institutions have increasingly asserted control over faculty time devoted to government-funded research.

All institutions accept reimbursement from contract funds for salaries of students, full-time professional assistants and nontenured faculty members such as instructors and assistant professors engaged in sponsored projects. Policies with regard to charging the salaries of tenured faculty to research contracts differ widely and are a source of controversy within some institutions. A few universities do not require that project budgets provide for salary reimbursement for the time of a tenured faculty member.[60] A somewhat larger number of institutions accept project budgets which provide for sponsor payment of all or part of the time devoted to

---

regular salaries from research funds during the academic year. The circular also prohibits the practice of compensating for intra-university consultation except when approval is provided in the research agreement.

[60] At Harvard University, "the traditional policy . . . has been to pay no permanent Faculty member from short-term research funds; if Federal funds were to be cut off tomorrow, Harvard would be able to honor its commitments to all its permanent Faculty members." Harvard is certainly one of few, and may be the only, university to follow such a policy and there is uncertainty that the policy can be maintained since the source continues: "But in order to maintain the essential quality on which all the rest of Harvard's scientific and medical activities depend—the quality of her tenure professors—it may be necessary to experiment cautiously to achieve greater flexibility by paying tenure salaries from Federal funds in certain departments for whose fields of interest steady and continuous Federal support may be most confidently predicted for the future" ("Harvard and the Federal Government, a Report to the Faculties and Governing Boards," p. 69). See also "Twenty-six Campuses and the Federal Government," *The Educational Record*, vol. 44 (April 1963), p. 109.

the project by tenured faculty. Some institutions do so within certain limits such as the institution's ability to support all its tenured faculty should the need arise.[61] Most administrations no doubt follow the policy that "maximum relief to academic salary budgets should be included" in faculty proposals.[62]

Besides changing patterns of compensation, the development of policies relating to sponsored research has stimulated changes in the definitions of the obligations of a faculty member to his institution. Appointment to a faculty position is increasingly a matter of formal legal contracts rather than the traditional informal letters.[63] However, the services to be rendered by the faculty member have come to be less frequently defined by reference to institution-wide policy and more frequently established by negotiation. The work loads of faculty members have always been difficult to define and administrators have avoided such conventional performance yardsticks as hours per week since they clearly obtained more from an understanding that best effort would always be applied.[64] It is clear, however, that teaching loads vary widely between institutions and between schools and departments within an institution. While the twelve-hour teaching load remains fairly standard in the colleges, three to six hours are much more com-

[61] At Princeton, 37 percent of the tenure faculty members who participated in government-sponsored research in 1959–60 had some fraction of their salaries charged to project funds, and the percentage is growing (William G. Bowen, *The Federal Government and Princeton University* [Princeton University Press, 1962]; "Twenty-six Campuses and the Federal Government," p. 109).

[62] Raymond Ewell *et al.*, "Developing Effective Proposals for Submission by Institutions and Individual Faculty Members," p. 39. The Committee on Sponsored Research of the American Council on Education in "Recommendations on Faculty Salaries Charged to Government Contracts" (1963) expressed its belief that "it is sound policy to regard the pro-rated portion of the salaries of faculty members working on such grants or contracts as a proper direct cost of research, and we believe that the Government should pay the full costs of the research work it sponsors in colleges and universities."

The practice of paying tenured faculty salaries from project funds is best established in the medical schools. In 1960–61, almost a third of all full-time members of medical school faculties received at least part of their salaries from federal project funds (*Journal of the American Medical Association*, Nov. 11, 1961, p. 633). See also Orlans, *The Effects of Federal Programs on Higher Education*, p. 121.

[63] Tyrus Hillway, "When Hiring Professors," *College and University Business*, vol. 26 (February 1959), p. 27.

[64] The numerous difficulties in defining the work load of university faculty members are well illustrated in Kevin Bunnell (ed.), *Faculty Work Load: A Conference Report* (American Council on Education, 1960).

mon in the universities. Leaves of absence from teaching in order to spend full time on research are also frequent.

Compensation practices continue to change. Many institutions now offer twelve-month employment contracts instead of, or as an alternative to, the traditional nine- or ten-month contract.[65] The shift to the twelve-month contract places the university in control over all of a faculty member's time and hence permits greater uniformity in faculty compensation policies. Summer and vacation periods do not provide extra income, reducing the pressure upon the faculty member to secure summer grants though the expectation that he may do so may remain.

Policies toward Sponsored Research

By exercising controls over funds provided by research sponsors, the university can establish and apply its own policy regarding participation in such research. The necessity for some policy follows from the pressures toward expansion inherent in the growth of the funds available, the initiative of faculty members, and the research process itself, but also more specifically from the necessity for some combination of research and training as a characteristic of the university situation.

Activities supported by funds available from outside sponsors might—many would say that they have—set the institution off upon an unguided drift with faculty reaction to the opportunities provided by federal agencies the only determinant of goals and methods. But federal funds might also be employed to meet identified institutional needs within a framework of planned objectives. Some institutions have established limited and specific objectives while others have looked upon whatever federal research grants or funds might be available as a source of growth—an attractive prospect to many institutions, given the highly competitive relationships between universities and the limitation on funds available from other sources.

Institutional growth from sponsored research rests upon the willingness of sponsoring agencies to recognize normal faculty salaries—in full or in part—as a legitimate charge against grants or con-

[65] The Committee on Sponsored Research of the American Council on Education, cited in note 62, recommended the twelve-month employment contract as "ideal" for "all faculty members carrying on scholarly work throughout the calendar year."

tracts. That willingness followed from agency recognition that part-time research could not support the rapid progress desired and it was encouraged by the desire of faculty members to pursue promising projects on the fullest possible scale. It is clear that the present level of university research activity could not have been reached if federal funds were not generally available to permit faculty members to supervise staffs of full-time assistants and associates and themselves periodically to devote a major part of their time to their projects.

While institutional growth is a product of a positive faculty recruitment and promotion policy it occurs also as a natural product of the research process. That process has been described as follows:

"Professor A at University Y applies for funds to carry on a project in this area although he may be the only one in the school with interests in it, and these interests may have been furthered by the availability of the federal funds. He employs several research assistants. They are paid for aiding Professor A on the project, and in the process obtain advanced degrees. One of the assistants is very capable. He is taken on the staff as an instructor or even assistant professor. He, too, applies for support for the same type of work and before long University Y has a strong department in the particular area."[66]

The description is accurate though incomplete in that it does not take into account the problems of the university. It is accurate if the institution has available uncommitted funds which it can apply to salaries as an investment in the possibility of securing grant support and if it has the physical facilities necessary to an expansion of research activities in the particular area. Within such limits, the process is that of normal growth for a research-oriented institution.

Problems arise when the university is faced with making permanent additions to its faculty or when additional physical facilities are needed to house expanding research personnel. To return to the illustration cited, the added man in a few years under normal university procedures becomes eligible for a permanent tenured appointment. The university then faces the necessity of providing for such an appointment, recommending to the man that he go

[66] National Science Foundation, *Government-University Relationships in Federally Sponsored Scientific Research and Development* (1958), pp. 17–18.

elsewhere, or offering him a nontenured appointment. There will be reluctance to lose a successful researcher, perhaps an important member of a team. It is clear that in deciding among the numerous competitors for uncommitted funds, university administrators have frequently found persuasive the possibility of adding to the university's activities those of which the university will have to meet only a fraction of the cost. If even a minimal teaching appointment cannot be made, an increasing practice in recent years has been to offer a nonfaculty, nontenured appointment. Such appointments clearly recognize the source and nature of the funds which support the researcher. At the same time, however, the university creates a class of employees who are qualified to be faculty members, who are paid as well if not better than the teaching faculty member, but who do not have the privileges and status associated with faculty membership. These people constitute a new and separate class of personnel not readily absorbed into the traditional university community.[67]

There are also risks, particularly since the universities in supporting the principles of academic freedom have traditionally felt a sense of obligation to their faculty members quite different from that which is characteristic of other institutions. The university is responsible for expenditures—under grants—which government auditors may determine after the fact to be unallowable. Government programs may change. Although it is rare and unusual, grants and contracts may be terminated at the convenience of the government.[68] Much more important is the fact that a faculty member may fail to secure new or renewed grants. In a rapidly growing scientific area such risks are relatively small, particularly when assessed in the light of the growing number of students and

[67] Some institutions apply to research personnel the same policies applied to teaching faculty, that is, appointment to a tenured position or termination within a stated number of years. This is Harvard's policy. Other institutions apply policies to full-time research personnel which are clearly different from the standard policies applied to faculty.

[68] Many university administrators will long remember the brief but disturbing crisis of 1957 that followed the Air Force's stop-work orders on university projects as part of an effort to cut down defense spending; see George A. W. Boehm, "The Pentagon and the Research Crisis," *Fortune* (February 1958), pp. 135 ff. The House Government Operations Committee expressed its disapproval of the DOD action in *Research and Development (Office of the Secretary of Defense)*, H. Rept. 2552, 85 Cong. 2 sess. (1958), pp. 35–41.

of other employment opportunities. The possibility of change in the funds available constitutes a hazard which some institutions have judged to be high and which others have for all practical purposes ignored.[69]

Contractual Terms for Researchers

The efforts of university administrators to apply some internal controls over sponsored research have been paralleled by efforts to establish contractual terms that would permit satisfactory working relationships. From the beginning of sponsored research programs, the universities found objectionable the efforts of some of the military agencies to apply to university research the same procedures and controls that were utilized in procurement contracts with industry. Such practices contrasted sharply with the easy relationships established by OSRD. These problems were ironed out by negotiations between the government and representatives of the universities as the agencies were able to establish new procedures.[70] A set of problems which have remained for a longer time a source of irritation to both parties related to costs that were

[69] While some data on project renewals is available from some government agencies, there is little information with regard to the continuity of sponsor support of principal investigators. One study of ONR contracts in the field of psychology concludes that ONR made "a better showing both in terms of longevity and annual dollar amount than local institutional support can probably make" (John G. Darley, "The Impact of Federal Support on Higher Education," *American Psychologist,* vol. XIV [August 1959], p. 484, citing the same author's "Psychology and the Office of Naval Research: A Decade of Development," *American Psychologist,* vol. 12 [1957], pp. 305–23). Over the twenty years of its operation there have been innumerable warnings against the uncertainty and capriciousness of federal contractual relations with the universities. It is, of course, inherent in the project system that there be terminations following technical appraisals of programs and projects. Except for the abortive 1957 Air Force episode, there has been no agency or government-wide reduction in contractual research with the universities.

[70] Difficulties between the Army and the universities led to the establishment in 1948 of the Advisory Committee on Contractual and Administrative Procedures for Research and Development for the Department of the Army, with its chairman, Robert B. Stewart, vice-president and comptroller of Purdue University. Its *Report,* issued October 15, 1948, was influential in establishing better relationships. The universities have been represented on a number of subsequent committees concerned with contractual relationships, working frequently through the American Council on Education. Currently, university administrative officials seem satisfied with the operations of the administering agencies. See survey data compiled by the House Select Committee on Government Research in *Statistical Review of Research and Development,* H. Rept. 1940, 88 Cong. 2 sess. (1964), p. 127.

properly contractual costs, including particularly reimbursement to the university of indirect costs which could appropriately be assigned to contractual projects. One source of difficulty was the very wide variety of practices pursued by the universities in computing indirect costs. While problems remain, a *modus operandi* was established in successive negotiations between the American Council on Education and the agencies. The guidelines were embodied in a circular of the Bureau of the Budget which provided all agencies with a standard procedure for determining allowable costs and for computing overhead.[71]

Grants vs. Contracts

Before 1950 virtually all federally sponsored project research performed by universities was for the Navy, Army, or AEC under fixed-price or cost-reimbursement contracts which varied in their provisions for overhead costs. Only the relatively small NIH program used the grant form of contract. Over the next decade, the grant-contract became highly important, accounting for about half of all federal expenditures for university research. The major factors were the growth of NIH programs and the establishment of the NSF and the expansion of its programs. Both operated through grants which provided for limited reimbursement of indirect costs. The scientists who supported the formation of NSF advocated the grant form since they sought funds as free as possible of such bureaucratic restrictions as reporting requirements. A plausible case could be made for distinguishing between the grant as applied by NIH and the contract as the latter has been applied by some agencies, particularly the Army in its early university research program. Given the prospect of limited funds, the scientists argued that all such funds should be used for research itself and they therefore opposed any but nominal payments to their institutions for the use of facilities.[72]

It was not fully recognized at the time that the changes made in

---

[71] Bureau of the Budget, "Principles for Determining Costs Applicable to Research and Development under Grants and Contracts with Educational Institutions," Circular No. A-21 (1958). The circular was incorporated in the Armed Services Procurement Regulations.

[72] On reasons why scientists opposed overhead cost allowances, see, for example, Frederick R. Furth in *Proceedings of the Conference on the Administration of Research* (New York University Press, 1955), p. 15.

federal procurement statutes and practices offered the possibility of making the contract a very flexible instrument and that the ONR was employing the research contract in a manner that aroused few if any objections. Instead, attention was focused on devising a method whereby the government could make funds available to scientists for work in exploratory or basic research but with a minimum of other restrictions. The grant, long used by private philanthropic foundations, was such a device. Its use had been suggested in the report of the President's Scientific Research Board which advocated grants for university research, defining grants as "a gift made to individuals or institutions whose competence has been demonstrated for the purpose of an investigation, whose outcome cannot be known precisely in advance."[73] To some degree, Congress appeared then and since to accept the concept of a grant as a gift. The conceptual differences between contract and grant appear to rest in some part upon a distinction between the clearly defined *quid pro quo* characteristics of normal procurement and the disposition of government property as a gift.[74] This distinction led Congress to restrict the grant-making authority to designated agencies until 1958 when the authority to make grants was extended to all agencies having authority to contract for R&D.[75] The Congress also thought of the grant as suitable only to nonprofit organizations, objecting to NIH's use of the grant in dealing with business firms.[76] The concept of the grant as a gift is

[73] John R. Steelman, chairman of the President's Scientific Research Board, in *Science and Public Policy*, vol. I (1947), p. 50.

[74] Congressional authority to procure rests upon Art. I of the Constitution; its power to dispose of property, upon Art. IV, sec. 3. This distinction is made in Interdepartmental Committee on Scientific Research and Development, *Report on Grants and Research Contracts* (Government Printing Office, 1950), pp. 6–7. Alan T. Waterman, director of the NSF, was the chief witness supporting the extension of grant-making authority. See *Science and Technology Act of 1958*, Hearings before the Senate Committee on Government Operations, 85 Cong. 2 sess. (1958), pt. 2, p. 309.

[75] P.L. 85–934 (1958), 72 Stat. 1793 (1958).

[76] Because of its limited authority to contract for research, the National Institutes of Health has made some use of the grant in dealing with profit-making institutions. Such use was criticized by the House Government Operations Committee (see its second report, *Health Research and Training*, H. Rept. 321, 87 Cong. 1 sess. [1961], pp. 45–46). Contracts were used under the delegation of authority available to the General Services Administrator and authority inferred from portions of the annual Department of Health, Education, and Welfare appropriations act (see *Government and Science*, Hearings before the House Committee on Science and Astronautics, 88 Cong. 2 sess. [1964], pp. 128–29). In 1965 NIH was given the authority, under

also a partial explanation of the congressional insistence upon limitations on reimbursement for overhead costs then attached to grants. Such limitations are a form of cost-sharing, a principle that is a common though not universal condition of federal grants-in-aid to state and local governments.

The difficulty of anticipating the evolution of federal programs and the inability to appreciate the full significance of changing federal policy toward research contributed to other efforts to rationalize a distinction between the grant and the contract.[77] Thus, efforts have been made to use different systems to finance research which an institution would do anyway, or was particularly anxious to do, and work inspired chiefly by agency wishes. If the initiative came from the university (or a faculty member), an agency-rendered support and a cost-sharing arrangement, whether by grant or contract, was appropriate. If the agency took the initiative, the relationship was one of procurement and required a contract.[78]

P.L. 89–115 (Health Research Facilities Amendments of 1965), to contract for research utilized by the military departments. However, such authority was limited to the fiscal years 1966–68, the Congress indicating that it intended a careful review of the use of the contract before considering an extension of the time limitation.

[77] On the legal differences between grants and contracts, see John W. Whelan, "New Federal Support for Basic Scientific Research," *Journal of Public Law*, vol. 8 (1959), pp. 462–98; Ellis A. Richardson, "Methods of Supporting Basic Research," *Federal Bar Journal*, vol. 17 (1957), p. 281; George Glocker, "The Contractual versus the Giant Approach to Basic Research Activities," *Federal Bar Journal*, vol. 17 (1957), pp. 265–78; Leroy Kahn, "The Lawyer and the Scientific Community—Procuring Basic Research," *Law and Contemporary Problems*, vol. 29 (Spring 1964), pt. II, pp. 631–46. For an NIH analysis of the differences between grants and contracts which also defends the grant form, see *Government and Science,* Hearings, pp. 128–31.

[78] The distinction between the procurement and the support of research had its origins in the debate over the National Science Foundation. In its first published study of federal scientific programs, the National Science Foundation attempted to develop a distinction between "purchased" and "supported" research and development in more detail. The report suggested that "agencies of the Federal Government have two main objectives in sponsoring scientific research and development at nonprofit institutions. They may be seeking scientific knowledge which will assist them in carrying out assigned programs. Or they may be augmenting the general fund of scientific knowldege as a matter of public interest. When motivated by the first of these purposes, the Government is, in effect, 'purchasing' research and development services. Although the specialized nature of the commodity, the purposeful production of new knowledge, may soften or blur the character of the negotiation, the relationship between Government and the institution is in essence that of buyer and seller. On the other hand, when the purpose is simply to increase scientific knowledge, the Government is providing financial 'support' for a type of activity which is in the general public interest." While acknowledging the difficulties of ap-

Such distinctions can exist only because of confusion regarding the role of basic research within an overall R&D policy and uncertainty regarding the role of university research. If research, whether classified as basic or applied, is recognized for its contribution to the stock of knowledge on which all other R&D is based, it follows that research is selected for support from limited funds, not in terms of who wants it done, but in terms of some set of priorities reflecting an evaluation of the alternatives that exist at any one time to further a program. The distinction made seems to establish a difference between research that is clearly in the public interest and other research which is less so, whereas the meaningful distinction is the use of public funds to secure the benefits of research judged to be in the public interest as that has been determined in the programming process.

The effort to apply to federal operations the concept of the grant as a gift did not succeed. Instead the grant became a legal instrument describing a *quid pro quo* in language that could

---

plying the distinction, the report suggested that the programs of the Department of Agriculture in making payments to state agricultural experiment stations, the grant program of NIH, the contract research programs of ONR, and the research support program of NSF were of the "support" character. These in 1951–52 amounted to slightly more than 20 percent of federal research expenditures with nonprofit institutions (National Science Foundation, *Federal Funds for Science*, vol. 1, pp. 10–11).

The military services made no significant effort to implement this distinction. However, the Atomic Energy Commission distinguished between two kinds of research: "(*a*) Basic research to solve a particular problem such as one dealing with reactor design or isotope separation. The Commission seeks the services of specific scientists under these contracts and usually pays the full costs. (*b*) Basic research of the typical university sort, undertaken to add to the general fund of knowledge applicable to atomic energy development. The Commission shares research costs of these projects to an extent arrived at by negotiation" (U. S. Atomic Energy Commission, *Atomic Energy and the Physical Sciences*, Seventh Semiannual Report [1950], pp. 151–52). The Interdepartmental Committee on Scientific Research and Development made a similar distinction (American Council on Education, *Sponsored Research Policy of Colleges and Universities*, Report of the Committee on Institutional Policy [1954], p. 65).

NASA's policy is to pay full cost. The agency distinguishes between solicited research projects which are funded by contracts and unsolicited projects which may be funded either by grant or by contract. The grant is considered the ideal instrument "when the defined element is the annual level of support, and the actual research accomplishments are impossible to define in advance." When "a definite set of specifications must be met by a particular date . . . the uncertainty of cost must be recognized and the ideal instrument is a contract that defines clearly the requirements but leaves the actual cost as an estimated variable" (*Government and Science, Hearings*, pp. 57, 59).

range from the very liberal to the very restrictive. In current use
the grant is a simplified type of procurement contract used principally by NIH and NSF for any type of research done within nonprofit organizations. As administered by those two agencies, the
award of a grant follows upon the selection of a proposal from
among those submitted for consideration. The grant is made in
the expectation that the work proposed will add to knowledge and
that the recipient will conscientiously do the research as described
in his work proposal and budget. The work to be done is described in broad terms and the investigator is left free to make
changes, although restrictions increasingly limit his authority to
deviate from the allocation of funds in his budget.

In legal form the grant is simpler than the standard contract.
Payments are made in advance of the work without the submission
of vouchers though evidence of expenditure must be retained for
audit purposes.[79] Grants are audited less frequently than contracts
and the audits have in practice been limited to the determination
that the funds have been used for the designated project. Disallowances of expenditures have been made on some occasions, however, and the institution is then responsible for restitution. The
usual reporting requirements are minimal: they call for semi-an-
nual accounting as to expenditures, and annual and terminal reports as to research progress and results. Termination is at the initiative of the agency after consultation with the grantee, but does
not affect firm financial commitments already made. Typically the
grant requires that the work be done under the supervision of the
designated principal investigator. Like contracts, grants are subject
by reference to all the terms and conditions established by the
agency.[80] Until 1958 title to equipment was readily transferred

[79] The lump sum prepayment policy is now being discarded in favor of periodic
payments or drawings against letters of credit. The change in procedure follows
from a GAO disclosure of and congressional objection to the fact that lump sum
prepayment permitted the universities to secure income by investing such funds.
Since many research and development contracts with industrial firms and universities as well provide for periodic progress payments, differences between grants and
contracts in this area have become minor (see *Government and Science*, Hearings,
pp. 261–72).

[80] NSF grant letters include the statement that the "grant be administered
in accordance with the Foundation's policies governing research grants as stated in
its publication, *Grants for Scientific Research*" (various dates). Typical NIH grants
include a similar reference to the applicability of all provisions in its 146-page
Grants Manual.

under grants but very difficult under contracts. That distinction has also been removed.[81]

All these characteristics of grants can be and have been closely approximated in the administration of contracts. The work statement of a contract can be written so as to leave the researcher with as much freedom as is possible under a grant. The number of controls applied to the grant have increased steadily so that from the points of view of both performer and administrator few differences remain.[82]

In 1966 the Bureau of the Budget's study of *The Administration of Government Supported Research at Universities* declared that "the traditional and practical distinction between the grant and the contract has now disappeared."[83] The study recommended that a new standard instrument, which it termed a research agreement, should be developed to replace the contract or grant for most purposes.[84] This research agreement would consist of a cover-

[81] In 1958 Congress passed S. 4039 which provided contracting agencies authority to transfer title to equipment to universities.

[82] The American Council on Education pointed out in 1955, "Now many grants contain a variety of conditions which have been associated traditionally only with contracts, such as the right of termination, patent provisions, requirements for prior approval, limitations on publication, and periodic reports. Consequently, the traditional distinctions between contracts and grants to some extent have disappeared" (*College and University Administration*, vol. II [1955], pp. 129–30). More recently, Howard P. Wile, executive director of the Committee on Governmental Relations of the National Association of College and University Business Officers, has asserted categorically that "the grant is in every sense of the word a contract" ("Federal Research Grants Can Bury Your Budget in the Underground Overhead," *College and University Business*, vol. 40 [March 1960], p. 71). And a government research administrator pointed out that "as a result of the evolution of contract and grant . . . it seems clear that the fluidity of the research relationships depends more upon administrative attitudes than it does upon the form of legal instrument used" (George Glocker, "The Contractual versus the Grant Approach . . . ," p. 279). See also James McCormack and Vincent A. Fulmer, "Federal Sponsorship of University Research," in the American Assembly, *The Federal Government and Higher Education* (Prentice-Hall, 1960), p. 81; and Raymond J. Woodrow, "Grants vs. Contracts," *Industrial Research*, vol. 6 (April 1964).

[83] Bureau of the Budget, *The Administration of Government Sponsored Research at Universities* (March 1966), p. 2. For an earlier discussion of the desirability of the "research agreement," see Leroy Kahn, "The Lawyer and the Scientific Community —Procuring Basic Research, *Law and Contemporary Problems*, Spring 1964, p. 643.

[84] The exceptions, requiring the standard cost-reimbursement or fixed-price contract, were those calling for a specific service or piece of hardware, for research directed toward the solution of a specific operating problem of the agency, where the agency finds it necessary to exercise close control over objectives, direction, specifications, costs, methods, or scheduling or where the research is classified (Bureau of

ing document specifying the contractual relationship in general terms and recognizing the special requirements for the effective conduct of university research. Supplementary statements would describe and provide for the funding of specific tasks or projects.

The Problem of Overhead Costs

There remains to be noted a financial difference between grants and contracts which is to many university administrators the only important distinction. While both grants and contracts might provide for payment of all direct costs until 1966, the contract provides for payment of all indirect costs as they may be negotiated, whereas the grant provides for payment of such costs as a statutory fixed percentage of the direct costs.

Fundamental to the concept of the grant as it has evolved is the willingness and capacity of the recipient institution to meet a share of the cost. If the university has unused capacity to house and equip research projects and to provide administrative services, the grant has usually been acceptable to university officials since it supplements their resources. However, if all resources are fully utilized, acceptance of a grant means that the institution must supply the necessary facilities and services. The university must then divert its resources to support the sponsored research, resources for which there are usually many other important uses.

University administrators evidenced little concern with such problems as long as the funds available involved merely a more intensive use of existing staff and facilities. The growth of funds made available under federal grants had long since passed that point. But, as funds mounted and as the prestige of research activity rose and was accepted by more faculty members, the universities with increasing frequency found their faculties requesting approval of projects which required the university to commit funds for the necessary facilities. To the degree that statutory limits on payments of indirect costs fall short of actual institutional costs, the grant operates as a cost-sharing arrangement which calls upon the recipient institution to provide physical facilities and supporting services with only partial reimbursement. One reaction on the part of many university administrators has been the development

the Budget, *The Administration of Government Sponsored Research at Universities* (March 1966), p. 3).

of a strong preference for contracts, and resistance to efforts to extend the use of grants.[85]

University administrators have also made strong efforts to secure full-cost reimbursement and have found considerable support from congressional committees concerned with research programs. The statutory limitation on overhead reimbursement under grants has been regularly increased from 15 percent paid by NSF prior to 1955 and 8 percent paid by NIH before 1957 to 20 percent in 1964. Because the circumstances of the universities, their accounting practices, and the needs of particular projects differ widely, the actual costs are subject to uncertainty and debate. Some projects in some institutions incur indirect costs below the statuory ceiling, but for participating universities in general, indirect costs exceed payments. One estimate places the gap between government overhead payments on grants and the costs to the universities at $40 million in 1964.[86] Since there are few if any differences between contracts and grants as they have been administered, and since indirect costs are reasonably satisfactorily handled under contracts, the statutory limitation on indirect costs of grants is an historical anomaly which has, as Congress sees it, served no purpose beyond bringing about slightly more research.[87] In the process, the government infringes upon the ability of the universities to perform functions not supported by federal funds.

[85] In passing P.L. 85–934 (1958) the hope was expressed in Congress that a substantial number of research projects would be transferred from contractual to grant form. The largest agency involved, the Defense Department, made substantial efforts in that direction but after some initial success met such resistance that its directives were amended to provide that either the grant or contract could be used, depending upon university preference. See "Attachment A, Department of Defense," from a report of the General Accounting Office, in *Government and Science*, Hearings, p. 276.

[86] The National Science Foundation, in *Indirect Costs of Research and Development in Colleges and Universities, Fiscal Year 1960*, estimated that in 1962 the colleges and universities would contribute $36 million to meet the differences between their indirect costs and the allowance made by the government. The higher estimate ($40 million) was made by Vincent Shea, comptroller of the University of Virginia, appearing as a representative of the Association of State Universities and Land-Grant Colleges, in *Government and Science*, Hearings, p. 577.

[87] The House Appropriations Committee in its report on the 1958 appropriations observed that holding to the existing statutory overhead allowance "will free $6,963,000 earmarked in the budget for overhead and will make it available for additional research" (H. Rept. 217, 85 Cong. 1 sess. [1957], pp. 17–18). The committee held to this position until 1965. See note 90 below.

University administrators on numerous occasions urged that the statutory limitations on overhead costs be eliminated. From time to time they found support from the agencies, the Executive Office, the GAO, the legislative committees of Congress, and others.[88] In 1964, the Daddario subcommittee reviewed the problem and recommended that the percentage limitations on overhead costs be dropped and that the Bureau of the Budget's regulations covering contracts be applied to grants.[89] It also offered its endorsement of "the concept of encouraging universities to share a portion of the costs of research projects where the university has a strong self-interest in the project," with the qualification that "cost-sharing should be agreed upon and understood in advance by all parties involved in the research agreement. . . ."[90] In 1965, the President recommended "that the Congress remove its restrictions on payments to universities for indirect costs of research grants."[91]

In 1965 the House Appropriations Committee abandoned restrictions on reimbursements of overhead costs and in its place established a "cost-sharing" principle, reasserting its view that the universities should contribute to the cost of research under the grant form.[92] The Congress left to the agencies the determination

[88] See the discussion of the problem in Charles V. Kidd, *American Universities and Federal Research* (Harvard University Press, 1959), chap. 5.

[89] It should be noted that the Bureau of the Budget favored cost-sharing "because it encourages universities to take some definite interest in the research to be undertaken. Furthermore, it has been traditional for universities to permit their senior faculty members to engage in research for a significant portion of their working time and some contribution of this sort should continue to be expected" (*Government and Science*, Hearings, p. 315).

[90] House Committee on Science and Astronautics, *Indirect Costs under Federal Research Grants*, Government and Science No. 5, 88 Cong. 2 sess. (1964), p. 41. Congressman Daddario personally presented the subcommittee report to the Subcommittee on Independent Offices of the House Appropriations Committee (*Independent Offices Appropriations for 1966*, pp. 884–91). The problem had been explored a few years earlier by the House Government Operations Committee, in *Payment of Indirect Costs of R&D by Colleges and University Contractors*, Hearings on H.R. 6984, 87 Cong. 2 sess. (1962).

[91] "Budget Message of the President," in *The Budget of the United States Government, 1966* (1965), p. 25.

[92] *Departments of Labor, and Health, Education, and Welfare, and Related Agencies Appropriations Bill, 1966*, H. Rept. 272, 89 Cong. 1 sess. (1965), p. 56, and P.L. 89–156. The same provision was applied to the DOD and NSF appropriations (P.L. 89–213 and P.L. 89–128). The committee report on HEW appropriations indicated that it was strongly influenced by the discussion of the indirect cost problem in the report of the NIH study committee chaired by Dean E. Wooldridge (*Biomedical*

of the amount of sharing to be required and it fell to the Bureau of the Budget to develop uniform guidelines. These guidelines, which appeared in the Bureau's Circular No. A-74, sought again to draw distinctions between research projects on the basis of their character and the motivations of the parties. The guidelines suggest that "a higher degree of cost participation should ordinarily exist when the cost of research consists primarily of the efforts of senior faculty during the academic year, or when the grantee institution's long-range interests are best served by substantial cost participation." However, "Cost participation should generally be lower when a major portion of the research costs consists of equipment, when the grant provides for a large component of services to be made available on a regional or national basis, or when, in the view of a federal agency, an area of research requires a special stimulus in the national interest." The circular instructed the agencies that cost-sharing "was to be more than a token" but did not suggest specific percentages. The agencies and the performing institutions were left with the task of negotiating the specific amount to be shared. Such sharing might be within the range of 1 to 5 percent, the figures suggested in the Appropriations Committee's discussion.

In application cost-sharing has had considerable impact upon universities. Since the university must demonstrate that it is meeting the cost-sharing requirement for each and every project supported by grant funds, research investigators must report their time and the university must provide data and analysis indicating its compliance.[93] It is possible that universities must make a larger financial contribution than had been true earlier, particularly since cost-sharing higher than the legal requirement in the case of a specific project cannot be applied to other projects. The American Council on Education in 1967 called for a "wholesale review"

Science and Its Administration [1965]). The Wooldridge report had suggested that, if less than full costs were to be paid, a cost-sharing fraction applying to all costs was preferable to a limitation on indirect costs. The House committee report also cited the suggestion in the Wooldridge report that "if the grantee institution must spend some of its own money it is more likely that it will propose only worthwhile research, and that it will supervise it adequately and conduct it economically" (*ibid.,* p. 52). The House committee ignored the observation of the Wooldridge committee that "we recognize no essential difference between a 'contract' and a 'grant' as the term is used by NIH" (*ibid.,* p. 29).

[93] Wile, "Federal Research Grants Can Bury Your Budget . . . ," p. 72.

of these and other fiscal relationships between the government and higher education charging that the effect of the cost-sharing policies has been to increase the concentration of federal funds in those institutions able to provide the funds needed, that those funds are drawn away from other important programs, and that the matching funds needed are being raised by increased charges to students.[94]

There is widespread agreement that in spite of many problems the net effect of federal programs upon the universities as a whole, and upon their teaching and research activities, has been highly favorable.[95] However, university administrators can correctly urge that the application of the cost-sharing principle imposes responsibilities upon them without commensurate control and that the ef-

[94] American Council on Education, *The Federal Investment in Higher Education: The Need for a Sustained Commitment* (1967), pp. 12–16. See also the Council's *Higher Education and National Affairs,* vol. 16 (Feb. 18, 1967), p. 3.

[95] The appraisal by administrative offices of participating universities regarding the impact of federal funds upon faculty research activities is unanimously favorable. See, among numerous others, those in "Twenty-six Campuses and the Federal Government," *The Educational Record,* vol. 44 (April 1963), pp. 106–8; Grayson Kirk, "University Research—Testimony on Federal Aid to Education," *Columbia University Forum,* vol. 7 (Winter 1964), pp. 38–47; Leo S. Tonkin, "Federal Research and the Universities," *Johns Hopkins Magazine,* October 1964, pp. 4–32. Generally overall favorable opinions are expressed in testimony in hearings before the House Select Committee on Government Research, *Federal Research and Development Programs,* 88 Cong. 1 and 2 sess. (1963–64), summarized in pt. 3, pp. 1161–62. Also generally favorable were several more elaborate surveys conducted by two House committees in 1965: *Conflicts between the Federal Research Programs and the Nation's Goals for Higher Education,* Hearings before the House Committee on Government Operations, 89 Cong. 1 sess. (June 1965), and *Responses from the Academic and Other Interested Communities to an Inquiry by the Research and Technical Programs Subcommittee,* H. Rept. 1158, concluding with a committee report, 89 Cong. 1 sess. (1965), pts. 1 and 2; and a study by the House Science and Astronautics Committee which was based upon a report of the National Science Foundation, published as *Higher Education in the Sciences in the United States* (1965).

There are, however, dissenters, principally concerned with the "overemphasis" on the grounds that the result is teaching of inadequate quality with deleterious effects on the forthcoming generation of prospective research manpower. A particularly important aspect of this problem is the inability of the liberal arts colleges to compete for faculty because of their very limited ability to provide research opportunities in those subject areas which are of principal research interest to the government. See John Gardner, *The Flight from Teaching* (Carnegie Foundation for the Advancement of Teaching, 1965); "The Liberal Arts College Struggles To Overcome a Shortage of Qualified Teachers," *New York Times,* Jan. 16, 1964; "College Controversy," *Wall Street Journal,* Dec. 28, 1964.

fect is to weaken the university in discharging its mission of supporting research in areas of knowledge which Congress does not find of interest.

The issue is, therefore, a fundamental one which reflects differences in understanding of the government-university relationship. Many congressmen and government officials view the relationship as one in which the government "supports" the universities in performing a function they should undertake in any case.[96] While that view is also held among many university scientists, virtually all university administrators take the position that the grant, like the conventional contract, purchases the effort of a faculty member selected by the government agency. Since any expenditure "supports" the recipient institution, the universities are not "supported" in any way that differs from the support industrial firms receive under procurement contracts. In this view the universities are, in fact, discriminated against to the degree that they are asked to meet part of the cost.

The University in a Research-minded World

The government's programs have been very successful in activating a capacity to conduct research which the limited resources available to the universities had long left under-utilized. It has made it possible for an increasing number of institutions to achieve the ideal of a graduate school faculty effectively intermingling teaching and research. The government's programs have been pursued in such manner as to avoid infringement upon academic freedom.[97]

There can be no question that the system described has been effective in increasing the nation's research efforts and its research capabilities. It has successfully drawn many thousands of the most

[96] Charles V. Kidd distinguishes between purchase and support in terms of agency motivations but recognizes that the grant or the contract can be used for either purpose. Kidd argues that there is a fundamental distinction and that it should be preserved but does not suggest how this might be accomplished (*American Universities and Federal Research*, pp. 5–9).

[97] Warnings of a threat to academic freedom have been frequent, but there is an absence of evidence of violations resulting from federal actions; see Charles V. Kidd, "The Implications of Research Funds for Academic Freedom," *Law and Contemporary Problems*, vol. 28 (Summer 1963), pp. 613–24. However, warnings are renewed as new types of programs are contemplated; see Harold Orlans, *The Effects of Federal Programs on Higher Education*, p. 294.

highly trained minds into participating in an organized process of identifying opportunities for increasing knowledge. It has retained, in large degree, the small unit of research performance—the faculty member and a small group of assistants—as the basic investigating unit, operating within the rich intellectual environment of a university. It permits periods of full-time research, if the university approves, or offers the stimulation that many find in a part-time teaching situation. The numerous graduate students involved constitute the nation's source of new creative manpower, contributing also to the flow of new research proposals.[98] The product is an ever-increasing body of knowledge, made public through research reports published in the scientific and technical journals.

A striking characteristic of the system is the fact that, after preliminary work has been done but before it is undertaken on a larger scale, a large proportion of American research is subjected to evaluation for its scientific promise by men whose experience qualifies them to judge it. In the process projects are, to some degree, ranked in order of scientific promise and also by importance to the sponsoring agencies' objectives. Such evaluations are not primarily concerned with the avoidance of duplicating efforts, although identification of duplications is one result.[99] Any given problem frequently attracts numerous research efforts, and a wide variety of approaches is not only typically possible but desirable. Scientific opinion guides and appraises such efforts, whether they represent new research proposals or involve projects coming up for extension through requests for renewal of a contract.

The appraisal system supplies a valuable service to the researcher as well as to the nation, increasing the effectiveness of the

[98] Reports from 1,309 institutions and including all but 3 of the 100 largest universities doing research for the federal government disclose that, in 1963, 31,877 students received $43.5 million from employment on such research, an average of $1,366 per student employed. In that year federal agencies under all programs provided financial assistance to 232,288 college and university students in an amount of $224.8 million (House Select Committee on Government Research, *Federal Student Assistance in Higher Education*, Study Paper No. 5, H. Rept. 1933, 88 Cong. 2 sess. [1964], pp. 85–92).

[99] What Michael Polanyi has termed the "coordination by mutual adjustment of independent initiative" ("The Republic of Science," *Minerva*, vol. 1 [Autumn 1962], p. 54).

total research effort in that less promising projects fail to secure support. The possibility does exist that such evaluations will fail to provide support for projects which show imaginative insight beyond that possessed by the evaluators. The magnitude of financial support for scientific investigation would seem to reduce such a possibility, but it also increases the number of opportunities for decisions that time may prove to be erroneous.[100] The diffused nature of sources of support tends to ensure, although it cannot guarantee, that all meritorious ideas will receive the support desirable for their exploration. Both scientists and society are in some degree protected from arbitrary rejection of new ideas by the number of possible sources of support within the federal government, the private foundations, and the scientist's own institution. Ultimately, of course, the scientist's faith in his own idea is its best defense.

The impact of federal programs upon the universities, however, has been not only quantitatively substantial but also qualitatively important. By virtue of their access to federal project funds, scientists and engineers have in significant degree reshaped the nature and functions of the university to their own image and convenience. University administrators have for the most part been permissive and adaptive to the interests of the scientists.

Among the quantitative results have been a marked reduction in the teaching done by many faculty members, and an increase in numbers of faculty. A different sort of result has been the growth of professional staffs who are not members of the tenured faculty, who are employed to do research and who do little teaching. These changes have had effects upon the university's teaching services.

The teaching of graduate students has undoubtedly improved in quality. Charges are made that the quality of teaching offered un-

[100] "For scientific opinion may, of course, sometimes be mistaken, and, as a result unorthodox work of high originality and merit may be discouraged or altogether suppressed for a time. But these risks have to be taken. Only the discipline imposed by an effective scientific opinion can prevent the adulteration of science by cranks and dabblers. In parts of the world where no sound and authoritative scientific opinion is established, research stagnates for lack of stimulus, while unsound reputations grow up based on commonplace achievements or mere empty boasts" (Polanyi, "The Republic of Science," p. 61).

dergraduates in the liberal arts colleges of the large universities as well as in the independent colleges has declined although evidence on the problem is at best conflicting.[101]

It is claimed that the cohesiveness of the university as an institution has diminished as the interests and loyalties of the scientists have turned to their peer groups and to some extent to their sponsoring agencies.[102] The ability of some university administrators to

[101] The best available study is Orlans, *The Effects of Federal Programs on Higher Education.* Donald F. Hornig points out that the debate over the effect of federal research programs on the quality of undergraduate education takes contradictory forms: "On the one hand, it is felt that good undergraduate education can be given in institutions where creative minds are at work and scholarly activity goes forward, where the students can sense the pulse and thrust of important enterprise in motion. It is argued that institutions which do not carry on enough research cannot recruit the faculties to provide a first-class education. On the other hand, it is sometimes argued that within institutions in which advanced education and research are active, the faculties lose all interest in undergraduates and leave them to junior members of the faculty. Surely, both cannot be true, or if they are, we should be able to devise a better way of doing things" ("Universities and Federal Science Policies," *Science,* vol. 150 [Nov. 12, 1965], p. 848).

[102] The problem of diversity can be dismissed by picturing the multiversity as Clark Kerr does in *The Uses of the University* (Harvard University Press, 1963). James A. Perkins, on the other hand, is much concerned with maintaining the integrity of the university, which he views as maintaining "the coherence of its various parts, and the harmony with which it is able to pursue its aims—whatever their specialized nature." To Perkins, "the integrity of the university involves, then, a resistance to overexpansion of any of its three institutional functions, and the accompanying requirement that each institution will select its fields of specialization. Integrity involves, perhaps, even more importantly, an insistence that all of the university's activities advance its capabilities to pursue each of its missions" (*The University in Transition* [Princeton University Press, 1966], pp. 33, 49).

Some scientists see the problem as a serious one. Donald F. Hornig, for example, has written that he is "worried that, having freed the creative and talented investigator from the petty bureaucracy of the departmental tyrant, we have also helped to remove him from the university as a whole and have turned the science departments into a collection of feudal fiefs rather than organic wholes" ("Universities and Federal Science Policies," p. 848).

The Committee on Science and Public Policy of the National Academy of Sciences, expressing concern that graduate teaching might be becoming a " 'poor relation' to research in the university," identifies the difficulty as arising "from a lack of strong policy within the universities themselves" and suggests that "university administrations need courage to be far-sighted in maintaining a balance between teaching and research" (*Federal Support of Basic Research in Institutions of Higher Learning* [1964], p. 93). See also Frederick Seitz, "The University: Independent Institution or Federal Satellite?" in Keenan (ed.), *Science and the University,* pp. 149–61.

Russell I. Thackrey observes of the NAS report that "we have the interesting

guide the evolution of their institutions and to act upon the competing claims to their resources has declined. They have limited *de facto* control over federal research funds which frequently require the allocation of supporting university funds. Changes in the relationship of teaching and research functions and in the relationships between subject areas supported by federal funds and those which are not have made of the university a different institution than it was a few decades ago. Some of those differences are a necessary reaction to the higher priority now given to scientific research. Other changes may be a sacrifice of established values in the interests of objectives that are not necessarily as important to the university's services to society.

The unique role of the university is that of transmitting and disseminating knowledge. In that role it holds a monopoly on the issuance of the symbols of education, certifying to the trainability of its graduates. It shares with other institutions—such as business firms and government organizations, particularly the armed services—the functions of providing specialized training.[103] As the university has accepted broader responsibilities for the advancement and application of knowledge, it has undertaken to provide an institutional setting for activities that have in varying degrees and with varying success also been undertaken elsewhere.

The claim is frequently made that the university provides a superior environment for creative endeavor. Unqualified, this claim

---

spectacle of a distinguished committee of the NAS-NRC recently giving whole-hearted endorsement to a continuance of past emphasis on grants to *individual scientists* and in the same report calling on university administrators (*not* individual scientists and their organizations) to be more vigilant in discharging *their* responsibilities for seeing that the possible conflicts of interest of the individual inherent in present programs don't get out of hand." Thackrey continues: "One result of all this is that some in higher education who have favored the segmented approach to Federal support of activities as contrasted with broad general support, on the ground that it is 'less likely to lead to Federal control,' are finding that in fighting the shadow of Federal control they have lost the substance of institutional control. A national policy of fragmented support is, after all, still a policy, and its effect is fragmentation" ("National Organization in Higher Education," in *Autonomy and Interdependence: Emerging Systems in Higher Education* [American Council on Education, 1964], pp. 79–80).

[103] See Harold F. Clark, "Potentialities of Educational Establishments outside the Conventional Structure of Higher Education," in Dexter M. Keezer (ed.), *Financing Higher Education, 1960–70* (Mc-Graw-Hill Book Co., 1959), pp. 257–73, for a brief survey and bibliography.

cannot be defended on the basis of historical experience.[104] Historically, the American university has not been a major source of creativity in the arts, humanities, or engineering, whereas very important scientific contributions have been made by men affiliated with other types of organizations. That historic experience of course need not determine the future course of university development, but it does suggest that the university's role is limited and specific. The university is not the only, nor need it be the best type of, institution to accomplish any one of the nation's scientific and technical objectives. It is merely clear that the university is a preferred environment for many scientists, though by no means all, and that the reasons for that preference are of significance to the administration of research in other types of institutions.

It is clear also that the types of research appropriate to the university cannot be rigidly delimited but are determined by circumstances such as the presence or absence of men possessing the relevant interests and skills. The effort to distinguish between research appropriate to the university and research which is not by claiming for the university research of a "pure" character and leaving to other institutions that which is "applied" is deluding. Much research is classified in one or the other category not because of any intrinsic difference but because of the motivations of the parties involved.[105] The effort to identify certain research as appropriate to the university because it is related to teaching is also of limited applicability. Much effective teaching can be and is done by observing and integrating the research work of others. However, this is neither more nor less true in the teaching of an "applied" subject than it is in the teaching of a "pure" subject.[106] Moreover, the desirability of pursuing research of the pure type very frequently

[104] John A. Perkins, *Plain Talk from a Campus* (University of Delaware Press, 1959), p. 145; Norman Kaplan, "Organization: Will It Choke or Promote the Growth of Science?" in Karl Hill (ed.), *The Management of Scientists* (Beacon Press, 1964), p. 108.

[105] There is, of course, research undertaken solely for the sake of new knowledge and other research motivated by the hope that a problem will be solved. The distinction is of little administrative significance. Kuhn writes: "I submit that these definitions are now so watered down and ambiguous that they serve very few useful functions. They do serve primarily to confuse us, inasmuch as there are a host of values and attitudes attached to the terms which affect people's behavior and attitudes considerably" (*The Structure of Scientific Revolutions*, pp. 34–35).

[106] See Harold K. Work, "The University's Role in Research," *Research Management*, vol. 5 (January 1962), p. 18.

arises from efforts to achieve an application objective. The fact is that more than half of the research now being conducted in universities is classified as applied. A good deal of research conducted within universities is not distinguishable from that done in other institutions.[107] Some has no more significant relationship to teaching than the training functions frequently conducted in other institutions. It is obvious that teaching duties are in many cases a handicap to the accomplishment of research objectives.[108]

Given current priorities for research objectives the university may be expected to adjust to accommodate those research functions for which the university environment is clearly superior to that which can be supplied by other institutions. University-affiliated scientists have tended to make broad and sweeping claims for the superiority of the university environment. Increasingly, however, university-based research has been subject to criticism. Research, for example, has been criticized as failing to provide adequately for the continuum from basic research into application which is desirable if not necessary in many areas.[109] University research has been accused of confining itself unduly to "soluble" problems rather than important problems.[110] More difficult to deal

[107] See Harold Gershinowitz, "Industrial Research Programs and Academic Research," *American Scientist*, vol. 46 (1958), pp. 24–32.

[108] The point is obvious from the willingness if not the desire of many university investigators to devote themselves full time to their research. The British scientist, A. P. Rowe, writes that "pending an analysis of the sources of important progress in science, I will make the guess that the great reputation of universities for their scientific research work largely stems from their research institutes in which research comes first and lecturing is mostly of a specialist character" ("From Scientific Idea to Practical Use," *Minerva*, vol. 2 [1964], p. 311).

[109] The rapid growth of basic and applied research in industry in support of government development programs suggests the accuracy of General Leslie A. Simon's observation that "we are beginning to see that research and development and engineering should be put back together again in a single field of technology" ("A Continuum of Applied Science in the Corporation," *Research Management*, vol. 2 [1959], pp. 251–59). Cf. C. Wilson Randle, "Problems of R&D Management," *Harvard Business Review*, January-February 1959; Frederic DeHoffman, "Technology and American Business," in Aaron W. Warner *et al.* (eds.) *Impact of Science on Technology* (Columbia University Press, 1965), p. 92.

[110] Alvin M. Weinberg, "But Is the Teacher Also a Citizen?" in Boyd R. Keenan (ed.), *Science and the University*, p. 167. Dr. Weinberg's point is that the university is less able to overcome the barriers of its discipline-orientation than are mission-oriented institutions. See also Peter H. Rossi, "Researchers, Scholars, and Policy Makers: The Politics of Large Scale Research," *Daedalus*, vol. 93 (Fall 1964), pp. 1142–61.

with is the further assertion that the interests of university faculty members in the "pure" aspects of their fields stand in conflict with the interests of society as expressed by government and industry in application.[111] And at least some spokesmen for the independent nonprofit organizations believe that their type of institution will prove a more effective basis for some types of research than universities since "the critical goals of big science are incompatible with the educational goals to which the universities must aspire."[112]

Whatever the ultimate validity of these criticisms, they serve to point out that there are some types of research which are the special province of the universities, some types which may be equally well carried on by other types of institutions, and some for which other institutions are superior.

The special province of the university in research is the encouragement of research on problems which emerge from and are integrated with the teaching process. Such research reflects the university's function of providing opportunity for the free exploration of whatever frontier of knowledge suggests itself to the faculty-investigator or arouses the interest of the graduate student. This freedom to take the initiative in exploring an unknown is a special characteristic of research in the university environment.[113] Such research is free of controls other than the hoped-for approbation of the investigator's peers. It is financed by the university's release of faculty time from other assignments.

In supporting research of the type mentioned, the university provides the resources for preliminary exploration of research

[111] Alvin M. Weinberg, for example, charges the university scientists with snobbishness in emphasizing pure and avoiding applied research and charges that one result is a lag in civilian technology ("Government, Education, Technology," in Aaron W. Warner, *et al.* (eds.), *Impact of Science on Technology* [Columbia University Press, 1965], pp. 66–70). See also similar testimony by Edward Teller in *Federal Research and Development Programs,* Hearings before the House Select Committee on Government Research, 88 Cong. 1 and 2 sess. (1963–64), pt. 2, pp. 938–42; and A. B. Pippard, "The Cat and the Cream," *Physics Today*, vol. 14 (1961), p. 41. Criticism of this nature is also being leveled against academic social science; see Mason Haire, "The Social Sciences and Management Practices," *California Management Review,* Summer 1964, pp. 3–10.

[112] Boyd R. Keenan, "Introduction: The Search for an Institutional System for Science," in Keenan (ed.), *Science and the University,* p. 8. See in the same volume Beardsley Graham, "The Nonprofit Research Institute: A Nonuniversity Approach," and James S. Triolo, "A New Community of Scholars in the Southwest."

[113] See Kidd, *American Universities and Federal Research,* pp. 32–34.

areas. Some of these projects will yield results justifying larger efforts. The university effort, in those areas in which government programs exist, permits the preparation of proposals to government agencies for support of larger-scale efforts. Those efforts vary widely in their dimensions. In most cases the principal investigator will continue some or all of his teaching but will pursue his research as a part-time effort, assisted by a small number of graduate students.[114] The research has emerged from a teaching situation and continues the teaching relationship in that the principal investigator works on the project part-time and the graduate students will typically earn their Ph.D. degrees from some phase of the work. Federal funds secured to finance work of this kind can properly be considered as supporting the university in its dual function.

Frequently, however, interest in a given project will lead to a larger-scale effort. The principal investigator may choose to secure the full-time assistance or participation of post-doctoral researchers. He may also choose to devote his own full time to the project. It is in arrangements of this type that the special character of university-based research loses its applicability. The teaching function is minimized if it has not disappeared. The training involved does not or need not differ significantly from that provided in other institutions. Full-time research by investigators trained through the Ph.D. is a function well performed in other types of institutions with which the university is now in competition. The university offers the advantage of some continuity of effort but once the teaching function has become minimal offers no clear or special advantage or competence in the administration of research. In accepting projects of this kind the university is undertaking a function which is a product of the expansion of federal programs since

[114] For example, Columbia University in 1964 had 748 sponsored research projects totaling $44 million. The average is somewhat less than $60,000 per funding agreement. However, if the ten largest projects are excluded, the average is $40,000, close to the national average for federal projects. The typical project is staffed by four graduate students and one postdoctoral fellow; 40 to 50 percent of the funds go to their salaries. Unlike most other universities Columbia does not charge allocable faculty salaries to federal project funds except when a tenured faculty member is relieved of teaching and a substitute hired. See Ralph S. Hanford, "Modern Science and Its Implications for the University," in Warner, *Impact of Science on Technology*, p. 183.

1940. The university can very properly consider itself a middle-man providing a method whereby research services can be sold with a minimum of organizational problems to the government. In playing that role the university may, however, suffer in its relations with other institutions which look upon it as a source of trained personnel, and in the esteem of its own students who look upon the university as an educational institution all of whose resources should be available to them.

Project Procurement vs. Institutional Support

There is widespread agreement that the competitive project system has operated effectively to the objectives it serves and that it should remain as the basis of the federal contractual research programs.[115] There are, however, a number of criticisms that suggest that the project system has been relied upon too extensively and for inappropriate objectives and that it should be supplemented by other types of research support.

The project system is better adapted, whether by contract or grant, to applied research as it is defined than to basic research, which is much less clearly definable as to objective or method.[116] It

[115] Regarding the competitive project system based on the merit of proposals, Donald F. Hornig writes, "I want to say most emphatically that I consider this approach a major invention in government support of science and one that is in no small measure responsible for the success we have had" ("Universities and Federal Science Policies," p. 848). Another observer identifies the values of the project system as follows:

"1. The system is well suited to meet specific short- and middle-range scientific and technological needs of a mission-oriented program.

"2. It permits early emergence of scientific competence within institutions with quite complex missions relating to instruction, service and research.

"3. It substitutes excellence for political considerations as a guide to support, and I use the term political here to encompass the many considerations apart from strict scientific merit which might bear upon the distribution of support.

"4. The project system makes possible access to multiple sources of support and diminishes dependence upon the terms and conditions of a single source.

"5. The project system helps strengthen the scientific environment within which the work is done, through detached assessment of staff capabilities and through maintenance of vigor within the environment" (James A. Shannon, "Science and Federal Programs: The Continuing Dialogue," *Science*, vol. 144 [June 22, 1964], p. 977).

[116] As Vannevar Bush pointed out, "the project idea, introduced largely as a necessity at war time, is far better adapted to applied research than to fundamental research" (cited in Eric Hodgins, "The Strange State of American Research," in the Editors of Fortune, *The Mighty Force of Research* [McGraw-Hill, 1956], p. 18).

has a further limitation in that while it is well adapted to support the work of the experienced investigator in a recognized area of endeavor, it does not operate as effectively for the young scientist. In the careers of many scientific investigators there exists a gap—in what are sometimes held to be the most productive years—which is filled by employment as an assistant or associate investigator. Such employment, while productive, may well encourage conformity rather than creativity.[117] There is room for concern also over the possibility that proposals are tailored to maximize the probability of acceptance, which may mean that they are conventional if not faddist, rather than true expressions of what the investigator may believe to be the most fruitful course of his activities.[118] It is charged by some that the creativity which the system seeks to nurture is, in fact, sometimes unidentified or discouraged by the present allocation system.[119]

[117] "Prolonged experience as an underling on a team contributes little to the development of an individual and may even be harmful" (Philip H. Abelson, "Group Activity and Creativity in Science," *Daedalus,* Summer 1965, p. 609). See also Melvin Schwartz, "The Conflict between Productivity and Creativity in Modern-Day Physics," *The American Behavioral Scientist,* vol. 6 (December 1962), pp. 35–36.

[118] The project system as administered is also subject to the criticism that undue emphasis is placed upon the conventional and upon the fashion of the moment. See Robert N. Kreidler, "The President's Science Advisers and National Science Policy," in Robert Gilpin and Christopher Wright (eds.), *Scientists and National Policy Making* (Columbia University Press, 1964), pp. 135–36. Radical ideas do frequently meet with irrational opposition in science as in all other fields of thought. (One analysis of this problem is A. Mangoshes and S. Litt, "Psychology of the Scientist: XII. Neglect of Revolutionary Ideas in Psychology," *Psychology Report,* vol. 16 [1965], pp. 621–24.) However, the problem of dealing with the "nonconformer" can be recognized as a challenge; see "Grants to Nonconformers," *Science,* vol. 143 (Jan. 24, 1964), p. 309, and "Nonconformers again," *Science,* vol. 143 (March 6, 1964), pp. 992, 994.

[119] For example, Dr. Harrison Brown points out that under present procedures, such scientific pioneers as Faraday and Maxwell would probably not have received financial support (*Saturday Review,* March 24, 1956). More recently it has been suggested that "with dependence on federal or state funds, under present policies the research which led to the Salk and Sabin vaccines would not have been possible" (Philip S. Broughton, "The Economic Function of Foundations," in F. Emerson Andrews [ed.], *Foundations—20 Viewpoints* [Russell Sage Foundation, 1965], pp. 22–23). These observations imply a lack of imagination and risk-taking in federal programs. In view of such programs as Mohole, Apollo, and others, there are at least very costly exceptions to the behavior pattern alleged. One of the virtues of the present system is surely the freedom with which different opinions can be discussed.

Such criticisms of the competitive project system are difficult to evaluate but they suggest the need for devising procedures that will minimize the limitations of the system. While the present organization for evaluating research projects no doubt identifies some which have little or no scientific merit, the claim sometimes made that any "worthwhile" project will receive funds reflects a highly subjective judgment. Historical experience strongly supports the suspicion that decisions on what is worthwhile are made within a set of assumptions that time may prove erroneous. While no clear alternative exists to evaluation boards in determining the use of public funds on large projects, the vitality of scientific research rests in some important degree upon the small and frequently the unconventional project. A dynamic element may be lost when the judgment of scientific peers dominates over the confidence of the individual scientist and possibly the judgment of his faculty colleagues and administrative superiors. It should also be pointed out that it is not clear in the case of thousands of small projects that the selection procedure accomplishes anything that could not be achieved as well and at less cost within an adequately administered university organization selecting research projects for financial support and accounting institutionally to the government for its use of federal research funds.

Taken together, these considerations strongly suggest the desirability of a program which places some fraction of federal funds available for university research in the hands of university administrators for allocation. In recent years, NSF, NIH, and NASA have established experimental programs of this kind. These programs seek to expand scientific training and research capabilities under conditions that provide the university with greater administrative responsibility and freedom.[120] Programs of institutional

[120] A few federal agencies have undertaken modest programs of institutional support though limiting them to the strengthening of science programs. Such programs require that the institution submit development plans. One early appraisal of the problems of a government agency in dealing with universities concludes that "In this as in other Federal forms of institutional support it is essential that there be careful and continuous planning which encompasses the total educational and research program of the institution and which takes into account the ways in which the program will be financed. Where an academic anarchy of autonomous departments and colleges prevails, an institution will have to bring order, if it is to keep its own autonomy and its control over the direction in which it wishes to go. The president and his top lieutenants in the administration will have to exert

support have received increasing support from the Congress and the Bureau of the Budget.[121]

Such a change in federal policy is consistent with the insistence of the Congress on cost-sharing responsibility which can be interpreted as a desire that the university exercise a role in project selection, whether independent of or supplementary to the present system. The suggestion is also consistent with the widespread interest of scientists, and of some university administrations, in reestablishing the freedom of research associated with the grant as contrasted with the contract.[122] The form of the grant would be

---

more authority in setting policy and seeing to its execution. There is bound to be resistance from faculty members who have been free agents and whose institutional loyalty has been less than their loyalty to their field of specialization. In many respects this loss of a certain amount of departmental autonomy may seem unfortunate but a complex social organism that functions as an effective unit cannot exist in a primitive state. Presidents cannot be mere channels through which government research grants flow to faculty scientists from their counterparts in Washington. Presidents cannot be just intermediaries, or just conciliators of opposing views. They alone are charged with the responsibility for the administration of the total institution, and they cannot discharge that responsibility effectively without controls which many of them have let slip away in recent years. Correspondingly, faculty members must start thinking institutionally and administrators of institutions will have to guide them into doing it" (H. E. Page, "Lessons of the NSF Science Development Program," *Educational Record,* Winter 1966, p. 55). See also articles by Page, Christian K. Arnold, and Don K. Price, in Harold Orlans (ed.), *Science Policy and the University* (Brookings Institution, 1968).

[121] By the House Committee on Government Operations, Eighty-ninth Congress, *Conflicts between Federal Research Programs and the Nation's Goals for Higher Education,* 89 Cong. 1 sess. (1965). In "Making the 1967 Science Budget," Elmer Staats, then Deputy Director of the Bureau of the Budget, observes that the policy was that of emphasizing institutional rather than project support (in Harold Orlans [ed.], *Science Policy and the University*).

[122] Support for arrangements which incorporate a minimum of restraints is nearly universal among scientific researchers as well as among administrators. The scientists think in terms of project funds, loosely controlled; the administrators tend to pursue the objective in terms of institutional grants. A return to simple grants has been advocated by the National Academy of Sciences in *Federal Support of Basic Research in Institutions of Higher Learning* (1964), p. 21; by the President's Science Advisory Committee in *Scientific Progress, the Universities, and the Federal Government* (1960), p. 9; and also by the House Select Committee on Government Research in *Administration of Research and Development,* Study No. 1, 88 Cong. 2 sess. (1964), p. 60.

Lieutenant General William J. Ely, Deputy Director (Administration and Management), Department of Defense, testified that "our experience in the use of grants has been that they give us and the university a flexibility and simplicity of administration that is beneficial to both of us, and the results from the research are equally

different, but by placing responsibility for administration with the university, it would permit the objective of research freedom with local responsibility for supervision.

Conclusion

American universities have experienced many substantial changes over their history and the present period is one of intensified experimentation as the universities seek to respond to new needs and opportunities. The variety of reactions has been very wide.[123] With few exceptions, the policy that has prevailed in many institutions has been one of permissive drifting, a policy not inappropriate to a period of experimental reaction to rapid change. Eventually, however, assessment is in order. After two decades of experience, dissatisfactions are being articulated, appraisals are becoming more frequent, and defenses are being mounted. What is at issue is once again the question of the appropriate role of the university as it faces changing conditions.

While many will contribute to the assessment process, the burden of policy formulation and application falls upon the administrative officials of the universities.[124] Those officials are being ad-

---

as good or better than from the contracts for the money invested." However, despite a drive to shift from contracts to grants, less than 25 percent of DOD's agreements with universities in the period 1958–62 were of the grant type and the percentage has been declining (House Committee on Science and Astronautics, *Geographic Distribution of Federal Research and Development Funds,* Government and Science No. 4, 88 Cong. 2 sess. [1964], pp. 8–9, 17).

[123] Fred R. Cagle classifies universities he surveyed by their attitudes toward federal research funds. Four phases are identified: In phase A the attitude is: "Can this be true? I need the money." In phase B: "It is true! We need the money!" In C: "Can't this be dangerous? The nation needs research!" And in D: "It is dangerous. The nation needs higher education." Cagle finds some of the southern universities with which he was concerned in phase A, the majority in B, a few in C, and a very few in phase D. The classification properly describes the situation across the nation except that a fifth phase, "We are sorry, Professor, that we cannot endorse your project since it is inconsistent with our objectives and resources," should be added. Whether any university has actually achieved phase E is uncertain, but a few appear to be moving to that position. See Southern Regional Education Board, *Federal Research Projects and the Southern University* (1962), pp. 53–57.

[124] University administrations have frequently been admonished that action relating to the nature of university activities is their responsibilty. For example, the Committee on Science and Public Policy of the National Academy of Sciences

monished to exercise their responsibilities more vigorously.[125] Although the federal government has conscientiously avoided actions directly interfering with the universities, it should effectively recognize that university administrators find themselves the vic-

states that "in dealing with federal agencies, university administrations should assert more clearly and emphatically the central purpose of American universities: the advanced education of American youth integrated with the scholarly activities of teachers; in the natural sciences these activities take primarily the form of scientific research. This purpose is not inconsistent with the purpose of the federal government in providing grants and contracts for basic research. It should be stated and restated lest both the government's purpose and the purpose of the universities be obscured by the administrative practices of the agencies" (in *Federal Support of Basic Research in Institutions of Higher Learning* [1964], p. 6; see also pp. 92–93). A similar position is taken in the NAS report, *Toward Better Utilization of Scientific and Engineering Talent—a Program of Action* [the Killian report], NAS Pub. 1191 (1964).

John W. Gardner suggests that "the best chance for the universities to play a role of genuine leadership in determining their own future is through the more effective operation of their associations, such as the American Council on Education." He adds: "But it will also require a level of awareness and a quality of statesmanship throughout the academic world that has not existed to date. A number of college and university presidents, deans, and professors have staunchly faced the larger issues, and we owe them a debt of gratitude, but they cannot do the job alone. They must be able to count on an informed and active constituency that knows very well what is at stake. If such a constituency emerges, then those very able leaders will receive the backing they deserve and their effectiveness will be multiplied. And then the universities will be not only magnificent resources, as they are now, but masters of their own fate, which now they are not" ("Government and the Universities," an address before the forty-seventh annual meeting of the American Council on Education, Oct. 1, 1964).

[125] The Bureau of the Budget report on *The Administration of Government Supported Research at Universities* (1966), while emphasizing the desirability of shifting the details of scientific administration from Washington to the campus and of providing greater local flexibility in deciding what is to be researched and by whom through institutional rather than project grants, also points out that the burden is on the universities to demonstrate that they can develop mechanisms that will make federal interference unnecessary. "Universities should recognize more fully the importance of both the quality of their business management and the type of professional conduct of faculty members when the university accepts Federal funds" (p. 126).

And a private observer, Norman Kaplan, notes that "if the universities are not to abdicate their responsibility (which they have only recently passively accepted) to promote the growth of basic science, then they must reorganize to cope more imaginatively with the problems that lie ahead. The direction is not toward more complicated bureaucracies, but rather toward a wholly new approach to research and its organization, as well as the other functions of the university" ("Organization: Will It Choke or Promote the Growth of Science?" in Hill [ed.] *The Management of Scientists*, p. 125).

tims of the indirect effects of the success of federal programs.[126]
With little control over research funds, university administrators
have very limited powers to establish and apply such policies as
would in their judgment best serve the interests of their institutions in meeting the demands properly made of them.[127]

[126] The Elliott committee concluded with regard to federally sponsored project
research in the universities that "the system's most important drawback has been
its influence on the university's administration and to some extent control over
its own destiny. Direct negotiations between the scholar and the agency leave the
university with little review power, and bypass the university's internal budget
systems. Thus a substantial portion of the university's expenditures may be
handled outside normal channels. These in turn commit some of the university's
own funds; they influence space assignments; they determine relationships of
teaching to research time; they establish the growth patterns between departments
in the university. All thus influence the balance of the whole university's organization in ways which the university may not control directly" (House Select Committee
on Government Research, *National Goals and Policies,* Study Paper 10, H. Rept. 1941,
88 Cong. 2 sess. [1964], pt. 1, p. 29). See also Clark Kerr, "The Frantic Race To
Remain Contemporary," *Daedalus,* Fall 1964, pp. 1063–65; and Christian K. Arnold,
"The Government and University Science: Purchase and/or Investment?" in Orlans
(ed.), *Science Policy and the University.*

[127] It is not suggested that an increase in university administrative controls over
research is easily and readily accomplished. Yet, "without administrative controls,
a program [of sponsored research] can develop in an amoeba-like fashion, render-
ing long range institutional goals almost impossible to attain. . . . Regardless of
centralized or nominally decentralized general plans of research administration,
a single review and approval check-point, at a level high enough to provide the
overall view, is the best insurance against disruption of university functions and
shattering of its objectives by the fiscal and physical burdens of sponsored research"
(W. C. Wheadon, "Organizing University Research," *Industrial Research,* April 1964,
pp. 46–47).

Ross L. Mooney points out that "faculty members who obtain help for their
research, whether through local committees or outside agencies, therefore do so
by special channels, separated from their normal departmental routes. Department
heads and deans, though they see the papers passing through, tend to become
spectators of a separate operation in which they have no crucial part. Department
heads tend to restrict their views of themselves to that of being supervisors of
arrangements for teaching, letting research become what it will as individual faculty
members are motivated and controlling committees decide. A coordinator of research, acting for a dean at the college level, becomes little more than a communi-
cative agent, serving between two poles of power, one held by the individual faculty
member who has the power of initiative and the other held by the agency which
has the power of specific approval" ("The Problem of Leadership in the University,"
Harvard Educational Review, vol. 33 [Winter 1963], pp. 43–44).

Don K. Price observes that "the qualities of independence and critical scholarship and leadership in basic theory, on which the whole research and development
enterprise depends, will be threatened unless the central structure of the university
is made strong enough to sustain the structure of specialized research grants" ("Federal Money and University Research," in Orlans [ed.], *Science Policy and the University*).

The interest of the Congress in implementing the principle of support rather than of purchase for some part of federal programs and in establishing greater institutional responsibility,[128] the need for halting the erosion of the role of university administrators and, indeed, strengthening their position, the recognition that the competitive project system, for all its merits, also has important limitations—these and similar considerations taken together strongly suggest that the universities should seek and be given greater direct control over larger portions of the funds that now support their research activities.

No source of the necessary funds exists other than the federal government. The objective could be achieved by earmarking for institutional allocation some substantial portion—perhaps 20 percent—of research funds now obligated to universities through competitive project grants and contracts. Such funds should not be disbursed as a reward for success in the competitive project system but should be related to the competitive project system much as the independent research funds of business firms are related to subsequent development contracts. The funds would be distributed among the universities as institutional grants matching in some realistic ratio the funds which the university makes available for research, preferably in all areas whether or not the government maintains supporting programs. The government thereby strengthens university administrations and strengthens also the university's special role in supporting small-scale, part-time faculty research. The government retains the function of selecting projects for large-scale support—perhaps those requiring full-time professional employment. However, adequate provision should be made so that the competitive process encourages the consideration of proposals from all types of research institutions.

These suggestions could hardly diminish and may well increase the effectiveness of university research. They provide an important step in the resolution of the relationships between the universities and the government and permit the universities greater freedom to shape their further development. They are, however, only a step, since the role of the universities in today's complex world can hardly be fully clarified without a more coherent federal policy toward higher education than now exists.

[128] As is recommended in the Bureau of the Budget report, *The Administration of Government Sponsored Research at Universities* (March 1966), pp. 5–6.

CHAPTER VIII

Other Groups Conducting Project Research

In the United States, nonprofit organizations other than colleges and universities have a long history of serving public objectives that in other societies have been undertaken by government if they have been pursued at all. Such activities have been financed by private philanthropy, public solicitation of funds, income from endowment or, in some cases, from membership dues and fees. Limitations in those sources of funds together with increasing public demands have led in the past to the usurpation by government of functions that the nonprofit organizations once performed —as in welfare. The nonprofit groups have, however, continued to expand the variety of functions they have undertaken. Moreover, since about 1950, they have increasingly carried out federal programs under contract. Research is one of the important functions performed by these organizations, but they have also carried out overseas technical aid projects. They have undertaken the management of domestic and overseas relief programs; they have administered manpower training programs and organized Community Action Programs for the Office of Economic Opportunity, and they serve as managers of federally financed housing projects.

The contractual relationship permits the government to delegate to private organizations responsibilities and functions that would not be as well carried out by civil service employees or by other forms of organization. For the nonprofit organization the contracts assure local responsibility as well as funds with which to pursue objectives important to those involved. The contract may require cost-sharing or, as happens more frequently, provide for reimbursement of all costs as defined by the government. The nonprofit institution must normally possess working capital and must provide for nonreimbursable costs. These requirements operate as limitations upon the effectiveness with which these organizations can carry out their roles. Such problems have attracted little attention.[1]

The following discussion is limited to independent nonprofit organizations in the R&D area, an area in which the contract relationship is perhaps best established.

Approximately 97 percent of federal expenditures for R&D go to the business firms and universities previously discussed, and the research centers, both contractually and directly administered, dealt with in the following chapter. There remain a large number of project-conducting organizations playing specialized roles of an importance not adequately measured by their small share of federal funds. Since these organizations are engaged in research rather than development, their contribution is better measured by the fact that they account for 7 percent of federal research expenditures.

Three groups are dealt with here. Most important are the nonprofit corporations not formally affiliated with any other institution and engaged wholly in research.[2] A second group consists of

[1] For an evaluation of some of these problems, see Alan Pifer, "The Nongovernmental Organization at Bay," *Annual Report of the Carnegie Corporation of New York* (1966), pp. 3–15.

[2] This distinction is in many cases an arbitrary one since many of the university-related institutes have only very tenuous ties with the university with which they are associated. Legally there is a difference if the university sponsors and administers the institute's contractual relations. However, some separately incorporated, university-controlled institutes such as the Syracuse Research Corporation and the Denver Research Institute enter into contracts in their own name and maintain their own staffs. A fuller study of such organizations than has been possible up to now is needed. Meanwhile we here follow the NSF practice of classifying such organizations with the universities.

Also excluded from consideration in this chapter but dealt with in chapter IX are those nonprofit groups which serve as contractual managers of research centers which are government-owned and those nonprofit groups which stand in a captive relationship with a sponsoring government agency. Excluded are a few consortiums of universities organized on a nonprofit basis and concerned with the

the professional scientific and technical associations which play a small and highly specialized role. The third group includes the foreign scientists and institutions that carry on project research sponsored by American government agencies.

The Independent Nonprofit Organizations

The independent nonprofit organizations are a diverse group of institutions which have little in common except their legal form of organization, their independence of other organizations, and their interest in research. Included are institutions wholly devoted to research and others which conduct modest amounts of research incidental to their principal interests. This latter group includes some private foundations, voluntary health organizations, museums, zoological and botanical gardens, and arboretums.[3]

Much more important are the independent organizations—most frequently calling themselves institutes—that are primarily if not wholly devoted to research or development. A 1964 survey identifies some 280 organizations of this type, employing some 9,750 scientists and engineers and expending $292 million.[4] About 2 percent of the nation's scientists and engineers engaged in research is associated with these organizations.[5] Although a few of the institutes maintain a broad range of staff capabilities, most direct their efforts to one or a few specialized areas. In the aggregate, however,

---

management of government-owned research centers. Among these are Associated Universities, Inc. (contractor for AEC's Brookhaven Laboratory, and the NSF's National Radio Astronomy Observatory); Association of Universities for Research in Astronomy (NSF's Cerro Tololo Inter-American Observatory); University Corporation for Atmospheric Research (NSF's National Center for Atmospheric Research); Midwestern Universities Research Association (AEC); and Gulf Universities Research Corporation. These organizations have normally limited their activities to broad managerial supervision. However, Associated Universities, Inc., in the early 1950's undertook responsibility for Project East River, a study of civil defense problems, under contract with the Department of the Army; see Associated Universities, Inc., *Report of the President to the Board of Trustees, 1951* (1952) and *1952–53* (1953).

[3] In 1964 an NSF survey identified 65 organizations classified as "nonprofit science exhibitors" reporting expenditures for R&D of $7.5 million. Federal funds constituted 27 percent of expenditures (National Science Foundation, *Scientific Activities of Nonprofit Institutions, 1964* [NSF 67–17], p. 29).

[4] *Ibid.*, p. 17.

[5] National Science Foundation, *Scientific and Technical Manpower Resources* (1964), pp. 45, 47.

they operate in virtually all areas of scientific, technical, and social science research.

From the point of view of their participation in government programs, it is useful to distinguish between those institutes which are program-oriented and those which are project-oriented, the latter deriving their programs in large measure from contractual projects.

The program-oriented institutes typically possess sources of income independent of specific research projects; incomes derived from endowments, fees, or contributions from business firms, and gifts or grants from philanthropic foundations. Many of these organizations accept research contracts from federal agencies when they conform to the organization's program and can be considered as forwarding its objectives. Compensation for government-sponsored work usually supplements the institute's own funds. Among these organizations some of the older and better known are the Woods Hole Oceanographic Institute, the Fels Research Institute, the Cranbrook Institute of Science, the Sloan-Kettering Institute for Cancer Research, the Carnegie Institution of Washington, the Boyce Thompson Institute for Plant Research, and in the social sciences, the Brookings Institution, the National Planning Association, and the National Bureau of Economic Research. Of a different type are the research organizations maintained by trade associations such as the Association of American Railroads Research Center, Institute of Textile Technology, the Institute of Paper Chemistry, or the Lithographic Technical Foundation.[6] Some are associated with, though independent of, a university, such as the Institute of Gas Technology at the Illinois Institute of Technology. There are a large number of smaller organizations.

The project-oriented institutions are of greater immediate interest since they have increased rapidly in the postwar period and since they are more active in government programs.[7] These insti-

[6] National Science Foundation, *Research by Cooperative Organizations: A Survey of Scientific Research by Trade Associations, Professional and Technical Societies, and Other Cooperative Groups, 1953* (1956), prepared by Battelle Memorial Institute; and John C. Green, *Technical Research Activities of Cooperative Associations,* Study Paper No. 21 of the Subcommittee on Patents, Trademarks, and Copyrights of the Senate Judiciary Committee, 85 Cong. 2 sess. (1959).

[7] The project-oriented institutes are not, of course, without program interests. Their program interests, however, tend to develop with their contractual activities. Three of the institutes are contractual managers of federal research centers: The

tutes frequently seek to maintain some areas of special interest and competence of a program nature, to provide flexibility in staff utilization and to explore new areas of possible interest. In large measure, however, their research capabilities are developed to accord with the interests of possible sponsors. These organizations are financed primarily by contacts with the federal government and private industry.

Some of the nonprofit research institutions offering their services under contract originated as local groups. Others came into being as philanthropists sought to provide a source of research services to meet the needs of industry. The oldest, the Mellon Institute of Industrial Research, took its present form in 1927 but had operated since 1912 as the Mellon Institute, a part of the University of Pittsburgh, and in 1966 announced its intention to merge with the Carnegie Institute of Technology. The Battelle Memorial Institute was founded in 1925 and the Haskins Laboratories and Armour Institutes—now merged with the Illinois Institute of Technology—followed in the 1930's.

The Franklin Institute of the State of Pennsylvania, established in 1824, engaged in a variety of scientific investigations utilizing the services of committees of volunteers. One of these—an investigation begun in 1830 of the causes of steam boiler explosions—attracted the attention of Congress and resulted in 1834 in a contract making available $1,500 to contribute to the costs of the work.[8] This appears to be the earliest recorded federal research contract with a private institution. The Institute continued to pursue research objectives through the organization of volunteer groups, but devoted its funds to educational activities. Not until

---

Franklin Institute in 1961 undertook to manage the Navy's Center for Naval Analyses. In 1964 the Battelle Memorial Institute entered into arrangements with the Atomic Energy Commission to operate the Pacific Northwest Laboratories, part of the former AEC Hanford works. The Research Institute of Illinois Institute of Technology is contractual manager of the Air Force Electromagnetic Compatibility Analysis Center. See *Systems Development and Management,* Hearings before the House Committee on Government Operations, 87 Cong. 2 sess. (1962), pt. 4, pp. 1487–88.

[8] The arrangement was made by the Secretary of the Treasury after he had been requested by the House to investigate boiler accidents and to submit a report. See John G. Burke, "Bursting Boilers and the Federal Power," *Technology and Culture,* vol. VII (Winter 1966), p. 10. A description of the present organization and research activities of the Franklin Institute appears in *Systems Development and Management,* pt. 4, pp. 1615–27.

shortly after World War I did it acquire a small laboratory staffed by full-time personnel. That laboratory operated under contracts with Office of Scientific Research and Development and Army Ordnance during World War II and since that time has engaged in contractual research.

Until World War II, the operations of the independent institutes were limited by the funds available from endowment income and modest amounts of contractual work for private industry. As in the case of the Franklin Institute, the facilities of the other institutes were also drawn to wartime needs, either directly by federal agencies or by private firms concerned with federal programs. With the postwar growth of federal R&D programs contractual project work for the federal government became an important source of income, in many cases, the largest.

In the postwar period a number of factors have combined to stimulate the growth of nonprofit research organizations. While industry expanded its R&D organizations, the heightened interest of the government as well as of business firms in research increased the demand for contractual sources. The nonprofit organization's contribution to technical development was substantial—as in metal alloys, magnetic recording, electrostatic copying and hypersonic wind tunnels. The success of the older organizations aroused the interest of groups in a number of states and localities in establishing similar research organizations in their areas. A nonprofit institute provides a method by which research personnel may be attracted to a given location. Typically what was sought by proponents after the war was a source of research services posessing the independence associated with university work but able to apply greater and more continuous effort in whatever areas of interest might develop. At the same time an increasing number of scientists and engineers found congenial the environment of the nonprofit institute.

The 1940's saw the formation of numerous contract-oriented nonprofit organizations.[9] Among the more important were the

---

[9] Useful general accounts of the nonprofit organizations include the following: National Science Foundation, *Research and Development by Nonprofit Research Institutes and Commercial Laboratories* (1956), prepared by Maxwell Research Center, Syracuse University; Beardsley Graham, "The Nonprofit Research Institute," in Boyd R. Keenan (ed.), *Science and the University* (Columbia University Press, 1966); Victor J. Danilov, "The Not-for-Profit Research Institutes," *Industrial Research*, February 1966, pp. 30–39.

Southern Research Institute, Southwest Foundation for Research and Education, Midwest Research Institute, Texas Research Foundation, Cornell Aeronautical Laboratory,[10] Stanford Research Institute and Southwest Research Institute. All were founded by private interests with private funds, some as collaborative efforts of business and university groups.

Among many other smaller institutes formed by private interests in recent years, the North Star Research and Development Institute in Minnesota, the University City Science Research Institute of Philadelphia, the Oceanic Institute of Hawaii,[11] and the Hudson Institute in New York[12] are among the more important.[13] Although some institutes tended in time to loosen their university ties, others remained closely affiliated and universities continue to participate in the organization of new ones. The Graduate Research Center of the Southwest, founded in 1961, differs from others in that, while strongly research-oriented, it also emphasizes graduate and postgraduate training. The Center does not grant academic degrees but collaborates with nearby universities in its training activities.[14]

In recent years, state legislatures have participated in the formation of some nonprofit research institutes. Typically, the legislatures have given financial and other support to the efforts of busi-

[10] The Cornell Aeronautical Laboratory is administratively a part of Cornell University. Because it was acquired by, rather than developed within, the university and because it is financially independent it is usually included in the independent nonprofit category. A similar relationship exists between IIT Research Institute and the Illinois Institute of Technology.

[11] *New York Times,* May 22, 1965.

[12] The Hudson Institute is described in Arthur Herzog, "Report on a 'Think Factory,' " *New York Times Magazine,* Nov. 10, 1963.

[13] The availability of research funds has stimulated the formation of many independent nonprofit institutes. Many are affiliated with medical schools and hospitals. Others are in essence private ventures. A recent example is the Basic Health Research Institute of Tucson, Arizona. The Institute is reported as having invited applications for association with the proviso that "each member must find his own financial support, although sponsorship of the institute will be available when applications are to be filed with grantor agencies." It was observed that "overhead from grants is enabling the institute to supply necessary facilities and services until it is sufficiently well established to enlist the support of private foundations" (*Science,* vol. 132 [Nov. 25, 1965], p. 1539).

[14] The ambitious plans for the Graduate Research Center of the Southwest are described in James S. Triolo, "The Independent Research Organization," in Keenan (ed.), *Science and the University.*

ness groups to increase the research activity within their states. Much current thought regarding local and regional economic growth assumes that a research center is an essential element in a program to accelerate economic progress.[15] The presence of a non-profit research institute can promote an expansion of research activities within a locality with a minimum financial burden. A research center is therefore considered desirable for its own sake, regardless of the problems to which it might address itself. What is sought is the stimulating effects of a scientific and technical organization upon an area with the hope of advantage from new business firms and new industries originating from their research. Such institutes differ from the earlier organizations in that they seek more specifically to supplement the scientific and technical personnel affiliated with nearby educational institutions as well as to attract other research organizations. The availability of federal funds is an important if not a determining factor.

It was considerations of this nature which led private enterprise with the cooperation of the state in 1959 to establish the Research Triangle Institute in North Carolina. The Spindletop Research Institute was formed in Kentucky in 1961 as a private organization, but with state funds for facilities and working capital; the Gulf South Research Institute was formed in Louisiana in 1965 with the assistance of state funds for facilities and some operation support. The Mississippi Research and Development Center is entirely an agency of the state.[16]

The survival and growth of these organizations rest upon their ability to compete in proposing research projects and to deliver a satisfactory product within prearranged limits of time and funds. It is characteristic of the internal structure of most of them that they consist of rather loosely controlled groups of specialists enjoying a large degree of independence as well as of responsibility. The responsibility includes securing sponsorship of projects in sufficient volume to keep the staff occupied. In consequence, groups which continue over a period of time do so by demonstrating skill

[15] For one such statement on the relationship of local research facilities to local economic growth, see Jesse Hobson, *The Role and Effect of Technology in the Nation's Economy*, Hearings before Senate Select Committee on Small Business, 88 Cong. 1 sess. (1963), pt. 1, pp. 68–79.
[16] Beardsley Graham, "The Nonprofit Research Institute," pp. 135–36.

in anticipating the interests of possible sponsors and by an ability to produce research reports satisfying to the client. Their work is largely in applied research, stopping short of development though some give considerable attention to basic research. Many nonprofit organizations have developed outstanding competence in some field of specialization. It is, however, also characteristic of these institutions that they maintain research capabilities in a wide variety of disciplines, thereby meeting the varied and changing needs of their clientele and permitting interdisciplinary approaches to a problem. Their ability to organize staff to provide a systematic approach to the analysis of a multifaceted problem seems clearly superior to that of most university researchers and supports rather than conflicts with normal industry interests. Unhampered by the restrictions that follow from institutional affiliations, these organizations can be highly responsive to a sponsor's problem in formulating a research project. They can quickly begin work on accepted proposals, and they have considerable flexibility in staffing.

Since they are free of organic ties, they can be selective of the projects they undertake and responsive to the interests of possible sponsors, rejecting proposals that may seem undesirable. However, since staff must be maintained, the nonprofit groups must be responsive to whatever problems come their way and aggressive in submitting proposals to potential clients. One result of such dependence may be a loss of sense of identity and an inability to establish organizational goals reflecting its sense of priorities.[17]

The work of the nonprofit research organizations is done on contracts of the fixed-price or cost-plus-fixed-fee types and infrequently under grants, since grants may not cover full costs.[18] Though organized as nonprofit institutions which have no stockholders and pay no dividends, these organizations must concern

[17] For an examination of such problems, as felt by Stanford Research Institute, see Spencer Klaw, "The Perils of Running a Nonprofit," *Fortune,* November 1966, pp. 158–61, 212–24.

[18] The problems of a nonprofit research center dependent upon grants and lacking other sources of funds were publicized in the case of the Laboratory of Quantitative Biology, Long Island, N. Y. This organization faced severe problems in maintaining over-age buildings. The Laboratory's director is quoted as pointing out that "we can easily get $5000 for that [a large microscope] but not $5 to paint the ceiling" ("Lab on L.I. Faces Building Crisis," *New York Times,* April 18, 1965).

themselves with problems of income. They are constantly faced with the problems of interregnums between projects, with the cost of preparing proposals that may fail of acceptance, and with the necessity of maintaining staff capabilities at high levels through unsponsored research and educational activities.

Possibly because they operate in a highly competitive milieu, these nonprofit research organizations have been subjected to little criticism. Such criticism as has appeared has come chiefly from the commercial laboratories and those relatively few organizations which compete directly with the nonprofit institutes but which are organized as profit-making corporations. The nonprofit institutions have responded to such criticism by reducing if not eliminating their activities in testing of the type done by the commercial laboratories. Criticism of them is also muted because the nonprofit organizations operate under restrictions imposed by federal tax law which limit their advantage over commercial research organizations. Any activity undertaken by a nonprofit organization which is judged to be of a commercial character risks the loss of the federal tax-exempt status. The Internal Revenue Service has ruled further that the nonprofit institutes are liable for taxes on revenue received for research which results in a proprietary advantage to the sponsor. Hence the institutes have no tax-privileged position when they undertake such work. Some, such as Stanford Research Institute, pay taxes on income from such sponsored research. Because of the problems involved, such as the need for complicated accounting procedures, other nonprofit organizations have elected to decline work that might subject them to tax liabilities.[19] Other bodies, such as Battelle and IIT Research Institute, have established and control conventional tax-paying organizations to perform functions which are competitive with commercial organizations subject to taxes.

Standing between the research interests and capabilities of the universities on the one hand and those of business firms on the other, the independent nonprofit institutes have groped their way to occupy a relatively small but clearly important niche among the

[19] Haldon A. Leedy, "The Role of the Independent Not-for-Profit Contract," *Proceedings of the Fifteenth National Conference on the Administration of Research* (1961), pp. 62–66; Herbert Solow, "Science for Sale—at a Profit," *Fortune,* March 1955, pp. 104–17, 136–44.

nation's R&D functionaries. Their reputations surely exceed their relative status since the independent contract-oriented institutes account for little more than 1 percent of national expenditures on R&D—two-thirds from the government and one-sixth from industry. It may also prove to be true that the independent research institutes can provide a way by which states and localities which seek greater participation in R&D activities can accomplish their objective. The institute route has some advantage in that such organizations can be promoted independently of the policies pursued by the state's institutions of higher education.

The Professional Associations

Professional associations operate under conditions which severely restrict them in undertaking research on their own account since such activities would normally conflict with the interests of their members who deal with sponsors through the organizations with which they are employed. As nonprofit organizations they are also inhibited by antilobbying statutes from taking action which might lead to advocacy of policy positions before Congress.[20]

Some professional associations have sought to deal with a common problem—such as the collection and analysis of statistical data —through collaboration with a wholly independent organization. Occasionally an association has undertaken such an activity or one related to teaching through committee management of a project. Other associations have sought to supply a need for services to a sponsor desiring work of a character not readily available from university faculty members. In the social sciences the American Political Science Association at one time had a subsidiary organi-

[20] See William J. Harris, Jr., "A View from Professional Societies," in Keenan (ed.), *Science and the University*. The Assistant Counsel of the House Science and Astronautics Committee, Joseph M. Felton, after examining the statutes relating to organizations tax exempt under section 501(c[3]) of the Internal Revenue Code of 1954, concluded "that there is no limitation on the extent such organizations may communicate with the Congress when the first step is specifically taken by the Congress, but that the attitude of such organizations not to offer unsolicited information to the Congress cannot be considered imprudent." Mr. Felton concluded that the nonprofit organizations probably did not come under the coverage of the Federal Regulation of Lobbying Act (House Committee on Science and Astronautics, *Scientific and Technical Advice for Congress: Needs and Sources*, Government and Science No. 3, 88 Cong. 2 sess. [1964], p. 69).

zation which performed contractual research. Some scientific areas have established a federation of the societies in the field, such as the American Institute of Physics. Aside from handling the publication of the journals of the member societies, the AIP, with funds from contracts or gifts, engages in translation activities, conducts manpower surveys, and manages a foreign visitors' program.

Somewhat similar is the American Institute of Biological Sciences, which was formed as a federation of the professional associations in biology for the principal purpose of assuming responsibility for research contracts in its fields, including the development of new teaching aids and techniques. Work undertaken by the AIBS is performed in facilities acquired under contracts with universities by arrangements with individuals, usually university faculty members.[21]

Many professional associations seek to provide their members with bibliographic information covering the new literature in fields of interest, and some have undertaken programs designed to develop new teaching aids and techniques. With the growth of scientific activity the provision of adequate bibliographic information has become increasingly difficult as well as of ever greater importance. One reaction to the problem is illustrated by the activities of the American Chemical Society. The Society is conducting a government-supported program seeking to apply advanced techniques and to broaden the coverage of the activities long conducted by its Chemical Abstract Service.[22] Similar programs are conducted by the American Psychological Association.[23] The training contracts of the American Association of Police Chiefs with the Agency for International Development provide a service not readily available in any other way. Other organizations which repre-

[21] On the American Institute of Biological Sciences, see *Science,* vol. 139 (Jan. 25, 1963), pp. 317–20, 321–22; vol. 139 (Feb. 1, 1963), pp. 392–93; and vol. 139 (March 1, 1963), pp. 814–15.

[22] American Chemical Society, *Annual Report* (1963). See also National Science Foundation, *Scientific Activities of Nonprofit Institutions* (NSF 67–17), pp. 23–26.

[23] The American Psychological Association in 1964 received grants totaling $404,000 from the National Science Foundation and the Public Health Service. The funds were used to support conferences, a national scientific register, studies of information exchange in psychology, and the publication of abstracts (*American Psychologist,* vol. 21 [May 1966], p. 418). The studies of information exchange are published as "Reports of the American Psychological Association's Project on Scientific Information Exchange," in *Psychology,* vol. 1 (APA, 1963) and vol. 2 (APA, 1965).

sent institutional rather than individual members also occasionally undertake contracts in areas in which they have some special expertise or which are appropriate for some reason. One example is the American Council on Education's contract to provide assistance in the award of grants under the Fulbright program of the Department of State.[24]

The role of professional associations is more important in the formulation and criticism of policy than in the actual performance of research. That role may be played by officers of an association usually speaking as individuals but presumably reflecting the views of the membership. The American Association for the Advancement of Science is particularly influential in this way.[25] Professional associations may also seek to make their views known in a more formal way, particularly on issues of special importance to the interests of the group. Aside from the inhibitions imposed upon them by their nonprofit character, problems internal to the operations of these associations have made it difficult to arrive at policy positions that are specific rather than platitudinous. For many of these groups, the machinery provided by the National Academy of Sciences–National Research Council and the National Academy of Engineering renders unnecessary the more narrowly professional organization as a vehicle to develop and communicate policy positions.

The special importance of the National Academy of Sciences–National Research Council follows from its unique relationship to the federal government which permits it to serve as spokesman for numerous scientific groups. In the future the National Academy of Engineering, formed out of the NAS–NRC in 1964 but in a close affiliation, may acquire similar status.[26]

[24] American Council on Education, *Annual Report* (1963), pp. 37, 76.

[25] The American Association for the Advancement of Science sponsored a Parliament of Science in 1958 in connection with congressional consideration of a Department of Science (see *Science*, vol. 117 [1958], pp. 852–58). Its Committee on Science in the Promotion of Human Welfare and other groups such as its Air Conservation Commission have issued influential reports. AAAS's prestigious weekly journal, *Science*, provides an important forum for the discussion of policy issues and trends. On the AAAS, see Wallace S. Sayre, "Scientists and American Science Policy," in Robert Gilpin and Christopher Wright, *Scientists and National Policy-Making* (Columbia University Press, 1964), pp. 97–112.

[26] An account of the circumstances that led to the formation of the National Academy of Engineering is given by John Lear, "Building the American Dream,"

The National Academy of Sciences was established in 1863 as an organization to afford recognition to a limited number of individuals who had made significant contributions in their fields of science and to be a source of scientific advice to the government. During its first half-century the organization served the second objective within the limits of the government's interest in science. The problems presented by World War I suggested a need for some arrangement which would permit the utilization of the nation's scientists and engineers, regardless of membership in the NAS. The result was the formation in 1916 of the National Research Council as an operating auxiliary of the NAS. The NRC was given permanent status by an executive order which enumerated its duties as follows:

1. In general, to stimulate research in the mathematical, physical, and biological sciences, and in the application of these sciences to engineering, agriculture, medicine and other useful arts, with the object of increasing knowledge, of strengthening the national defense, and of contributing in other ways to the public welfare.

2. To survey the larger possibilities of science, to formulate comprehensive projects of research, and to develop effective means of utilizing the scientific and technical resources of the country for dealing with these projects of research.

3. To promote cooperation in research, at home and abroad, in order to secure concentration of effort, minimize duplication, and stimulate progress; but in all cooperative undertakings to give encouragement to individual initiative, as fundamentally important to the advancement of science.

4. To serve as a means of bringing American and foreign investigators into active cooperation with the scientific and technical services of the War and Navy Departments and with those of the civil branches of the government.

Saturday Review, Feb. 6, 1965, pp. 49–51. See also "The Engineer Goes to Washington," interview with Augustus B. Kinzel, first president of the new National Academy of Engineering, in *International Science and Technology,* June 1965, pp. 49–52.
The Government Liaison Committee of the Engineers Joint Council—a federation of national and regional engineering societies—has also sought ways and means of contributing to the discussion of policy issues. See statement by William J. Harris, Jr., in *Establishment of a Congressional Science Advisory Staff,* Hearings before the House Committee on House Administration, 88 Cong. 1 sess. (1963), p. 61.

5. To direct the attention of scientific and technical investigators to the present importance of military and industrial problems in connection with the war, and to aid in the solution of these problems by organizing specific researches.

6. To gather and collate scientific and technical information, at home and abroad, in cooperation with governmental and other agencies, and to render such information available to duly accredited persons.[27]

Until World War II, these functions were exercised on a modest scale. As has been pointed out, government calls upon NAS-NRC increased rapidly in the years immediately preceding the war and were maintained at a high level throughout the conflict. Since the war, federal agencies have continued to utilize the resources of NAS-NRC, and its activities have increased with the proliferation of federal R&D programs. Much of its work has related to the more narrowly defined programmatic and feasibility problems of agency programs, frequently involving the establishment of advisory panels.

With the emergence of organized representation of science in the Executive Office of the President, the NAS-NRC offered machinery whereby the government might readily obtain authoritative scientific advice. At the same time, NAS-NRC acquired a channel of communication of vastly greater potential than the agency contacts which it had long possessed, a channel by which it might, to use the language of the Executive Order of 1916, "survey the larger possibilities of science, . . . formulate comprehensive projects of research, and . . . develop effective means of utilizing the scientific and technical resources of the country for dealing with these projects of research." To respond to invitations or opportunities to deal with broad questions, NAS established a Committee on Science and Public Policy, its only committee representing all fields of NAS interest but restricting its membership to the members of the Academy.[28] The Committee has prepared a number of broad-ranging and influential studies, usually at the invitation of

[27] *Science and Technology Act of 1958*, Staff Paper of the Senate Committee on Government Operations, 85 Cong. 2 sess. (1958), p. 116.

[28] See Lee Anna Embrey, "The Role of the National Academy of Sciences in Long-Range Planning for Science," *NAS-NRC News Report*, vol. 14 (September-October 1964), p. 75. A useful, more critical survey is D. S. Greenberg, "The National Academy of Sciences: Profile of an Institution," *Science*, vol. 156 (1967), pp. 222–29, 360–64, 488–93.

OST or one of its constituent groups.[29] Such studies are ordinarily prepared under contract although the Committee has sought private financing on a few occasions.[30] The National Academy of Engineering in 1966 established a similar group, the Committee on Public Engineering Policy.

A significant further effort to apply the unique ability of NAS-NRC to direct the expertise of the scientific community toward evaluations of the status and potentialities of areas of scientific activity occurred in 1963. The NAS-NRC entered into a contract with the Subcommittee on Science and Research of the House Committee on Science and Astronautics to prepare studies on areas selected by the Committee.[31]

Most of the work of the NAS-NRC is done through fourteen subject-area divisions and a number of other administrative units. Depending upon their interest or the requests made to them, the divisions work by means of standing, interim, or *ad hoc* committees. These committees sometimes accomplish their objectives through their own membership but frequently draw from the nation's scientific community to form staff technical panels, conferences, symposia, workshops, task groups, and in a number of cases, boards with full-time staffs. A frequent activity is that of inventorying the state of knowledge in a field, of further identifying problems and methods of solution, and recommending policies and programs.

Evaluation of proposed research or of ongoing research pro-

---

[29] National Academy of Sciences–National Research Council committee reports appraising the status, problems, prospects, and significance of areas of science are frequently highly important documents. Among recent reports the following may be mentioned: *Toward Better Utilization of Scientific and Engineering Talent—a Program for Action* (1964); *Desalination Research and the Water Problem* (1962); *More Effective Organization and Administration of Materials Research and Development for National Security* (1960); *Chemistry: Opportunities and Needs* (1965); *Physics: Survey and Outlook* (1965); *Digital Computer Needs in Universities and Colleges* (1965); *The Growth of United States Population* (1965); *Ground-based Astronomy: A Ten-Year Program* (1964); *Federal Support of Basic Research in Institutions of Higher Learning* (1964).

[30] The NAS-NRC report, *Growth of World Population* (1963), was financed by a private source; see D. S. Greenberg, "Birth Control: National Academy Issues Report Calling for Major Effort in Population Planning," *Science,* vol. 140 (1963), p. 281.

[31] The first product of the contract was *Basic Research and National Goals, A Report to the House Committee on Science and Astronautics by the National Academy of Sciences,* 89 Cong. 1 sess. (1965).

grams is also an important function. Some NRC committees operate jointly with a federal agency as in the case of the Armed Forces-NRC Committee on Bio-Astronautics and the Armed Forces-NRC Committee on Vision. In other instances NRC supplies an advisory evaluation service as in the case of the long-standing NAS-NRC Advisory Board on Quartermaster Research and Development. The advisory evaluation panels which serve the Army's Research Office are less formal. Some committees have standing responsibilities for surveillance of research, such as that conducted under the National Blood Program, naval medical research and the Veterans Administration research program.

The performance of research is not a primary NAS-NRC function. However NAS occasionally undertakes a contractual research project that requires the assembly of a full-time staff, frequently relying heavily on consultants.[32] Some NAS-NRC divisions employ small full-time research staffs and in a few cases research performance on a large scale is undertaken.[33] The NAS-NRC, for example, serves as the contract manager of the Army's Prevention of Deterioration Center. Under a long-continued contract with the Bureau of Public Roads, supplemented by private funds, the NRC Highway Research Board has for many years served as a principal research agent in its area. This function has now been assumed by the National Academy of Engineering. The NAS-NRC has long been engaged in research on housing which its Building Research Advisory Board has pursued under contracts with the Federal Housing Administration. The same board under a National Bureau of Standards (Federal Construction Council) contract has also provided technical services to federal agencies interested in building construction and maintenance. Contract research also has been performed for the Office of Civil and Defense Mobilization.

In addition, the NRC performs a variety of contractual services involving the promotion of scientific activity. Its Office of International Relations administers a refugee scientists' program under contract with the Department of State, an international program in documentation with National Science Foundation support, and

[32] A recent example is an NAS contract with the Department of Housing and Urban Development to perform research aimed at development of an urban transit bus that would be free of "noise, pollution, and other disruptive effects" (*New York Times*, Feb. 2, 1967, p. 31).

[33] National Academy of Sciences, *Annual Report (1960–61)*, pp. 103–7.

provides scientific committees to advise the Agency for International Development on some of its development programs abroad. Its Office of Scientific Personnel administers a number of fellowship programs financed by government agencies (such as those of AID, and the senior parts of the Fulbright and Smith-Mundt program of the Department of State) as well as studies of scientific manpower.

The ability of the NAS-NRC to organize and make effective use of panels composed of outstanding representatives of the scientific community constitutes a valuable if not indispensable function. The resulting appraisals of the near or long-range projects of a given field or of broader areas of science and the policies and programs recommended make up a vital part of the communication between the nation's scientists, the federal government, and the public. The role of the NAS-NRC while authoritative is nevertheless advisory and is not inclusive of science in its coverage.[34] The NAS-NRC panel recommendations are published and therefore

[34] NAS-NRC interests are virtually co-terminous with science, but its influence varies with the nature of the organization of each field of science. NAS-NRC has been particularly influential in some areas as in the space program (on the activities of the Space Sciences Board, see John Walsh, "Space National Academy Panel Recommends Exploration of Mars as Major Goal in 1971–85 Period," *Science*, vol. 146 [Nov. 20, 1964], pp. 1025–27; and Gordon J. F. MacDonald, "Science and Space Policy: How Does It Get Planned?" *Bulletin of the Atomic Scientists*, May 1967, pp. 8–9). There has been less NAS-NRC activity in nuclear physics although the COSPUP report, *Physics: Survey and Outlook* (1966), was an important effort to increase and reorient research in that area. The sources of policy proposals and review in the high energy physics field are reviewed in Joint Committee on Atomic Energy, *High Energy Physics Program: Report on National Policy and Background Information*, 89 Cong. 1 sess. (1966).

In medical research, the National Institutes of Health with the support of numerous advisory panels together with influential members of Congress have been the principal sources of policy. The NAS has not been a particularly important influence in the area—NAS does not have a medical category although NRC has a Division of Medical Sciences—nor is there a single professional organization dominating the field. The American Medical Association in 1963 established a special committee intended to enable the association "to present expert opinion on the subject of federal support of medical research." No report had been made at the time of writing. See letter by Dr. F. J. L. Blasingame, Executive Vice-President, American Medical Association, in *Federal Research and Development Programs*, Hearings before the House Select Committee on Government Research, 88 Cong. 2 sess. (1964), pt. 2, p. 959.

The Association of American Medical Colleges has been active in dealing with the administrative problems of large-scale involvement in research. The absence of a strong professional organization in medical research has prompted the suggestion that a National Academy of Medicine is needed (Irvine H. Page, "Modern Medicine," *Saturday Review*, Feb. 6, 1965, pp. 59–60).

open to discussion and dissent by other interested parties as they are also subject to appraisal by government agencies, particularly the OST and ultimately by the Congress as the executive responds with program proposals. The desirability of the reliance of both the Congress and the executive on this one source of advice has been questioned.[35] The larger issue is the ability of both branches of the government to interpret the public interest in the recommendations of the scientists, particularly the ability to establish priorities between fields, a function which the NAS-NRC has little or no capacity or apparent inclination to undertake.

Overseas Programs

The federal government also supports a variety of R&D programs in foreign countries. One type involves the application of known technology rather than the discovery of new. In the late 1940's the Economic Cooperation Administration financed a number of efforts to accelerate the technological development of the recipient countries. Such programs were, with a few exceptions, administered by the foreign government. The technical assistance programs administered by the Technical Cooperation Administration eventually absorbed those of the ECA and have been continued by the Agency for International Development. AID and its predecessor agencies have used contractual performers on a large scale to carry out its programs of technical assistance to underdeveloped countries. The agency also finances contract research on the problem of economic development.

Federal overseas programs directed to research in the physical and medical sciences and to development include cooperative military development agreements, the world-wide trading nation operations of NASA, AEC support of Euratom, and programs sponsored by DOD, NSF, PHS (NIH), and DA in basic research which supplement domestic programs. Expenditures for project research by foreign functionaries increased from approximately $3 million in 1953 to an estimated $86 million in 1966.[36] There have

[35] See Kenneth Kofmehl, "COSPUP, Congress, and Scientific Advice," *Journal of Politics*, vol. 28 (February 1966), pp. 100–120.

[36] National Science Foundation, *Federal Funds for Research, Development, and Other Scientific Activities, Fiscal Years 1964, 1965, and 1966*, vol. 14 (1965), pp. 31–33. Data for 1953 are estimated from reports of the military agencies.

also been a number of programs involving international cooperation as the International Geophysical Year in which various agencies have participated with NSF serving as coordinator.

The Department of Defense maintains a number of programs
with foreign countries which relate to weapon development and
which involve some sharing of costs. Included are the Mutual
Weapons Development Program, the Mutual Weapons Development Data Exchange Program, Defense Development Exchange
Program, the United States–Canadian Defense Development Sharing Program and the Cooperative R&D Program. Most important
in terms of expenditures are arrangements with Canada and the
United Kingdom calling for the cooperative development of aircraft and tanks.[37]

As the research programs of the three military services grew,
some attention was given to identifying European scientists whose
interests might contribute to program objectives. The number of
such scientists under contract and the further opportunities discovered led the Air Force in 1952 to establish a European Office for
Research in Brussels.[38] In 1956 the Navy followed with an office in
London and the Army established one in Frankfurt. A similar office was established by the Army in Tokyo in 1959. A Rio de Ja-
neiro office, established in 1962, became in 1965 a joint activity of
the Army, Air Force and Public Health Service. The Public
Health Service, the AEC and the NSF also have research offices in
Europe and in Japan.

In 1958 the Department of Agriculture organized a Foreign Research and Technical Programs Division to administer the Foreign
Agricultural Research Grant Program. The Division makes grants

[37] Richard U. Sherman, "The Mutual Weapons Development Program," in Richard
A. Tybout (ed.), *Economics of Research and Development* (Ohio State University
Press, 1965), pp. 386–400. The Army's current program is described in *Army Research
and Development Newsmagazine*, April 1965, pp. 8–9.

[38] *Foreign Operations Appropriations for 1962*, Hearings before House Committee
on Appropriations, 87 Cong. 1 sess. (1961), pt. 3, pp. 185, 298; *Basic Scientific and
Astronautic Research in the Department of Defense*, Hearings before the House
Committee on Science and Astronautics, 86 Cong. 1 sess. (1959), pp. 176–80, 202;
Inquiry into Satellite and Missile Programs, Hearings before the Senate Committee
on Armed Services, 85 Cong. 1 and 2 sess. (1957–58), pt. 1, p. 711; John W. Barnes,
"International Cooperation in Army Research and Development," *Military Review*,
vol. 43 (1963), pp. 48–56; Howard J. Lewis, "How Our Air Force Supports Basic
Research in Europe," *Science*, vol. 131 (Jan. 1, 1960), pp. 15–20; *Army Research and
Development Newsmagazine*, March 1961, p. 14, and June 1962, p. 5.

from foreign currencies released by the Treasury to foreign institutions which can provide trained personnel and facilities for the conduct of proposed work. Agricultural attachés act as liaison between the Department, the institute receiving the grant, and the ambassador of the country involved. The program was established following the authorization provided by the 1959 amendments to the Agriculture Trade Development and Assistance Act of 1954 (P.L. 480). By this amendment foreign currencies accumulated under federal programs and in excess of the government's needs for the purpose of encouraging the agricultural sciences in cooperating countries.

Expenditures on project performance by foreign nationals overseas increased from approximately $3 million in 1953 to approximately $86 million in 1965, distributed by agency as shown in Table 6. Expenditures have concentrated in the European countries, particularly the United Kingdom, with about a third of

TABLE 6

United States Obligations for Research and
Development by Foreign Performers

(In Millions of Dollars)

Agency	1965		1966[a]		1967[a]	
	Total	Foreign Currency	Total	Foreign Currency	Total	Foreign Currency
Department of Defense	33.2	0.9	25.1	0.6	17.9	0.6
National Aeronautics and Space Administration	0.6	...	0.5	...	0.3	...
Atomic Energy Commission	4.1	...	6.0	...	8.3	...
Health, Education and Welfare	19.8	6.5	27.6	13.8	35.9	21.3
Agriculture	8.9	8.9	10.3	10.3	10.6	10.6
National Science Foundation	0.5	...	0.6	...	0.8	...
Commerce	0.7	0.7	1.0	1.0	0.9	0.9
Other	0.7	0.2	0.9	0.3	1.6	0.3
Total	68.5	17.2	72.1	25.9	76.3	33.7

Source: National Science Foundation, *Federal Funds for Research, Development, and Other Scientific Activities*, vol. 15 (1966), p. 145.
  a. Estimated.

funds obligated to the support of project research by European scientists. The program, however, has grown most rapidly in Canada, Australia, and New Zealand and in Latin America. Israel, which enjoys the combination of a supply of capable investigators and available P.L. 480 funds, in 1963–65 received close to 10 percent of overseas project funds.

Difficulties with the international balance of payments led the Bureau of the Budget in 1963 to establish ceilings on those overseas research expenditures which affected the "gold budget." Somewhat earlier the Federal Council for Science and Technology had recommended a gradual phasing out of United States financing of research in prosperous countries as governments involved found it possible to provide the support. An important factor in the FCST recommendation was the desirability of avoiding any stimulation to the migration of foreign scientists to the United States.[39]

Emphasis on using excess foreign currencies where possible and the operation of Bureau of the Budget ceilings has curtailed the growth of the use of dollars in purchasing overseas research. These controls have not been sufficient to avoid severe criticism by the House Committee on Government Operations of this form of the

[39] The migration of scientists and engineers from foreign countries to the United States amounted to an estimated annual average of 4,869 over the period 1956–61. About a quarter were from Canada and a slightly larger number from Western Europe, principally the United Kingdom and Germany. The problem is serious to the losing countries since emigrating scientists and engineers as a percentage of 1959 output of science and engineering graduates amounted to 32 percent in the case Canada, in excess of 10 percent for Norway, Switzerland, Greece, and the Netherlands, and 7 percent or more for West Germany, the United Kingdom, Ireland, and Sweden. There is some evidence, historical and contemporary, that the migrants are of high quality. See National Science Foundation, *Scientific Manpower from Abroad* (1962); Organization for Economic Cooperation and Development, *Resources of Scientific and Technical Personnel in the OECD Area* (OECD Third International Survey; Paris, 1963); E. M. Friedwald, "The Research Effort of Western Europe, the USA, and the USSR," *The OECD Observer*, February 1966, pp. 13–15.

International movements of scientists and other highly trained personnel present numerous problems and conflicts in objectives and values. Some of these considerations are brought out in *The International Migration of Talent and Skills*, Proceedings of a Workshop and Conference sponsored by the Interagency Council on International Educational and Cultural Affairs, Department of State, October 1966, and in ICIECA's "Some Facts and Figures on the Migration of Talent and Skills" (processed, 1967). See also Charles V. Kidd, "The Loss of Scientists from Less to More Developed Countries," *United Nations Conference on the Application of Science and Technology for the Benefit of the Less Developed Areas* (Geneva, 1963), pp. 18–26.

dollar drain.[40] The Committee held that too many nonurgent projects were being approved, that some projects could be conducted within the United States, and that greater use should be made of excess foreign currencies.[41]

It follows that United States policy toward supporting overseas research activity is in process of reexamination and probable change. The overseas contract programs in countries with well-established traditions of research—as in Western Europe—have had a small but significant impact. These expenditures have generated significant research, stimulated some European governments to increase their support for science, and encouraged American business firms to establish laboratories abroad. Elsewhere the programs, though not without scientific significance, appear to be primarily a part of the American effort to aid in the economic growth of the underdeveloped countries.

[40] See *Federal Foreign Research Spending and the Dollar Drain,* Hearings before the House Committee on Government Operations, 89 Cong. 2 sess. (1966); and the same committee's *Plugging the Dollar Drain: Cutting Federal Expenditures for Research and Related Activities Abroad,* H. Rept. 1453, 89 Cong. 2 sess. (1966).

[41] However, the Committee on Appropriations determines. That committee, reporting on the 1967 appropriations for the Departments of Labor and of Health, Education and Welfare, approved HEW's request for an increase in funds for its Office of International Research, expressing the belief "that these international programs play a vital role in the total biomedical research effort of this country, and that they should not only be continued but be expanded as opportunity offers in the years ahead. Curtailment of these valuable programs to alleviate a chronic balance of payments problem with which we have had to live during most of the postwar period is not in the best national interest. Unique opportunities to advance biomedical knowledge which contributes to the steady improvement of the health of the American people should be exploited wherever they occur" (*Departments of Labor and Health, Education and Welfare, and Related Agencies Appropriation Bill, 1967,* H. Rept. 1464, 89 Cong. 2 sess. [1966], pp. 30–31).

CHAPTER IX

Government Centers for Research and Development

The performance of research and development discussed in the three preceding chapters is of a project type—controlled by the work statement describing a sequence of activities to be completed within a given period of time and within a budget which is fixed in the case of most basic and applied research. In the case of development contracts there is more flexibility in costs, even though the sponsoring government agencies are making strenuous efforts to improve cost estimates and to hold expenditures within those estimates. Such projects are normally selected from a number of more or less directly competitive proposals, with contracts being awarded in accordance with the agency's evaluation procedure.

There remain for consideration those R&D organizations supported by funds allocated by the sponsoring agency on the basis of a mission or program assignment rather than on a project basis. Such organizations typically use the project to organize their work but such projects are selected internally, subject in many cases to review by the sponsoring agency but not to direct competition with proposals from outside sources. Three classes of institutions engage in such administratively assigned research: the intramural organizations of the sponsoring agencies, the federal research centers which are contractor-operators of government-owned facilities, and a group of nonprofit organizations which own or lease the facilities used, but which stand in a captive relationship to their

373

principal sponsoring agency or, in any case, to the government. Since the ownership of facilities is not necessarily an important difference, these organizations are dealt with together as federal research centers.

Classification as a contractual research center according to the criteria discussed below is clear in most cases. It was pointed out in Chapter VII that government agencies and the universities are entering into an increasing number of program-oriented arrangements. Some of these are intended both to increase research capabilities and to heighten emphasis on the training of students. Others are focused on more immediate research objectives, though with more flexibility than the project approach permits. Their arrangements differ significantly in administrative and other ways from project contract and grant research and have clear resemblance to the recognized research centers. However, the reports of the National Science Foundation do not differentiate and in the following analysis the NSF's classification is followed.

Federal Contractual R&D Centers

The federal R&D centers represent the use of the contract to establish and operate facilities which, before World War II, would have been intramural organizations if it had been possible to establish them at all. The National Science Foundation lists fifty-eight such centers in operation in 1964.[1]

The centers are a highly diverse group of organizations, but they share some characteristics which distinguish them from other types of research institutions:

1. All are managed by private institutions under contracts which have a marked continuity. Since 1946 some changes in contractors have occurred but only a very few research centers have been disbanded.

2. The centers are closely identified with a single government agency. The bulk of the work of each center is done by one agency which is its sponsor. Some centers accept contracts with other government agencies, frequently after securing the consent of the

[1] National Science Foundation, *Federal Funds for Research, Development, and Other Scientific Activities, Fiscal Years 1964, 1965, and 1966*, vol. 14 (1965), pp. 69–70.

principal sponsor. In a few cases, a center, though identified with a single agency, is in fact supported by two or more in a joint program.[2] The long-term and intimate relationships of most research centers to the sponsoring agency are reflected in the frequent reference to them by name in budget submissions and testimony of the agency to the Congress.

3. The centers have contractual responsibilities for furthering the interests of the sponsoring agency in broad mission or program terms. In some situations the specific projects to be undertaken are identified and outlined in periodic discussions between the agency and the center; in others the center exercises considerable independence in selecting its projects. All projects, however, are assigned through administrative procedures rather than through competition with proposals submitted by possible alternative R&D groups.

4. The government's objectives could not be effectively accomplished by conventional types of organizations. Such determination may follow from a congressional decision regarding the nature of the public interest in an objective, as in the case of atomic energy. In that case there followed an AEC determination that the designated objectives could best be accomplished through contractor management of government-owned facilities. In other circumstances an agency may determine that an organization standing between itself and conventional institutions is necessary to accomplish an objective. Such a decision may be strongly influenced by an agency's lack of the necessary personnel but may follow also from the decision of agency administrators that a source independent both of government and of conventional private organizations could best perform a necessary function.

5. Since the centers are managed by private organizations, their personnel policies are not controlled by civil service regulations, salaries, and procedures. Although they are, in varying degrees, influenced by the personnel policies of the parent institution, the centers also typically operate independently of them. Restraints on personnel policies do exist, but they are contractual. The most

---

[2] As in the case of the work of Columbia University's Radiation Laboratory on lasers, which is supported by the three military services (*Army Research and Development Newsmagazine*, April 1961, p. 16).

common and important restraints are provisions for reviewing the general salary structure, and particularly salaries above a certain level—frequently $25,000 per year.

Origins of the Contractual Centers

The federal research centers originated during World War II. Early in its career, the Office of Scientific Research and Development sought the expeditious accomplishment of some R&D objectives which required assembling scientific talents together with supporting technical skills to work in close proximity under a single management. There were precedents for the establishment of such centers in the existence of a number of research institutes attached to universities, and some industrial corporations had consolidated their research programs in separately incorporated organizations. To carry out its objectives in nuclear energy, the Office of Scientific Research and Development sought to mobilize all available specialized knowledge and skills and to provide whatever support was needed. The OSRD minimized the problems of achieving a large and rapid expansion of effort by building upon existing centers of activity, and entering into contracts with private institutions to establish and operate its programs. As the nuclear energy program yielded results calling for intensive development requiring massive engineering support, the program was transferred to the Army Corps of Engineers. The existing contractual arrangements were compatible with the procedures of the Corps of Engineers since it had long relied upon contractors to do the work required on its projects. Expansion of the program by the Corps of Engineers proceeded then through contracts with private industrial firms and universities to provide management for building and operating the Manhattan Project facilities.

The need for considerable expansion of what had been a small effort emerged also in other areas. For example, the OSRD was interested in accelerating the development of an effective proximity fuze for anti-aircraft shells. The OSRD organized an effort to this end by entering into a contract with Johns Hopkins University to establish an appropriate laboratory, the Applied Physics Laboratory. When that project reached the early stages of production in

1944, OSRD turned administrative responsibilities over to the Navy as the interested service. The Navy thereupon assumed the contract supporting APL.[3] Since that time APL has held mission responsibilities for the Navy's ship-to-air weapon programs.

The Jet Propulsion Laboratory originated in a somewhat different manner. The Army Air Force in 1943 entered into a contract with the California Institute of Technology to support a small faculty group which had been engaged for a decade in research in rockets. That group was organized as the Jet Propulsion Laboratory, a division of the Institute. Army support of JPL increased slowly until 1950 when mounting interest in rockets, together with promising research developments, generated a substantial increase in funds.[4]

Postwar Growth

The postwar appraisal of the nation's R&D policies resulted in continued use of privately managed federal research centers. The Atomic Energy Commission chose to apply the policy of contractor management to all its facilities, with the AEC "responsible for what is done and the contractor for how."[5] Though some of the other OSRD-founded centers were closed, the Army or Navy assumed sponsorship for most. In one case—that of the Naval Ordnance Testing Station—a contractual center was converted into an intramural organization of the Navy.

Since the end of World War II, the number of contractual research centers has more than doubled. Expenditures of federal research centers increased from slightly less than $300 million annually in 1953–55 to $1.2 billion in 1967.

The expenditures of research centers operated under AEC contracts (Chart 11) increased from $181 million in 1955 to $824

---

[3] *Systems Development and Management,* Hearings before the House Government Operations Committee, 87 Cong. 2 sess. (1962), pt. 5, p. 1500. These hearings are the most important single source of information on the so-called nonprofit or not-for-profit research organization.

[4] *Systems Development and Management,* Hearings, pt. 5, p. 1737.

[5] James T. Ramey, "Economy in Government Contracting—Atomic Energy Commission Experience," *Law and Contemporary Problems,* vol. 29 (Spring 1964), p. 381.

CHART 11
Federal Obligations for Contract Research Centers by Agency

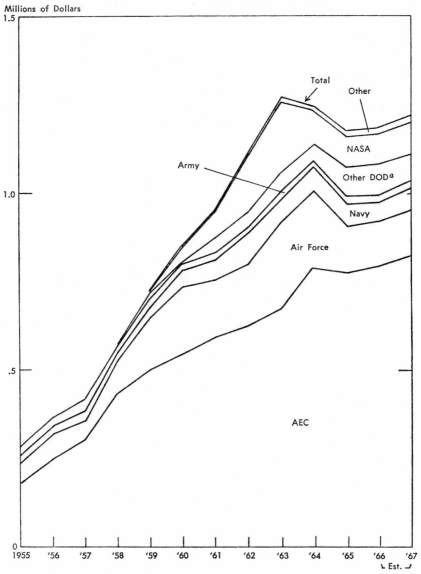

Source: National Science Foundation, *Federal Funds for Research, Development, and Other Scientific Activities,* vols. 5–15.
a. Includes Advanced Research Projects Agency and department-wide funds.

million in 1967. AEC expenditures accounted for 63 percent of all research centers expenditures in 1955 and slightly more in 1967. The expenditures of centers supported by the military agencies increased from 1955 to 1963 by more than three times but have since decreased significantly. The Air Force accounts for more than half of DOD support of research centers. The Navy and DOD-wide activities account for 20 percent each. The Army has made use of this kind of arrangement on a smaller scale. Moreover, its largest contractual research center, the Jet Propulsion Laboratory, was transferred to NASA in 1958. The JPL remains the sole NASA contractual research center.

The research centers tend to be specialized in function, but as a group their activities range from basic research to prototype production and include such services as operations analysis, weapons evaluation, and strategic planning. All these functions can be and are performed in other forms of organization. The very heavy reliance of the AEC upon its research centers has followed from administrative policy. Most of the other centers have been established as a recognized deviation from normal procedures and after determination that the use of conventional institutions imposed obstacles or limitations which could best be overcome by utilizing a contractual center.

Basic and Applied Research Centers

About half of the government-sponsored, contractor-operated centers are devoted to research; all save one are managed by universities. Such centers as those of the Atomic Energy Commission came into being when a level of research effort was desired that substantially exceeded the facilities of a university.[6] A university-like environment was desired but expensive equipment was necessary together with large professional staffs and supporting personnel. Similar considerations motivated the establishment of such centers sponsored by the Department of Defense as the Arctic Research Laboratory, the Navy Biological Laboratory or the Army Mathematics Center. (See Chart 12 for the different types of management for contractual research centers.)

---

[6] The history and work assignments of the AEC centers are described in Joint Committee on Atomic Energy, *The Future Role of the Atomic Energy Commission Laboratories*, 86 Cong. 2 sess. (1960).

CHART 12

Federal Obligations for Contract Research Centers by Type of Management

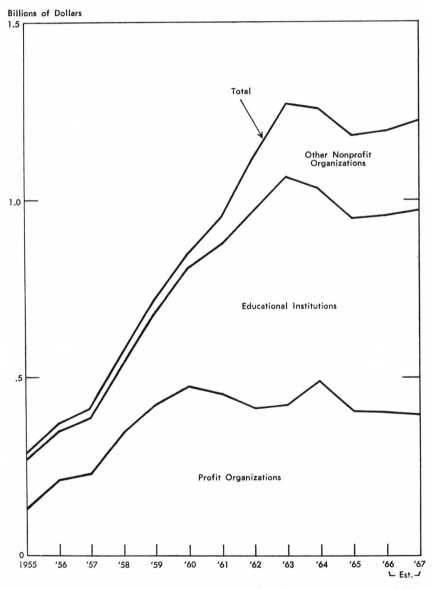

Source: National Science Foundation, *Federal Funds for Research, Development, and Other Scientific Activities*, vols. 5–15.

The three centers sponsored by the National Science Foundation originated from a need to supply expensive facilities that would be available to scientists regardless of their university affiliation.[7] The NSF is prohibited by statute from operating its own laboratories. The agency, however, can respond to proposals that provide for contractor operation of a large undertaking involving expensive equipment. In these instances one objective was to permit widespread utilization of the facilities by interested institutions and their scientists. The NSF chose to ensure that objective by arranging for multi-institutional management and did so by contracting with consortia of universities for the operation of the laboratories.[8]

For the university, a contract center represents an opportunity to extend its research activity in an area far beyond what would otherwise be possible. The strength of the faculty group which attracted the formation of the center to begin with is further enhanced by the addition of impressive facilities and new staff.[9]

While many of the centers are physically located on or adjacent to the campus of the contracting university, such proximity is not particularly important. Interchange of personnel between the university's teaching and the center's research staff does occur but tends to be limited to a very few key people and to some larger numbers of graduate students.[10] The staffs of the centers are typi-

[7] See the explanation of National Science Foundation Director Alan T. Waterman, in *Systems Development and Management*, Hearings, pt. 1, pp. 184–85.

[8] At least two others have been organized. One is the Gulf University Research Corporation, formed by eight southern universities to operate a government-owned Gulf Coast Marine Science Center (*Congressional Record*, daily ed., March 16, 1965, pp. 5050–51). The other is Universities Research Association, Inc., formed in 1965 by 34 universities, joined in 1966 by 12 others, for the purpose of offering their services as the contracting agency for the construction and operation of the AEC's proposed high energy particle accelerator—the 200 Bev accelerator (*Annual Report to the Board of Trustees* [URA, December 7, 1966]).

[9] "Approximately 20 percent of the R&D scientists and engineers at all colleges and universities are employed by 11 universities to work in 22 separate governmentally supported research laboratories and institutes. They operate apart from the universities' regular departmental structure and they contribute in varying degrees to the main research and educational functions of the institutions that manage them" (Leland J. Haworth, in *Nation's Manpower Revolution*, Hearings before the House Committee on Labor and Public Welfare, 88 Cong. 1 sess. [1963], p. 2661).

[10] About 5 percent of the scientists employed in university-managed federal research centers were in 1958 also faculty members of the sponsoring university.

cally full-time scientists and technical supporting personnel without faculty status.

The presence of a center, however, adds to the luster of the institution's research reputation, and normally permits the parent university to give special emphasis to training in the fields in which the center operates. It also has the advantage of access to the center's resources and the results of its work. Some of its graduate students are likely to develop interests in the subject area and a certain number will wish to qualify for employment with it.

Development Centers

A second group of centers has broad responsibilities to support an agency's needs for development in some area. Most of these centers are managed by industrial firms. A large part of their effort as measured by expenditures relates to the development of applications of atomic energy. There is also a small group of business-managed federal centers engaged in specialized development in explosives, missile fuels, and electronics.

The development center managed by a business firm is a phenomenon arising for the most part out of the special circumstances relating to the development and application of atomic energy. The business firms that have served as managers of federal centers have not done so primarily for profit. Fees have been modest and in some instances nominal. University administrators of development centers receive a management allowance or a negotiated lump sum to cover management expenses.[11] Such advantages are, however,

---

Some of these were, of course, key people. The fact remains that 95 percent of the scientific staff of the organization had no formal affiliation with the university faculty. See National Science Foundation, *Reviews of Data on Research and Development*, No. 23 (October 1960), p. 4. Student employment by such centers is also of very modest proportions. In 1964, 22 of the 30 university-affiliated centers employed 1,773 students at a cost of $3,999,000. Much of such employment was for the summer vacation period. More than half the number were employed at the Lawrence Radiation Laboratory and the Los Alamos Laboratory, both operated by the University of California. See *Federal Student Assistance in Higher Education*, Study Paper No. 5, House Select Committee on Government Research, H. Rept., 1933, 88 Cong. 2 sess. (1964), pp. 22–23.

[11] AEC industrial contractors receive a fee which ranges from 1 to 4 percent of a negotiated fee base which excludes government furnished materials and some other items. The AEC policy with regard to university contractors is to pay a management allowance to cover central office expenses or negotiated lump sum

small compared with those to be had through expanding technical capabilities. It is clear that a few of the contractors have made use of the experience gained by their employees for the development of products and techniques not directly associated with the government's programs.

The expanding interest of business firms in R&D in areas of interest to the government and the accumulation of experience on the part of both business firms and the government in working together on federal programs have apparently rendered more centers of the AEC type unnecessary. There have emerged, however, a small number of university-managed centers with responsibilities for research through applied development extending upwards in some cases to the production and utilization of operational prototypes. Such centers pose some particularly difficult problems since they infringe upon even if they do not disrupt the conventional division of functions between types of institutions.

If, in the R&D process, knowledge accumulates slowly from widely scattered contributors and is broadly diffused, the successive steps from research to exploratory and then to applied development can be dealt with by normal procedures. It must be kept in mind that an objective selected for intensified R&D efforts is frequently identified with the contribution made by one person or a small group of research people. If these successive steps occur within a single organized group with minor contributions from outsiders, the problems of accelerating development are minimized by providing an appropriate organization for the group, avoiding the difficulties that may be encountered by a transfer to another type of institution. If the principals are employed by a business firm which can provide the necessary technical support and administer a large-scale effort, a normal contractual relationship is established. This is true even for such complex projects as that launched by the Army's Nike contract with the Bell Laboratories. If the principals are employed by the government, the scale

in lieu of indirect administrative expenses. For fees actually paid in 1962 see *Systems Development and Management,* Hearings, pt. 5, p. 1668. Such negotiated fees overcome differences of opinion regarding allocation of indirect costs and may result in financial gain for the university. See "AEC Contracts May Permit Profit for Nonprofit Institutions," *New York Times,* Jan. 21, 1962.

of operations may be expanded, sometimes to a degree leading to the establishment of a new facility. An illustration is the formation of the Army Ballistic Missile Laboratory to support the von Braun research team.

Occasionally, a development objective emerges from the work of a research group whose principals are members of a university faculty and who are uniquely qualified to continue the work. Small groups of this type sometimes transfer as a whole or in part to another form of organization. If the group is a large one and prefers to remain at the university, it becomes necessary to provide some form of organization which will permit the group to acquire the necessary facilities and to expand as its operations call for new skills. This is particularly true if the supporting agency views the objective as urgent.

Situations of this type led to the formation of some of the early contractual organizations in the nuclear energy area. In the postwar period, related considerations prompted the establishment of the Lawrence Radiation Laboratory of the Atomic Energy Commission under contract with the University of California, the Air Force's Lincoln Laboratories with the Massachusetts Institute of Technology, and the Navy's Hudson Laboratories with Columbia University.

A special problem exists when an agency does not have the staff necessary to collect and to evaluate ideas and proposals from a variety of sources. If the agency's staff is inadequate, the agency will seek a business firm with a capability which it can hope to expand. If, however, the necessary capabilities are widely dispersed among business firms, a contract assigning responsibilities to a single business firm will be ineffective since other firms will be reluctant to share their knowledge with a competitor. Under such conditions the agencies have sought to provide arrangements whereby proposals can be invited, assembled, and evaluated from the government's point of view.

Two devices have been used. One is the formation of an independent nonprofit corporation. The other is to induce a business firm to undertake the function of assembling and evaluating technical data under conditions which permit the cooperation of other firms. This is accomplished by contract with the firm which includes a "hardware ban." The firm agrees to refrain from competing for contracts for advanced development and production relating to the project on which it serves as technical evaluator. Under both systems the agency delegates in some substantial measure the functions of gathering information and providing technical advice, appraisals, and evaluations.

System Managers

The standard way to deal with the complex problems of a development project is by the selective consolidation of business proposals and agency ideas into a program statement. The work of the contractor selected is then coordinated through system management within the agency or, if that is not feasible, by assigning such functions to a business firm as prime contractor. Such an assignment is made only after the agency has assured itself that the contractual firm has available most of the relevant technical information, that it can obtain what it needs through subcontractors, or that the firm will accept technical support and direction from the agency itself. A number of the AEC development centers are managers of integrated systems.

On a few other occasions, advanced knowledge required for an objective has been acquired by groups so situated that they could not easily be utilized through standard procedures. The Jet Propulsion Laboratory administered by the California Institute of Technology has held systems management responsibilities for NASA's programs for unmanned exploration of the moon and planets—the Ranger, Surveyor, and Mariner projects. The JPL's designs are fabricated by numerous subcontractors under its managerial and technical direction. The JPL then performs some functions which are normally provided by agency staff and others which are normally contributed by industrial firms.[12]

The Applied Physics Laboratory has also held mission responsibilities for the Navy's surface-to-air missile programs for many years. Its role has differed from that of JPL in that its management responsibilities were limited to furnishing analysis and advice on the technical aspects of development tasks which had been contracted by the Navy to business firms. Such firms were designated as associate contractors, and were responsible for produc-

[12] *Systems Development and Management,* Hearings, pt. 5, p. 1698.

tion.[13] Production contracts were let but overall responsibility was retained by the Navy as in the case of the Polaris program by the Navy's Special Projects Office.

One of the results of the work of Lincoln Laboratories for the Air Force was the determination of the feasibility of SAGE, a complex air defense system. Attainment of the objective required that the Lincoln technical people serve as system engineers, integrating Lincoln capabilities with those possessed by business firms. There was reluctance on the part of MIT to permit Lincoln Laboratories to undertake such functions. The solution was the formation of Mitre Corporation in 1956, the transfer of a large number of Lincoln Laboratories staff members to the new organization, and the transfer of Lincoln responsibilities, first through subcontracts, and eventually by direct Mitre contracts with the Air Force.[14]

The origin of the Aerospace Corporation, the Air Force's other research center which functions as a systems manager, was quite different. Until 1960 the Air Force relied upon the Space Technology Laboratories, a subsidiary of Ramo-Wooldridge Corporation, to perform the functions of systems manager in the development of its intercontinental ballistic missile programs. By 1960, however, a substantial number of business firms had acquired capabilities in one or more aspects of missile development. While the competence of the technical staff of STL was high, it was also necessary that the Air Force have access to the knowledge and skills which had been developed elsewhere. The firms involved not unnaturally objected to revealing the results of their work to a competitor. This situation had been anticipated and the contract with STL provided that it would not enter into the competition for production contracts. However, STL's parent firm, Ramo-Wooldridge, was increasingly interested in participating in production contracts and was anxious to secure release from the hardware ban.[15] STL faced a potential conflict-of-interest situation that threatened to dilute its effectiveness in missile development for the Air Force.

This problem attracted the attention of the House Committee

[13] *Ibid.*, pt. 4, p. 1497.

[14] *Ibid.*, pt. 3, pp. 989–1013, 1229–76.

[15] Under this ban a business firm accepts a contract in which it agrees to develop an item but to refrain from competing for a resulting procurement contract (*Systems Development and Management—1963*, Hearings before the House Committee on Government Operations, 88 Cong. 1 sess. [1963], pp. 76–78).

on Government Operations. A GAO report on AF-STL relationships recommended that the Air Force develop a technical staff competent to handle its problem intramurally. The Air Force, however, was concerned with the need for continuity of effort. With the approval of some members of Congress the Air Force sought the solution to the problem in the formation of a new trustee-managed nonprofit corporation, the Aerospace Corporation.[16] Aerospace acquired part of the STL staff and the Air Force assigned to it program responsibilities for projects extending beyond those retained by STL. Among its functions was that of "working with the various associate contractors in such a manner that the client—the Air Force—receives the product which meets its requirement in an economical and timely manner and which is qualitatively superior to that available to any potential enemy by the utilization of the maximum that science and engineering has to offer."[17] This meant that the Corporation exercised authority to give technical direction to contractors within the framework of the contractual relationships between the government and the contractor.

It is generally acknowledged that organizations like these have contributed effectively to the accomplishment of agency objectives. However, all the research centers engaged in systems management have been subjected to severe criticism. Industry critics contend that they perform no service which industry cannot perform as well. Some government critics contend that their functions should be performed by agency staff. Congress has added to such criticism concern with the rapid growth of some of these organizations and their apparent immunity from both market and statutory controls over costs, particularly salaries.[18] In the absence of such controls, Congress clearly expects the sponsoring agency to exercise its contractual powers to limit expenditures. The Air Force's relations with its Aerospace Corporation have been particularly subject to criticism—criticism that may well lead to closer financial controls.

[16] See House Committee on Government Operations, *Organization and Management of Missile Programs*, 86 Cong. 2 sess. (1960), and the same committee's *Air Force Ballistic Missile Management (Formation of Aerospace Corporation)*, H. Rept. 324, 87 Cong. 1 sess. (1961).

[17] *Systems Development and Management*, Hearings, pt. 3, pp. 953–87, 1103–1228.

[18] John R. Donnelly, "The Aerospace Corporation: Fish or Fowl or Government Instrumentality?" *Federal Bar Journal*, vol. 22 (Fall 1962), pp. 298–306; "Missile Managers," *Wall Street Journal*, Dec. 4, 1961, pp. 1–2.

Operation and Policy Advisers

A final group of research centers includes those which specialize in supplying expert analysis, evaluation, and advice relating broadly to the application of new technology to operations and policy problems. It has been common practice since World War II for government agencies to seek analysis and advice on specific problems through project contracts. The centers here considered are nonprofit corporations which supply agencies with such services as a continuing mission responsibility on annually renewable contracts. The practice has been confined to the military agencies, although civilian agencies are experimenting with it.

During World War II, OSRD found that new types of equipment made available to the services as a result of its development programs were often used ineffectively. It therefore established an Office of Field Service which made available to both the Army and Navy teams of specialists to advise on the use of such equipment. Such advice almost inevitably dealt also with the problems of integrating new techniques into existing procedures as well as generally subjecting operating procedures to rational analysis, frequently by applying the new techniques of operations research. The contribution made to World War II through these services was very impressive.[19]

During the war the Navy had assembled a small staff assigned to the analysis of operational problems. With the disbanding of OSRD at the end of the war, the Navy arranged for the continuation of such services by establishing an Operations Evaluation Group managed under a contract with the Massachusetts Institute of Technology. In 1958 the Navy established another group with the assignment of analyzing the longer range problems of the Navy. This was the Institute for Naval Studies which was managed by the Institute for Defense Analyses, an organization discussed below. These two groups were brought together in 1962 as the Center for Naval Analyses which was given some additional responsibilities. At that time, the arrangements with MIT and IDA were terminated and the Franklin Institute accepted the contractual responsibility for managing the new organization.[20]

[19] Lincoln R. Thiesmayer and John E. Burchard, *Combat Scientists* (Little, Brown & Co., 1947), chap. 7.

[20] *Systems Development and Management*, Hearings, pt. 4, p. 1487.

The Army also profited from OSRD's assistance in analyzing some of its operations as well as from OSRD advice on the utilization of new equipment. Although an interest existed in continuing the application of the new science of operations research to military problems, the Army did not act until 1948. It then established a General Research Office to make such services available to its commands. That attempt to establish an intramural group was abandoned within the year, after which the Army entered into a contract with the Johns Hopkins University to administer a new Operations Research Office. The contract with the Johns Hopkins University was terminated in 1961 and in its place the Army established the Research Analysis Corporation, an independent nonprofit organization which took over the facilities as well as much of the personnel of ORO. The new organization was assigned responsibilities relating to operations analysis of combat, logistic, and management systems.[21]

The Army also arranged for sources of expert analysis and advice in two other areas. Since 1957 the George Washington University has administered the Human Resources Research Office which is concerned with applied psychology as it relates to the problems of Army organization and tactical operations.[22] The desirability of securing expert attention to the problems of unconventional warfare led to the establishment of another nonprofit organization. This is the Special Operations Research Office which since 1955 has been administered by American University.[23]

Late in World War II the Army Air Corps acted upon proposals from various sources that it maintain a continuing program of research bearing on military planning, a concept much broader than anything then contemplated by the Army or Navy. That program was established under a contract with the Douglas Aircraft Company in 1945 to administer Project Rand. The staff assembled was to conduct research on the "broad subject of intercontinental

[21] *Ibid.*, pt. 4, p. 1431.

[22] HumRRO operates in support of the Army's Human Factors and Operations Research Division. See *Army Research and Development Newsmagazine*, August 1965, pp. 28–29, and September 1965, pp. 20–21; and Meredith P. Crawford, *A Perspective on the Development of HumRRO* (George Washington University, 1967).

[23] The operations of SORO were explored in hearings before the House Foreign Affairs Committee (*International Organizations and Movements*, 89 Cong. 1 sess. [1965]) in connection with the difficulties in Chile with its Project Camelot.

warfare other than surface, with the objective of recommending to the Army Air Forces preferred technique and instrumentalities for this purpose."[24]

By 1948 the project was judged to have established its value but the association with the Douglas Aircraft Company, slight though it was, had been criticized, particularly by other aircraft firms. The solution was the transfer of Project Rand to a new nonprofit corporation formed for the purpose, the Rand Corporation. Since that time the Air Force has maintained a continuing contractual relationship with Rand. Rand's services to the Air Force cover a wide range of research including highly technical studies, cost estimates of new weapons systems, and estimates of the changing capabilities of foreign countries.[25]

Rand's work in certain technical areas generated requests by the Air Force for an expansion—an expansion so great as to alter the fundamental character of the organization. The problem was met by forming a new organization to which some of Rand's functions and some of its staff were transferred. This was the Systems Development Corporation, formed in 1956 to provide technical and training services in the field of advanced communication systems.[26]

Another research center emerged as a solution to the problems of the Joint Chiefs of Staff in evaluating the operational significance of new weaponry. The Joint Chiefs of Staff had sought to supply themselves with such services by establishing in 1949 a Weapons Systems Evaluation Group as a staff division. The second Hoover Commission reviewing the operations of the JCS approved the concept of WSEG but noted that the staff was too small and that efforts to expand it had been unsuccessful. The Commission recommended that the development of a more adequate staff be sought through a private organization. The course chosen—to establish the Institute for Defense Analyses—following the Rand pat-

[24] *Systems Development and Management*, Hearings, pt. 3, pp. 917–52, 1088–1101.

[25] The most useful, available study of any on the dependent nonprofit organizations is Bruce L. R. Smith, *The Rand Corporation: Case Study of a Nonprofit Advisory Corporation* (Harvard University Press, 1966). The study includes an informative case study of AF-Rand relationships although in general it reflects the classified nature of Rand's work. See also *The Rand Corporation—the First Fifteen Years* (RAND, 1963).

[26] *Systems Development and Management*, Hearings, pt. 3, pp. 989–1013, 1229–76.

tern except that the trustees of the corporation were selected from the top administrators of a number of universities. It was anticipated that the university association so established would lead to close relations between IDA and university faculties.[27]

Two other research centers have been formed recently to meet quite different problems. Both are small and both are intended to supply highly qualified advisory services in relation to the responsibility of the Air Force's Director of Development Planning for estimating the technical effectiveness and cost of proposed developments. Previously, short-term studies with both profit and nonprofit organizations had been used to assist in such work. While such studies continued to be made, greater efficiency and speed were sought by concentrating such preliminary studies in a single organization. In 1957 the Air Force entered into a continuing contract with a small engineering firm to maintain a technical staff to provide the technical studies necessary. These arrangements were judged successful until the engineering firm was absorbed by a large industrial corporation. Though the arrangement was continued, it became unsatisfactory because other industrial firms were reluctant to supply proprietary information to a possible competitor.

The Air Force then requested Rand to undertake the functions and to assemble the necessary staff. Rand instead recommended that a new nonprofit organization be formed. The result was the formation in 1958 of Analytical Services Inc. ANSER has remained a small organization capable of reacting quickly in appraising the desirability of larger scale efforts in exploring new technical developments.[28]

The most recently organized research center is the Logistic Management Institute, which came into being because of the need of the Office of the Secretary of Defense for an expanded and independent source of advice on the logistical factors in the procurement of weapons.[29] Like ANSER, LMI directs all its efforts to the needs of its sponsor.

[27] *Ibid.*, pt. 2, pp. 615–39; Charles R. Donnelly, *The United States Guided Missile Program*, Print of Senate Committee on Armed Services, 86 Cong. 1 sess. (1959), p. 51.
[28] *Systems Development and Management*, Hearings, pt. 3, pp. 1073–86, 1357–72.
[29] *Systems Development and Management—1963*, Hearings, pp. 130–31.

Functions and Roles

The research centers vary in size, from a score or two employees and modest facilities to very large organizations employing several thousand scientific and technical personnel and operating very expensive facilities. All exist because of the conviction held by their founders and supporters that existing organizations could not effectively serve the goals sought. The decision to seek private rather than government management for the new research organizations was based on a belief that the restraints historically associated with government operations must be avoided. In large part, the advantages possessed by these organizations stem from their freedom, both from their sponsors and from the contractual managing institution. It follows that they can recruit and retain personnel with a minimum of restraints. They can also negotiate from strength on their course of action within their assigned missions even if they are not altogether free to determine it. Such advantages are at the same time obvious targets of criticism from established organizations upon which the centers infringe and which may be fearful of departures from historical patterns of institutional functions and responsibilities. The principal defense of the centers against such criticisms is their record of positive accomplishment.

Those federal research centers which are devoted to basic and applied scientific research short of production have on the whole escaped serious criticism. Since there are no generally accepted criteria regarding the productivity of basic research efforts, assurance of the effectiveness of such efforts rests upon providing an environment that attracts and stimulates research people. For many, the university environment, permitting some limited teaching, the stimulus of contacts with graduate students and other faculty representing diverse disciplines, and a high degree of freedom in work habits is clearly the most productive environment.[30] Some,

[30] The President's Science Advisory Committee, for example, recommended with reference to basic science that "new research laboratories for a special field should be attached to universities whenever it is practicable, and universities should make full educational use of such facilities." From what it judged to be the "best cases," it concluded that these laboratories enjoyed the following advantages from their university connection: "they have had the active participation of outstanding university scientists; their own ability to attract first-rate research men has been strengthened by the university's sponsorship; [and] they have been stimulated to

disliking teaching, have found other environments more satisfying. It is clear, also, that a research center managed by a business firm can develop and maintain vigorous programs involving intimate relationships with universities.[31]

On the other hand, university-associated and independent research centers functioning as managers of large development projects have been subject to severe criticism. The appropriateness of such activity for a university is questioned.[32] Some spokesmen for industry have contended that the universities perform no service which industry cannot perform as well while the existence of such centers deprives industry of the opportunity to employ the skills represented and thus reduces industry's ability to meet the technical requirements of government programs.[33] The element of truth

---

high standards of excellence by the standards of the university itself. At the same time the university has benefited from opportunities for research and for the advanced training of graduate students, and its own ability to attract first-rate scientists has been strengthened." The committee also expressed the belief that "members of such installations should be more fully associated with teaching in the universities than is now usual and conversely we think the installations themselves should always be full of learning students" (*Scientific Progress, the Universities, and the Federal Government* [Government Printing Office, 1960], p. 21).

[31] As is demonstrated by the experience of the Oak Ridge National Laboratory, which was administered by the Union Carbide and Chemical Corporation. The ORNL'S Oak Ridge Institute of Nuclear Studies (now the Oak Ridge Associated Universities) established close relationships with approximately forty participating institutions of higher education. See "Oak Ridge National Laboratory: Aim Is Change Along with Growth," *Science*, vol. 150 (Nov. 26, 1965), pp. 1133–36.

[32] A thoughtful analysis of the place of this type of nonprofit institution is provided by Major General James McCormack, vice-president of Massachusetts Institute of Technology, in "The Not-for-Profit Research," *Proceedings of the Fifteenth National Conference on the Administration of Research* (Denver Research Institute, 1961), pp. 47–51.

[33] The Stanford Research Institute, in its study *The Industry-Government Aerospace Relationship*, vol. 1 (1963), pp. 33–34, summarizes industry's views on nonprofit organizations as systems engineering and technical directors: "The Aerospace industries are not concerned about the existence of these organizations. They are concerned about the fact that these organizations, in their role as technical advisors to the government, appear to be taking over a portion of industry's one-time role in conceptualizing new systems and components. These organizations, too, are becoming increasingly active in the conduct of research, the capacity for which also exists in industry. In effect, this represents increasing government 'in-house' research." The report continues: "A critical concern of industry is the relatively aloof and sometimes competitive attitude of these special organizations in their consideration of industry's ideas. This is important because the livelihood of industry is increasingly at the R&D level, where proprietary ideas are crucial. In

in such a contention is offset by the fact that the government needs more than the ability to meet specific technical requirements; it needs objective sources of technical information and analysis. The government also needs this alternative so as not to be entirely dependent on industrial advice.[34]

While the sponsoring agencies staunchly defend their contractual relations with the systems-management nonprofit corporations, criticism from other government sources has been vigorous at times. The charge that the centers perform functions which should be performed within the government is met with the response that the specific functions at issue have never been conducted within government. The response to the charge that the centers pay excessively high salaries is that their salary scales are set in competition with industry, not with government, and that salaries are reasonable by that standard.[35] Despite such attacks from some congressional quarters, many congressmen have consistently supported these organizations.

The research centers carrying on policy-related analysis have also been subjected to criticism which, on the whole, reflects an uneasiness with the assignment of work affecting public policy to

---

this regard, it is said, however, that companies, increasingly must be careful not to mix fancy with facts in their proposal submissions."

Ralph J. Cordiner has asserted that the nonprofit organizations "are usurping a field traditionally served by private consulting firms and producer companies and hence are little more than a blind for nationalized industry competing directly with private enterprise—on a subsidized nontaxpaying basis" ("Competitive Private Enterprise in Space," a speech reprinted in *Congressional Record,* vol. 106, Append., 86 Cong. 2 sess. [1960], p. A4719). See also "Will Congress Regulate 'Non-Profits'?" *Missiles and Rockets,* Aug. 28, 1961, pp. 12–13.

[34] "The really valid reason for having such entities in existence is in part their inherent professional environment. Much more significant, however, is the fact that they, as long as they perform only a public function, can go to a General Electric, and a Westinghouse and a RCA and Arthur D. Little, and anywhere else, and ask how those organizations go about solving a problem. They can collect and compare concepts. And hear many competitive concepts from competitors. It could not be that such a contract would be assigned—it should not— to a Westinghouse and then they go around to GE or Raytheon and say, Tell us how you would solve such a problem, and so forth" (Helge Holst in *Systems Development and Management,* Hearings, pt. 1, p. 115).

[35] Max Golden, "The Nonprofit Corporation, Gimmick or Godsend in Weapon System Development?" remarks before Federal Bar Association, Sept. 14, 1961 (mimeographed).

contractors with no clear line of responsibility to the public. To a large degree the work of this group of organizations is classified and therefore not subject to public appraisal. However, the Rand Corporation releases a substantial amount of its output to the public; the Research Analysis Corporation and the Center for Naval Analyses make public a lesser part of their activities. This, supplemented by indirect and inferential evidence, permits some judgment.[36] In the course of time, too, certain general rules have been developed to define and limit the role of these organizations: (1) they must be sufficiently independent so as to provide objective studies, some of which should be on subjects of their own choice; (2) they should supplement and not substitute for agency staff capabilities; (3) their work should increase the policy alternatives available, and (4) they must not constitute a sole source of policy analysis since they then become *de facto* formulators of policy.[37]

The contributions of these centers must then be independent of such policy positions as the sponsoring agency may have acquired. They cannot serve merely to supply highly trained personnel to an agency nor must they be placed in a position of directing the work of government personnel.[38] They must also be independent of any affiliations which might be suspected of influencing their conclu-

[36] For appraisals of the "think" groups, see Edward L. Katzenbach, Jr., "Ideas: A New Defense Industry," *The Reporter,* March 2, 1961, pp. 17–21; Herbert Roback, 'The Not-for-Profit Corporation in Defense Contracting: Problems and Perspectives," *Federal Bar Journal,* vol. 25 (Spring 1965), pp. 195–206; Gene M. Lyons and Louis Morton, *Schools for Strategy* (Frederick A. Praeger, 1965), chap. 11. On the Rand Corporation, see John McDonald, "The War of Wits," *Fortune,* vol. 43 (March 1951), pp. 99–102, 143–58; Gene Marine, " 'Think Factory' De Luxe," *Nation,* vol. 188 (Feb. 14, 1959), pp. 131–35; Saul Friedman, "The Rand Corporation and Our Policy Makers," *The Atlantic,* vol. 212 (September 1963), pp. 61–68; "Rand: R&D Nonprofit Pioneered a New Kind of Organization; Served as a Model for Others," *Science,* vol. 144 (May 29, 1964), pp. 1113–14, 1164; E. E. Halmos, Jr., "IDA's 'Brain Factory' Guides Weapons Choices," *Missiles and Rockets,* Jan. 5, 1959, pp. 20–21. Bernard Brodie, "The Scientific Strategists," in Robert Gilpin and Christopher Wright (eds.), *Scientists and National Policy Making* (Columbia University Press, 1964), pp. 240–46; James L. Trainor, "Government Use of Nonprofit Corporations," *Harvard Business Review,* vol. 44 (May/June 1966), pp. 38–52, 182.

[37] See James D. Grant, "The Future of Nonprofit Research and Development Organizations," *California Management Review,* Summer 1965, pp. 84–89.

[38] Problems of the kind cited created difficulties and criticism of the relationships between the Institute for Defense Analyses—and also the Advanced Research Projects Agency—and the Weapons Systems Evaluation Group of the Joint Chiefs of Staff.

sions. Inevitably these organizations must on occasion take positions in conflict with the official views of their sponsoring agencies, but in only a few cases have such conflicts reached the public's attention.[39]

The research centers oriented to policy analysis differ from other research centers in that they do not normally operate government-owned facilities and in that with one exception they are administered by independent trustee-controlled nonprofit corporations. An important advantage of an established institution as contractor is its ability to supply promptly the facilities and staff necessary to begin operations. Such organizations as Rand, RAC, and CNA each had a predecessor and were going concerns when their present form of organization was adopted. In those and other instances the need for assistance in the formative period was judged less important than the need for an independent status. Experience has shown that once these centers are firmly established, their operations and their contacts with the sponsoring government agency are handled by the managerial and technical staffs of the center. The functions of broad policy guidance remain with the contractor.[40] The independent nonprofit institutions receive such

[39] For example, in the 1963 hearings on the Navy's appropriations, Secretary of Defense McNamara supported his objections to building new nuclear-powered aircraft carriers by citing a study prepared by the Center for Naval Analyses. A letter from the Chief of Naval Operations reproving the Center for Naval Analyses for taking a position contrary to official Navy policy was read into the record. See *Nuclear Propulsion for Naval Surface Vessels*, Hearings before Joint Committee on Atomic Energy, 88 Cong. 1 sess. (1963), p. 173.

[40] Differences between the nonprofit management staff and the sponsoring agency have on a few occasions produced major changes. Policy differences with the management of the Operations Research Office led the Army to terminate its contract with Johns Hopkins University and to the formation of the independent Research Analysis Corporation (*New York Times*, May 28, 1961). Efforts by the management of the Systems Development Corporation to diversify its sources of contractual work were objectionable to the Air Force, leading the corporate trustees to change management and restate the corporation's sphere of activities (Herbert Roback, "The Not-for-Profit Corporation in Defense Contracting," *Federal Bar Journal*, vol. 25 [Spring 1965], p. 199).

The Air Force has also had difficulties in its relationship with the Rand Corporation. A curious, overall judgment is that of Major General Dale O. Smith, who writes: "It is indeed ironical that the scientific research organization established to assist the Air Force in the solution of its postwar problems was instrumental in creating the greatest problem ever faced by the Air Force—that of its imminent extinction as a separate air arm" (*The Eagle's Talons: A Military View of Civil Control of the Military* [Spartan Books, 1966], p. 247).

guidance from qualified men willing to serve as corporate trustees.

Almost all the research and development centers manage government-owned facilities although in some cases, such as that of the Applied Physics Laboratory, the plant and equipment used are a mix of government and private property. All the policy analysis centers, however, are housed in privately owned facilities. Some lease their buildings, some devote part of their fees to the acquisition of buildings, and some have found private funds to erect their own buildings which are then amortized under the contract. While the amounts involved are not large, the accumulation of property wholly from government funds by nonprofit corporations has raised some questions regarding the disposition of the property in the event of dissolution.

The existing arrangements vary. The Research Analysis Corporation contract provides that ownership reverts to the government.[41] Rand's charter provides for disposition to a charitable foundation,[42] while the Applied Physics Laboratory specifies accumulation of a "Stabilization and Contingency fund" intended to protect its employees should the workload decline markedly or the contract be terminated. The disposition of the residual sum is to be negotiated.[43] The Bell report (which has been discussed in Chapters III and IV) recommended a uniform policy which would minimize the accumulation of capital assets. According to this study, such assets as were accumulated by research centers should revert to the government in the event of the center's dissolution.[44]

The contractor-managed research centers are a type of organization new to the American scene. They have come into existence in response to needs not readily met by standard procedures. They may, however, infringe upon the functions of other organizations, and their freedom from the controls that operate upon business firms and the universities, and within the government arouses concern. The contractor-managed research centers have, therefore, been viewed critically if not skeptically, and, in some quarters, resentfully.

The 1962 *Report to the President on Government Contracting for Research and Development* (the Bell report) was the first

[41] *Systems Development and Management,* Hearings, pt. 4, p. 1434.
[42] *Ibid.*
[43] *Ibid.,* pt. 4, p. 1504.
[44] *Ibid.,* pt. 1, p. 238.

large-scale appraisal by the executive branch of the contractor-managed research centers. Its conclusions were that

university-associated research centers are well suited to basic or applied research for which the facilities are so large and expensive that the research acquires the character of a major program best carried out in an entity apart from the regular academic organization. . . .

Not for profit organizations (other than universities and contractor-operated Government facilities), if strongly led, can provide a degree of independence, both from the Government and from the commercial market, which may make them particularly useful as a source of objective analytical advice and technical services. These organizations have on occasion provided an important means for establishing a competent research organization for a particular task more rapidly than could have been possible within the less flexible administrative requirements of the Government.

Contractor-operated Government facilities appear to be effective, in some instances, in securing competent scientific and technical personnel to perform research and development work where very complex and costly facilities are required and the Government desired to maintain control of those facilities. Under such arrangements, it has been possible for the Government to retain most of the controls inherent in direct Federal operations, while at the same time gaining many of the advantages of flexibility with respect to staffing, organization, and management which are inherent in university and industrial operations.[45]

These evaluations were accepted by Congress without critical comment.

The Bell report recommended that any new organization of the research center type should be formed under new legislation providing for government institutes. That recommendation received little attention. Continuing assessment is appropriate to new institutional forms, particularly where their origins suggest that they may be temporary in nature and therefore subject to dissolution when their missions are completed or as older forms of organizations can be adapted to meet the needs which generated the new forms.

There are, however, problems, inherent in the fact that most of the research centers are highly specialized means to specific ends—

[45] *Ibid.*, pt. 1, p. 221.

ends which have "finite dimensions."[46] While the programs of the centers are subjected to periodic review by the administering agencies, that review differs from the assessment periodically made of contractual project research. Project research terminates in the absence of positive action on a request for extension or renewal. The centers, in contrast, are concerned with complex programs and the administering agency must appraise the character and progress of those programs to determine their continuation, reduction, redirection, or termination. The complexity of these programs and the large size of many centers make such appraisal difficult, at the same time attracting the persistent critical attention of the interested public and of Congress.[47] The Atomic Energy Commission has undertaken a substantial redirection in the assignments of the Oak Ridge National Laboratory. The AEC is also engaged in a major realignment of the contractual management and utilization of the resources of its Hanford facilities, an experiment which may cast some light on the problems of terminating large-scale R&D programs and finding other employment for facilities and personnel. The Air Force, meanwhile, in 1966 changed its relationship to the Systems Development Corporation. The captive relationship has been terminated and the Air Force will deal with SDC as it deals with other private organizations.[48] There has also been some tendency for these nonprofit organizations intimately related to their sponsoring agency to seek to do research for other organizations.[49]

[46] Alvin Weinberg, "Future Aims of Large Scale Research," *Chemical and Engineering News,* May 23, 1955, p. 2188.

[47] For example, *The Future Role of the Atomic Energy Commission Laboratories,* Hearings before the Joint Committee on Atomic Energy, 86 Cong. 2 sess. (1960); and *The Aerospace Corporation: A Study of Fiscal and Management Policy and Control,* Hearings before the House Committee on Armed Services, 89 Cong. 1 sess. (1965). For public comment, mostly critical, see n. 33.

[48] *Air Force Relations with the Not-for-Profit Corporations,* Report of Air Force Systems Command Board of Visitors (1966). The report dealt with achievements, functions, and problems of Mitre, Aerospace, and SDC.

[49] The Rand Corporation has been particularly active in seeking research contracts from sponsors other than the Air Force. The Institute for Defense Analyses has also undertaken research for government agencies other than DOD, as, for example, a $498,000 research project for the President's Commission on Law Enforcement and Administration of Criminal Justice. In this case, the results form part of the Commission's report.

Intramural R&D Organizations

Intramural R&D organizations merit brief attention here because of the impact of contractual policies and procedures upon them and because they are integral parts of the overall system by which federal contractual programs are managed. The intramural R&D organizations operated as organic parts of federal agencies continuing the characteristic prewar practice of using civil servants to conduct the government's programs. These organizations have been affected in varying degrees by the growth of private execution of federal projects and programs, although the performance of such functions within the government has also increased.[50]

Since 1940, expenditures by the federal government allocated to R&D functions performed within the government have increased by approximately ten times, amounting in 1966 to approximately $3.2 billion (Chart 13).[51] An estimated 30,000 scientists were employed by the federal government in 1947, including "persons with professional civil service ratings as physical, biological, or agricultural scientists plus those engineers engaged directly in scientific activities."[52] The number of federal civil service employees assigned to work classified as Research, Development, Testing & Evaluation was estimated at 58,000 in 1952 and at 141,000 in 1964.[53]

[50] A brief history of federal policy regarding the establishing and utilization of intramural facilities is in House Committee on Government Operations, *A Case Study of the Utilization of Federal Laboratory Resources,* 89 Cong. 2 sess. (1966), chap. 3.

[51] That growth has not been continuous. From 1946 to 1950 expenditures for intramural R&D moved from $470 million to $1.4 billion. In the period 1953–55, this trend was reversed and intramural expenditures fell to a low of $950 million in 1955. Since that time intramural expenditures have increased each year.

[52] President's Scientific Research Board, *Science and Public Policy,* vol. 3, p. 141.

[53] Data for 1952 from Eugene W. Scott, *Applied Research in the United States* (National Academy of Sciences–National Research Council, 1952), p. 18; data for 1964 from House Select Committee on Government Research, *Federal Facilities for Research and Development,* Study Paper No. 3, 88 Cong. 2 sess. (1964), p. 16. No complete list of government-owned and -operated RDT&E organizations appears to exist. There are difficult problems of definition since many R&D organizations have small and scattered units which support the overall program in some manner. There are also numerous organizations that perform some R&D function as an incident to their primary responsibilities. A list of the principal intramural facilities of the Department of Defense is in *Impact of Federal Research and Development Policies on Scientific and Technical Manpower,* Hearings before Senate

The data on intramural R&D expenditures and employment covers not only research and development activities within government facilities, but also testing, evaluation, and administration. As overall federal expenditures have increased, administrative functions relating to establishing programs and identifying projects, to selecting sources and monitoring the work of private performers, and testing, evaluating and applying results have similarly increased. Although the costs of such functions cannot be segregated from performance costs with any precision, management functions are responsible for a substantial part of intramural R&D expenditures. Administrative costs necessarily vary widely with differences among the programs, e.g., as between the administration of a grant program and the administration of a highly complex development project. Costs of administering large and complex development projects likewise vary widely between agencies in part because of differences in the management responsibilities delegated to the contractor and hence in the distribution of costs between the government and contractor. No precise breakdown of intramural expenditures into the various functional categories such as research administration, management, performance, testing or evaluation is available. The costs of administration may range from approximately 2 percent of an agency's total R&D expenditures for the AEC, 2½ percent for NIH's grant program, 6 percent for NSF, and up to possibly 20 percent for some military development projects which, though contractor performed, nevertheless provide for close surveillance and in some cases for contributions of detailed technical support.

It seems clear that much of the absolute increase in intramural R&D expenditures is to be accounted for by the increased requirements for administrative work generated by research which is carried on in whole or in large part by private groups. By the same token, the activities of many government R&D performing organizations are strongly influenced by the extent of their participation in administrative activities. Given the sharp increase in the cost of R&D it is probable that effort directed to the performance of re-

Committee on Labor and Public Welfare, 89 Cong. 1 sess. (1965), pp. 449–52. The problems of inventorying federal intramural R&D in terms of personnel or facilities are dealt with in House Committee on Government Operations, *A Case Study of the Utilization of Federal Laboratory Resources,* 89 Cong. 2 sess. (1966).

CHART 13

Federal Obligations for Intramural R&D by Agency

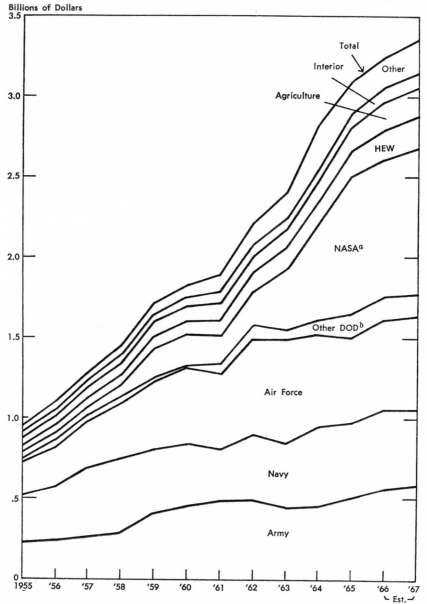

Billions of Dollars

Source: National Science Foundation, *Federal Funds for Research, Development, and Other Scientific Activities*, vols. 5–15.

a. Figures for 1955–57 are for the National Advisory Committee for Aeronautics (NACA).

b. Includes funds for Office of the Secretary of Defense, Advanced Research Projects Agency, and other department-wide activities.

search within government organizations increased significantly until the early 1950's. Since that time growth has been rapid in the areas of management, testing, and evaluation but, with a few exceptions, moderate in the actual operation of R&D.

Military Intramural R&D Organizations

Immediately after the war the existing military intramural R&D facilities were looked upon as organizations which had operated with reasonable effectiveness within a system that had demonstrated numerous and serious inadequacies. The inadequacies were to be corrected by new policies and procedures which would assure that private institutions would contribute as they were able to the development and execution of programs. A policy utilizing private institutions in government programs assumed a core of intramural capabilities as necessary to the effective use of contractors but did not assume that intramural operations were not to be expanded if expansion seemed desirable. To some degree, the absolute increase in government-owned and -operated facilities has followed from an expansion of intramural facilities doing the R&D work required by agency programs.

Virtually all the R&D organizations in existence before World War II continue in operation today. Those military laboratories which had developed strong positions before or during the war have retained their mission responsibilities, particularly in such areas as artillery, explosives, fuzes, mines, and torpedoes. Some have had their area of responsibility substantially broadened.

New organizations have also appeared. After the war a relatively small number of war-created privately managed R&D organizations were relinquished by the private contractor and became intramural operations. An example is the Naval Ordnance Testing Station (China Lake, California) which had been operated under contract by the University of California and which became a directly managed facility of the Navy's Bureau of Ordnance. The Army in 1957 acquired by transfer from the National Bureau of Standards a group which had been formed when the National Defense Research Council undertook to study the feasibility of a proximity fuze. As the Harry M. Diamond Laboratories, the organization has acquired wide-ranging responsibilities.[54] Another

[54] *Army Research and Development Newsmagazine,* vol. 6 (July 1965), pp. 32-35.

source of growth of intramural R&D facilities was the establishment of wholly new facilities to deal with the new areas of science and technology. Some of these represented efforts to establish agency competence in support of large programs conducted primarily by contract. The Army Quartermaster Corps, for example, during World War II conducted a substantial R&D contractual program through the National Academy of Sciences. Though the NAS continued in an advisory capacity, after the war the agency chose to establish its Natick Laboratories as the R&D administering and performing organization around which its contractual programs were built. In some instances an agency developed a new R&D facility because at the time no suitable contractor could be found to assume the necessary responsibilities. An example is the establishment of the Army Ordnance Missile Laboratories at Huntsville.[55]

Another factor making for a changing role for the intramural organizations derived from the success of the massive R&D programs in generating new devices and processes. Testing and evaluating prototypes before approval and acceptance for production, and evaluating the application and operational characteristics of new equipment are functions that have required increased staff attention as well as new facilities. While such functions are sometimes supported by contractual assistance in their technical aspects, overall appraisals and operational analysis are not delegable activities. Activities of this nature are essential parts of the terminal developmental process and account for some substantial part of the growth of intramural R&D expenditures.

The laboratories of the Army and Navy continue to operate along the lines of the traditional arsenal systems in conventional weaponry such as firearms, artillery and explosives and some components such as fuzes.[56] The approach has also been applied to

[55] The circumstances were unusual in that the Army had the problem of finding some way of making effective use of the group of German scientists headed by Wernher von Braun brought to the United States by Project Paperclip. Most of the scientists coming to the United States as a result of that operation found private employment. The problems presented, particularly by the von Braun group, are dealt with in Clarence G. Lasby, "Project Paperclip: German Scientists Come to America," *Virginia Quarterly Review*, vol. 42 (1966), pp. 366–77. A brief account by von Braun is "Management in Rocket Research," *Business Horizons*, vol. 5 (Winter 1962), pp. 41–48.

[56] *Ordnance*, July-August 1964, p. 72.

more recently developed technology as in some of the earlier missile systems such as the Army's Redstone and Jupiter and the Navy's Sidewinder.[57]

The functions performed by intramural organizations for the agencies of which they are a part have undergone significant changes. Prior to World War II and for varying lengths of time thereafter, these organizations exercised central responsibilities for the R&D programs of their agencies, activities which were usually subordinated to other agency functions. They were characterized also in the case of the Army and Navy by a point of view which visualized the responsibilities of the intramural R&D agency as extending through the preparation of specifications sufficiently precise and detailed to permit competitive bidding by private suppliers when production was desired. That concept of development objective was, of course, necessary under the statutory restrictions that prevailed prior to World War II. An important advantage was claimed for the system in that it provided for any expression of special military requirements throughout the development process. A further advantage was that procurement could be sought from industrial firms which had no R&D capabilities or very limited ones.

Producing a prototype or the complete and detailed specifications of a new device is no longer a principal but is an unusual function of the military organizations. With the resources available through the R&D contract, the interface between intramural R&D performing staffs and private organizations may occur at almost any point in the process of defining a technical objective. The precise point of contact will depend not upon the intramural organization but upon the decision of higher management, varying widely with the agency, the specific technology involved, and the institutional location of competent technical capability.

Non-Defense Intramural R&D

The intramural R&D organizations in the nonmilitary agencies are, with some exceptions, service- rather than mission-oriented, which means that their problems are different from those affecting the military organizations. Most of the prewar organizations, such

---

[57] *Systems Development and Management,* Hearings, pt. 4, pp. 1408, 1455.

as those of the Department of Agriculture, the National Bureau of Standards and the Coast and Geodetic Survey of the Department of Commerce, or the Bureau of Mines of the Department of the Interior continue to carry on specialized programs long established as governmental functions.[58] Their growth, however, has been at comparatively low levels, as Chart 14 shows. Some new programs utilize contractors, such as the program for water desalination. And in other instances, like bituminous coal research, independent, parallel contractual programs have been established.

A marked growth in intramural research has, however, occurred in two areas. One is the mission-related operation of NASA. Upon its formation, NASA acquired the facilities of the NACA as well as a large part of the Army's Missile Laboratories at Huntsville. The NASA policy involved maintaining an inhouse level of scientific and technical competence which would permit knowledgeable control of its procurements from private industry. In the words of Robert C. Seamans, "The University industry and the government . . . can't have a good impedance match if, in the government, we have what are primarily administrators or clerical type people. We must also have people that really understand the fundamentals of science and technology. You can't maintain that competence unless you have people who are actually working at it and have a zest for it and are themselves making a major contribution."[59] To do so it established two new, large laboratories and is currently in the process of staffing a space electronics center.

The second area in which there has been a marked postwar growth of intramural research is that of health. The NIH had its origins in a small intramural operation which eventually established a small contractual research program. In the postwar period, NIH has followed a policy of maintaining an intramural op-

[58] At the request of the Secretary of Commerce, the National Bureau of Standards was the subject of an intensive study by the National Academy of Sciences (*The Role of the Department of Commerce in Science and Technology* [1960]) which recommended substantial expansion. The report formed the core of a presentation to Congress which met with a favorable response. The Congress found that NBS had inadequate facilities and funding and that it needed to be "placed in a better position with respect to recruiting and retention of senior scientists." The result was the appropriation of funds for a wholly new plant for the Bureau as well as substantial increases in operating funds (H.R. 711, 87 Cong. 1 sess. [1961]).

[59] In National Security Industry Association, *Motivation and Support of R&D To Achieve National Goals* (Government Printing Office, 1965), p. 91.

CHART 14

Federal Agency Total and Intramural Obligations for Research and Development, 1954 and 1967

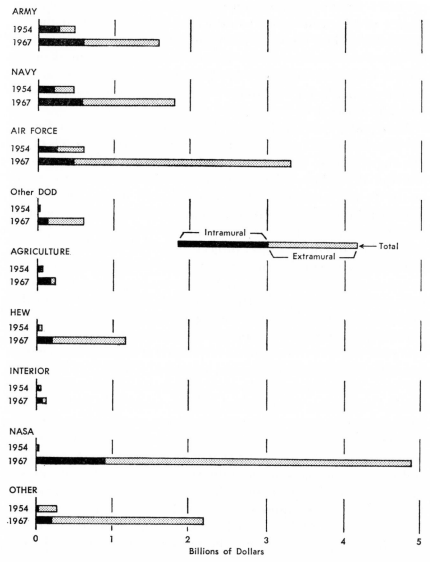

Sources: for 1954: National Science Foundation, *Funds for Scientific Activities in the Federal Government* (1958), p. 96; estimated figures for 1967: National Science Foundation, *Federal Funds for Research, Development, and Other Scientific Activities,* vol. 15 (1966). pp. 94–95. Figures include pay and allowances but not obligations for R&D plant.

eration and has established such staffs for each new program. Administration of NIH's contract program was clearly separated from its intramural operations almost from its beginnings. Congress established an advisory committee procedure for recommending awards which dealt with a contract officer and not with the research institutions themselves. The intramural staff members have no closer relationship to the agency contract program than do private scientists. Members of NIH research staff do serve on the advisory panels from time to time although, in proportion to their numbers, no more frequently than private scientists.[60]

As is pointed out in Chapter IV, the postwar period has been characterized by the assumption at high administrative levels of increasingly specific control over R&D programs. With the loss of much of the policy and program responsibilities which were formerly theirs, the inhouse R&D organizations became specialized units within a complex structure supporting management groups in dealing with multi-faceted programs. The performance of R&D assignments whether of task, project, or system size is carried out where management determines that it can best be done. Such determinations are in some situations a choice between clear alternatives but are more frequently compromise decisions made in the light of presently available or potential capabilities.

From the point of view of the responsible administrator, carrying out research or development projects is only one service rendered by R&D organizations and personnel within an agency. In the view of the chairman of the Civil Service Commission, "federal scientists have the responsibility for leadership, for directing and reviewing, and must also do enough research on their own to maintain their expertise."[61] In the view of the Director of Research and Engineering of the Department of Defense the scientific and engineering staffs of the military services must "continuously investigate rapidly changing fields of science and engineering to find materials, techniques, processes and ideas which may prove to have some as yet undetermined military value," and in the course of such activities "must bring the problems of the Armed Forces

[60] National Institutes of Health, *Biomedical Science and Its Administration* [the Wooldridge report] (1965), p. 36.

[61] John W. Macy, Jr., "The Scientists in the Federal Service," *Science*, vol. 148 (April 2, 1965), p. 52.

before the broad scientific and technical community expressed in the terms of technical discourse."[62] It is assumed that scientific and technical intramural staffs will reflect a sensitivity to the needs of the agency and an ability to evaluate proposals with a degree of objectivity not available elsewhere. Such characteristics enhance the usefulness of the scientific and technical personnel of intramural organizations as sources of advice to responsible administrators and in assisting in the management of contractual weapons systems development and programs. They can provide day-to-day technical advice to systems managers, aid in the selection of R&D contractors, perform such research tasks as are not assigned or perhaps not assignable to a contractor, and assist in the evaluation of contractor performance as well as providing technical education and training for military officers.[63]

Any appraisal of the intramural establishments must recognize that they differ widely in the functions they are expected to perform. Some are purely research organizations, which contribute to public objectives in exactly the same way that private organizations do. Some are assigned key roles in supporting the development objectives of their agencies. Others are primarily engineering organizations concerned with the details of programs and developmental objectives. Still others are primarily concerned with testing and evaluation. Regardless of type, some are relied upon for scientific and technical advice to assist R&D administrative officials in conducting contractual programs, while others do little advisory work, either because of statutory or organizational arrangements or because higher officials have preferred to seek other sources of advice.

The effectiveness of the government's intramural research oper-

[62] Harold Brown, "Research and Engineering in the Defense Laboratories," remarks at the Naval Research Laboratory, Defense Department news release, Oct. 19, 1961. See also *Federal Budgeting for Research and Development,* Hearings before the Senate Committee on Government Operations, 87 Cong. 1 sess (1961), pp. 15, 222–26.

[63] A survey of "primary work activity of scientists by type of employer" suggests that scientists employed by the government are involved in management and administration to a degree only slightly greater than those with other types of employers: 32 percent of the scientists employed by the government; 30 percent, by industry; 7 percent, by universities; 24 percent, by nonprofit organizations. These data are based on 224,000 respondents out of 415,000 canvassed (National Science Foundation, *American Science Manpower, 1964,* NSF 66–29 [1966], pp. 15, 33–40).

ations has frequently been attacked. The Hoover Commission accepted the view of one of its task forces that government research and development operations, whether in military or civilian agencies were "generally at a lower level of effectiveness than could be realized if suitably placed in the civilian economy." It suggested further that "even where operations must be done in military installations, frequently increased effectiveness and efficiency will be realized through operations by civilian economy organizations."[64]

More recently, C. C. Furnas, while recognizing certain advantages of intramural R&D, saw serious disadvantages in that "exposure to an involvement in the cloying effects of governmental bureaucrats seems inevitable, with resulting hindrance to progress and detraction of individual motivations." Among other disadvantages of R&D performance within the government he also noted that "the organizations are subject to an undue amount of public analysis and criticism; life is too much in a goldfish bowl; prestige is currently low in the minds of scientific and industrial communities; and because of the bureaucratic system, it is very difficult to remove incompetents from the ranks."[65]

Similarly James A. Perkins expressed the view that the scientists "will be underused when placed in Government laboratory and given detailed instructions and blinders and told to 'solve the specific problem, please!' . . . Experience," Perkins said, "has long since demonstrated the value of an arm's-length arrangement that makes it possible for a scientist to bring to bear his creative imagination on a widely and loosely defined problem. Scientific laboratories under military direction have frequently not prospered."[66] As a congressional investigation has indicated, the practice of placing R&D organization under military command has not always

[64] U. S. Commission on the Organization of the Executive Branch of the Government (1943–44), *Research and Development in the Government* (1958). L. A. DuBridge argued in 1953 that "the Government is not getting its money's worth out of many existing military laboratories. Military organization, military customs, practices and rules, military traditions are all made for fighting and not for research" ("Science and Government," *Chemical Engineering News,* vol. 31 [1953], p. 1384).

[65] Testimony in *Federal Research and Development Programs,* Hearings before the House Select Committee on Government Research, 88 Cong. 1 and 2 sess. (1963–64), pt. 2, p. 1006.

[66] *Federal Budgeting for Research and Development,* Hearings before Senate Committee on Government Operations, 87 Cong. 1 sess. (1961), pp. 460–61.

yielded good results.[67] Other criticisms of intramural R&D seem to rest on ideological grounds. The view that government organizations should do no research that a private institution is able to do appears frequently, and, on the other hand, government personnel sometimes hold the position that the government weakens its position and receives less than it should because of an excessive reliance upon contractors.[68]

If it be conceded—in the face of important contrary evidence[69]—that the government's R&D facilities are by and large less productive than private organizations, the problem of the competence of the government's R&D staffs as sources of technical advice remains. A high level of technical competence within the government is clearly essential if effective use of private sources is to be achieved.[70] Research and development projects require that alter-

[67] The issue was developed at some length in *Organization and Administration of the Military Research and Development Programs,* Hearings before the House Committee on Government Operations, 83 Cong. 2 sess. (1954).

[68] One example of the view that government should undertake no research that a private institution is able to do is the criticism of the intramural programs of the National Institutes of Health made by the Wooldridge committee, *Biomedical Science and Its Administration* (1965), pp. 37, 146–47. For one statement of the position that the government makes excessive use of contractual R&D, see William B. McLean, "The In-House Government Laboratory," *Proceeedings of the Fifteenth National Conference on the Administration of Research* (1961), pp. 52–56.

[69] A major DOD study of the sources of contributions to the development process credited intramural scientific and technical staffs with 39 percent of the "events" —discrete identified contributions—in the nineteen development projects that were analyzed (C. W. Sherwin and R. S. Isenson, *First Interim Report on Project Hindsight (Summary),* Office of the Director of Defense Research and Engineering [Government Printing Office, 1966], pp. 6, 15).

[70] The point has been made many times. Forceful analyses are those of James R. Killian, Jr., "Can Government Maintain Vital Scientific Leadership?" (National Civil Service League, n.d.); Glenn T. Seaborg, "The Federal Manager and the Third Revolution," *Civil Service Journal,* October-December 1964, pp. 1–5; and Bernard I. Spinrad, "Why Not National Laboratories?" *Bulletin of the Atomic Scientists,* vol. 22 (April 1966), pp. 20–22. Representatives of business firms frequently note the government's need for technically qualified personnel. Ralph J. Cordiner, for example, observed with regard to NASA that "the government needs a certain number of experienced technical men to help make realistic choices as to future missions, to set high standards of performance, and to provide technically sound policy guidance. That cannot be done by men who are not actively engaged in space research and development. Hence a certain percentage—perhaps as much as five percent—of the technical work of the space program is best done in Government Laboratories. They should be well staffed and well financed" ("Competitive Private Enterprise in Space

natives be analyzed and decisions made at very numerous steps in the process. Such decisions range from concern with the minute details of a subcomponent of a research task upwards to a choice between different systems performing the same function. The qualifications necessary to effective decision-making differ. The details are of critical importance to the satisfactory functioning of the total project and require that intimate and specialized knowledge be applied. The broader questions must be approached on the assumption that the detailed questions have been dealt with effectively and that true alternatives exist to be judged against more extensive technical knowledge. Chalmers W. Sherwin, then Deputy Director of Defense Research and Engineering, has emphasized that "where technical details of either science or of law are the dominating factors, one simply cannot divorce authority and knowledge," adding that "the gap between the working scientist and engineer and the upper echelon government technical manager is far too great."[71] For such reasons programmed development requires scientific and technical capabilities in depth.

Some decisions can be delegated to contractors. Under the competitive proposal system, however, contractors submit their solutions to a problem in considerable detail. Their proposals must be judged by government personnel technically qualified to express opinions, to evaluate differences, and perhaps to make suggestions. A wide variety of skills must be brought to bear on such tasks, skills which must be maintained at the frontiers of rapidly changing scientific and technical areas. Once a contract has been let, it is necessary to deal with changes in the work proposed as well as to introduce new concepts from wherever they may emerge.

A high level of competence is clearly essential but there exist substantial differences of opinion and practice as to the necessary depth of staff competence. Agencies and, indeed, programs within the same agency differ widely in their approaches to the management of development projects. Both the size of intramural scientific and technical staffs and the nature of their utilization vary. Such differences are reflected in the nature of the contractual

---

Research," reprinted in *Congressional Record,* vol. 106, Append., 86 Cong. 2 sess. [1960], p. A 4721).

[71] Chalmers W. Sherwin, "The Management of Science in the Public Interest," *Bulletin of the Atomic Scientists* (June 1964), pp. 11–12.

relationships which are maintained. Given the complexity of many R&D programs, it is exceedingly difficult to distinguish the effectiveness of large versus small intramural advisory groups in the conduct of programs. Whether the intramural technical staff be small or large, the critical element is the quality of its advisory service.

The competence of the government's scientific and technical personnel has been questioned, not on the basis of case studies—which would be very difficult—but from the clear evidence that government organizations have found it increasingly difficult to retain many of those government employees who were most experienced or who were judged to be the most productive.[72] Congress has also on occasion expressed doubt that federal agencies can apply an adequate level of competence to the administration of the system.[73]

Government agencies have had few or no difficulties recruiting people newly entering scientific and technical fields since civil service salaries at the lower levels have been competitive. However, while turnover of federal scientific and technical personnel has not been high, government agencies have tended to lose their best and most productive people while being unable to recruit comparable replacements. In the competition for men who have proven themselves of superior ability, the agencies have been unable to offer salaries comparable with those to be had elsewhere, while the conditions of employment—such as the freedom to select projects, to publish results, ease in securing supplies and equipment, and participation in professional organizations—have in some agencies suffered by comparison with practices of private institutions. Such problems are not new; they were pointed out in a 1938 study of the National Resources Board, in the Steelman report of 1947 and on numerous occasions since. The 1962 Task Force on Government Contracting for Research and Develop-

[72] Federal Council for Science and Technology, *The Competition for Quality* (1962), reprinted in *Systems Development and Management,* Hearings, pt. 1, pp. 403–21.

[73] The Defense Procurement Subcommittee of the Joint Economic Committee, for example, recommended that "a vigorous recruiting and training program be instituted so the Government will have the in-house capability to obtain what it needs from industry and know that what is received meets the specifications" (from its *Report* [July 1963], p. 19).

ment, chaired by David Bell, found, as has been noted,[74] that the contractual system was basically sound and urged that the government's programs be carried out by the most effective source available. The task force implied that the government's intramural organizations should be competitive with private organizations in the recruitment of personnel, particularly because of their important advisory role in the administration of the contractual system. The Bell report was influential in incorporating in legislation the principle of comparability of salaries with private practice. The principle of salary comparability, however, requires periodic adjustments in salaries. With regard to the higher salaried classifications, such adjustments have not been made in full conformity with the comparability concept. Government organizations therefore continue to claim that they suffer serious competitive disadvantages.[75]

In addition to salary comparability, the task force sought also to establish comparability in employment conditions.[76] Under the leadership of the Bureau of the Budget, the agencies were requested to revise their regulations with regard to such matters as the publication of research results and attendance at professional meetings, and to provide some freedom to select projects comparable with arrangements common in private organizations. The Department of Defense made special efforts to assure its laboratory staffs that it would henceforth seek to assign to them projects of greater intrinsic interest and significance.[77]

The Bell task force accepted, as did other groups, the proposition that the government must develop its own higher level scientific and technical staff from within its own employees and facili-

[74] See Chapter III.

[75] The continuing substantial lag in salaries paid government scientists and engineers is documented in Edward M. Glass, "Comparative Analysis of Compensation Patterns for Scientists and Engineers," in *Proceedings of the Twentieth National Conference on the Administration of Research* (University of Denver, 1967), pp. 33–42.

[76] A useful review of the problems of maintaining comparability in salary and working conditions of government scientific and technical personnel, their history, the many studies that have been made, and the objectives that should be achieved is Albert F. Siepert, "Creating the Management Climate for Effective Research in Government Laboratories," in Karl Hill (ed.), *The Management of Scientists* (Beacon Press, 1964).

[77] A review of agency efforts to implement the recommendations in the Bell report is in *Systems Development and Management—1963*, Hearings, pp. 222–70.

ties. On that assumption it is clear that there is no alternative to action which will make government employment at least as attractive to scientific and technical personnel as employment elsewhere.[78] It will take considerable time before the effectiveness of such actions can be appraised. Given the intense competition that exists for the kind of personnel required there is some significant probability that the results will fall short of needs.[79]

The Bell report did not specifically explore alternative methods of meeting the government's needs for scientific and technical personnel of high quality. One alternative might be to establish more effective procedures for bringing into the government mature scientific and technical people of recognized accomplishment and established reputation who have reached a point in their careers when a role in the decision-making process becomes attractive.[80] Such a program was envisaged when the scientific and technical supergrade positions were established in 1946 under P.L. 313, relating to the Department of Defense with subsequent similar legislation for other agencies. Unfortunately that program operated on a small scale in the face of pressing needs for more personnel. Though there were instances of successful recruitment of new high-level personnel, the program succeeded principally in retaining people who might otherwise have been lost. While the actions undertaken as a result of the recommendations of the Bell report do not neglect lateral entry into government service, such recruitment possibilities are submerged in an undiscriminating concern with the employment conditions of all levels of scientific and technical personnel. A program emphasizing the government's needs for highly experienced scientific and technical personnel to sup-

[78] On the attitudes of scientists and similar groups toward federal employment, see Franklin P. Kilpatrick, Milton C. Cummings, Jr., and M. Kent Jennings, *The Image of the Federal Service* (Brookings Institution, 1964), pp. 115–17, 140–45.

[79] Such evidence as is available suggests that there has been little change in the quality of government R&D personnel that is traceable to the efforts made since 1962. See, for example, testimony of Harold Brown, in *Department of Defense Appropriations for 1966*, Hearings before a Subcommittee of the House Committee on Appropriations, 89 Cong. 1 sess. (1965), pt. 5, pp. 33–34.

[80] There is some evidence that many of the more successful scientific and technical personnel in the government enter government service only after employment experience elsewhere. A study of a sample of federal scientist-administrators indicates that more than two-thirds "had pursued a nongovernment career prior to joining the federal service" (Eugene S. Uyeki and Frank B. Cliffe, Jr., "The Federal Scientist-Administrator," *Science*, vol. 139 [March 29, 1963], pp. 1267–70).

port its decision-making functions would at a minimum provide another source by which high competence might be secured. The problems are exceedingly difficult and solution rests upon the evolution of occupational values broader than those now characteristic of the scientific and technical profession. It has been suggested that "the scientific community must invent a system of nonmaterial rewards corresponding to those which make a judicial career desirable. Objectivity, impartiality, and broad technical competence must be recognized as desirable *in addition* to the traditional factors of individual creativity in the practice of science, pure or applied."[81] Initiative on the part of the government in nurturing such values seems essential.

A substantial need for intramural performance of R&D remains. To the degree that research performance by such staff is incidental to the tasks of supporting management, or to performing tasks which cannot readily or appropriately be delegated outside the government, the case-by-case judgment of management must prevail. Lack of private interest or capacity is, however, now only rarely a valid reason for intramural R&D while the advantages of multiple, competitive proposals are in most, if not in all, circumstances very considerable. It is to the interest of all concerned that R&D assignments be conducted, as the Bell report suggests, where they can best be done. But the Deputy Director of the Bureau of the Budget noted in 1966 that the difficulty of maintaining some balance between inhouse and extramural research was a chronic one and that "we still don't have a clear picture of when it is best to undertake research inhouse and when it is best to undertake it by outside grants and contracts."[82]

[81] Chalmers W. Sherwin, "The Management of Science in the Public Interest," *Bulletin of the Atomic Scientists*, June 1964, p. 11.
[82] Elmer B. Staats, "Making the 1967 Science Budget," in Harold Orlans (ed.), *Science Policy and the University* (Brookings Institution, 1968).

CHAPTER X

Some Continuing Problems

The federal government's commitment to the support of research and development on a grand scale arose in large part from defense requirements but has come to mirror a broad-based public interest in accelerating the rate of technological change. The contractual procedure must be considered as a fundamental factor not only in establishing the public commitment but also in underwriting the effectiveness with which objectives can be pursued. Those contractual procedures operate in cooperation with rather than in conflict with existing institutional arrangements, providing multiple sources of knowledge, ideas, and proposals as well as of performance, and offering flexibility of relationships, and specialization of function.

It is essential to recognize that the contractual system is more than a device to get work done for a government agency. An agency's program in its broad outlines as well as in its specific objectives as expressed in projects is prepared by drawing upon contributions from many public and private sources. In this process of program-building there exist numerous channels by which interested and knowledgeable groups may present their evaluations of needs and opportunities and suggest specific courses of action to accomplish broadly defined objectives. The formal contract is therefore not the beginning but one culminating point in a process of interaction between the private and public groups which have an interest in a scientific or technical area. In this process the

417

government agency exercises the initiative, in that it must prepare programs and defend them through the normal governmental processes of authorization and budgeting, and also in that it selects from the proposals made to it those that it will include as contractual projects in its approved programs. In both the formulation and the execution of its programs the agency is heavily, and sometimes wholly, dependent upon the initiative of R&D institutions in developing the expertise necessary to prepare the proposals and do the work.

After two decades of experience, the policy of massive federal initiative and support in selected areas of scientific research and technical development is firmly established. So also is the policy of utilizing private institutions to contribute to the formulation of programs and projects and to do the work. As general principles these policies have been subjected to little significant criticism; on the contrary, they are being employed for a broadening range of public purposes.

The contractual system is, however, still in the process of evolution. While numerous changes have occurred, existing institutional relationships as well as the contractual terms and the administrative procedures which effectuate them continue to bear many signs of the improvisation that accompanies rapid growth. At the same time the capabilities sought through contracting are growing and changing.

Numerous problems exist. One group of problems relates to achieving more effective operations of the contractual system. This affects the government as administrator, private institutions as performers, and the relationships between them. The evolution of the system, its internal structure, and many of its problems, past and present, have been discussed in the preceding chapters.

Problems also arise from the impact of the system upon institutions which are only indirectly involved. In this study, attention has been concentrated upon the growth and internal character of the system. The peripheral effects of that growth are important, both as they bear upon the effectiveness of the contractual system and as ramifications of the contractual system manifest themselves in values held by elements in society and differing from the immediate concerns of government policy. The priorities established for the government's programs have far-reaching effects, as, for example, upon the volume of research for privately determined objectives, the nature of university programs and activities, and the economic and social position of scientists and engineers as compared with that of people in other occupations. There are many others that follow less directly as, for example, the supply of nurses as compared with laboratory technicians.[1] Different types of problems follow from the suspicion that the system may have generated an internal momentum that eludes if it does not defy control. Among the possible results are the channeling of resources into low rather than high priority goals and the sacrifices of values that are important for reasons other than immediate scientific and technical objectives.

The Goals of Research and Development

With the contract providing ready access to the R&D capabilities of the nation, the federal government has assumed heavy responsibilities for the wise use of scarce abilities. It has been pointed out that the system has established effective procedures for communication between the government and outside R&D institutions. That machinery includes procedures by which private researchers can and do anticipate the evolution of the government's interest. Indeed, to an important degree, the government's formulation of programs responds to and follows selectively from proposals made by private organizations.

However, this communication mechanism does not provide in any similar manner for consideration of the interest of the public in that large and important area of technological change which continues to be the responsibility of private business responding to the forces of the market. Government programs draw in large measure from the same pool of skilled manpower that private firms must draw upon as they seek to promote technological progress relating to private interests. That supply of skilled manpower is lim-

---

[1] Increased research programs may draw manpower from related fields. Successful research increases demands for the new services, and when new social values are established as through Medicare, the pressure upon trained manpower can present difficult problems. See House Committee on Interstate and Foreign Commerce, *Investigation of HEW*, H. Rept. 2266, 89 Cong. 2 sess. (1966), pp. 78–83, and Herman M. Sturn, "Technological Developments and Their Effects upon Health Manpower," *Monthly Labor Review*, January 1967.

ited, but no machinery exists whereby the objectives sought by a government-supported program can be weighed against the competing objectives which might be favored by private interests. The real alternatives in such situations call for more analysis than has yet been attempted.

The problems are the more difficult because the procedures whereby the government's goals and the magnitude of its efforts are determined are very different from those that apply to the broad areas of interests held by private business. The effective relationship between the programs established by the government and those sought by private industry (aside from the very important exchange of information) is to be found in competition for the available qualified manpower. While it is true that much of the government's work is done by private firms, such work is frequently sharply differentiated from the firm's efforts directed to private markets. Much of the effort directed to private markets is made by firms that hold few or perhaps no government R&D contracts.

Problems of this nature have stimulated an interest in the establishment of some procedures which would identify and assign priorities to national goals to which R&D activity might be directed.[2] The interest in the establishment of more formally rationalized and comprehensive R&D goals arises in part from the suspicion that some areas are supported excessively and others inadequately. The fact that R&D objectives that compete for scarce manpower are established in the absence of machinery by which differing objectives can be compared, even roughly, for their prospective value relative to their claims upon manpower invites doubt that the nation is pursuing that mixture of activities which would represent something approaching an optimum use of its resources. The very expensive area of high energy physics enjoys lavish support for equipment, operations and the training of more physicists because of its great promise of yielding new fundamental knowledge. What economic significance such knowledge might

---

[2] A useful discussion of the need for and problems involved in establishing national goals is *National Goals and Policies,* House Select Committee on Government Research, H. Rept. 1941, 88 Cong. 2 sess. (1964), pt. 1. See also the President's Commission on National Goals, *Goals for Americans* (1960), in which Thomas J. Watson, Jr., advocates the formulation of social goals for technological development.

have is at this time unpredictable. In contrast, chemistry, a field that has greatly enriched our technology appears to be comparatively neglected although the possibilities of new knowledge are far from exhausted. Whatever the merits of this specific comparison, it is clearly desirable to review the nation's programs as a whole and to consider more specifically and precisely than is or can be done now, the relationships between the support given to the performance of research and the training programs in the various fields of science.

Furthermore, since the beginning of the government's interest in promoting science and technology, there has been concern with the impact of new knowledge and technology upon man and upon the organization of society. Yet relatively little provision is made to support the work of those disciplines that might contribute to anticipating and meeting the related problems.

There is relatively little difficulty in finding support for research when support is associated with a search for solutions by clearly recognized problems—as in the case of materials research or in biological research related to cancer. There is a broad consensus among scientists that more research not so directed is desirable. Since the subject matter of such research is not susceptible to evaluation, selection for support rests upon judgments as to quality—of the area, of the man, and of his proposal. It may be true, as the first chairman of the National Science Foundation, Chester Barnard, said, that "we cannot spend as much [for basic research] as would be economically advantageous. The bottleneck, I believe, will be lack of men and women who have the capacity, the interest, and the willingness to pursue science."[3] The subjectivity inherent in selection of areas and projects establishes a very flexible yardstick which permits, on the one hand, the assertion that the government is supporting more scientific work than we have good scientists,[4] and, on the other, proposals that would provide funds

[3] National Science Foundation, *Third Annual Report, Fiscal Year Ending June 30, 1953*, p. vi. Jerome Wiesner expresses a similar view in "The Impact of Scientific Technology upon Industry and Society," in *NASA Conference on Space, Science, and Urban Life*, NASA SP-37 (1963), p. 69.

[4] Vannevar Bush, for example, replied affirmatively when asked whether the nation had "reached the point where our support of research exceeds the supply of first-rank scientists" (*Federal Research and Development Programs*, Hearings before the House Select Committee on Government Research, 88 Cong. 1 sess. [1963], pt. 1, p. 463).

for practically all university faculty scientists in a field such as chemistry.[5] These issues are attracting an increasing amount of attention though they remain unresolved.[6]

In the areas of technological development directed to clearly public responsibilities such as defense, space, and air transportation, the ability of the government to appraise the public interest is, in practice, determined by the assumption that this nation must hold and maintain a position of international superiority. In other areas, impending crises provide justification for the support of development programs, particularly when plausible proposals for solutions become available.[7] As has been pointed out earlier, one of the significant by-products of the government's experience with development projects has been an increasing ability to deal with problems that have heretofore escaped effective action. Such problems pose a variety of difficulties. Many are very large in scope. Many are local in nature and present jurisdictional problems. The contract system, however, provides a method whereby a solution can be sought and, together with the grant-in-aid, a method whereby application can be promoted. More difficult problems are

[5] "Federal Support of Basic Chemistry," in *Government and Science*, Hearings before the House Committee on Science and Astronautics, 88 Cong. 2 sess. (1964), pp. 823–30.

[6] The problem was the first subject assigned by the House Science and Astronautics Committee to the National Academy of Sciences under their contractual arrangement. The product of the NAS study was a volume which reflected the widely differing views of fifteen contributors (*Basic Research and National Goals* [National Academy of Sciences, 1965]). An important contribution to the dialogue, constituting also a critical appraisal of *Basic Research and National Goals*, is Stephen Toulmin, "The Complexity of Scientific Choice, II: Culture, Overheads or Tertiary Industry?" *Minerva*, vol. 4 (1966), pp. 155–65. An economist's effort to supply relevant criteria and procedures is Frederic M. Scherer, "Government Research and Development Programs," in Robert Dorfman (ed.), *Measuring Benefits of Government Investments* (Brookings Institution, 1965), pp. 12–70.

[7] "What we lack in many of the civilian problem areas identified by the committee is not a consensus on their importance. Rather, it is a lack of solid R&D program proposals that will satisfactorily answer the questions I have raised. We cannot buy and create progress in a field which is not ready to progress. We need to know where we are going and have enough people of the necessary competence to work out the programs. Once a program is underway, the possibility of doing something new and useful will tend to stimulate additional allocation of resources. It will also tend to stimulate the interests of other people to come within the field" (Donald F. Hornig, in *Federal Research and Development Programs: The Decision-making Process*, Hearings before the House Government Operations Committee, 89 Cong. 2 sess. (1966), p. 6.

apparent when the interest in promoting technical change relates to a problem involving private industry. Here, too, the contract with some cost-sharing provision is emerging as a device which promises to be effective in securing desirable objectives which neither government nor industry acting alone can attain. The application of such analytical tools as cost-effectiveness analysis promises to contribute some increased objectivity to decision-making even though the process is and remains political in character.

It has long been recognized that improvements in applied technology have been basic to the nation's economic growth and to its security.[8] Qualitative changes in economic well-being have their source in scientific and technical effort. Annual rates of economic growth—of which technological change is a major component—have been and promise to continue to be matters of broad interest and great importance. The nation is so growth-conscious that increases in productivity have become a major element in wage policy. Industries are distinguished from one another by growth rates, and there is a universal expectation of a continuous flow of new products.

The heavy claims made by federal programs upon the available scientific and technological manpower have aroused concern regarding federal encroachment upon traditional private roles[9] and fears that the growth of a civilian-oriented technology has or will

---

[8] Recognized principally and somewhat vaguely by economic historians. Economists have more recently supplied statistical analyses which permit more precise evaluation of the contribution of technological change to economic growth. See Edward F. Denison, *The Sources of Economic Growth in the United States and the Alternatives before Us* (Committee for Economic Development, 1962), chap. 23. Other measures are provided by Robert M. Solow, "Technological Change and the Aggregate Production Function," *Review of Economics and Statistics,* vol. 39 (1957); Mark S. Massell, "Capital Formation and Technological Change in United States Manufacturing," *Review of Economic Statistics,* vol. 42 (1960); Jora R. Minasian, "The Economics of Research and Development," in *The Rate and Direction of Inventive Activity* (National Bureau of Economic Research, 1962), p. 93; Wassily Leontief in *Economic Aspects of Government Patent Policies,* Hearings before the Senate Select Committee on Small Business, 88 Cong. 1 sess. (1963), pp. 231–32, 250–51.

[9] One statement of the relationship of federal to private R&D functions is by J. Herbert Hollomon, "Government Systems Affecting Industrial Technology," in National Security Industry Association, *Motivation and Support of R&D To Achieve National Goals* (NSIA, 1965), p. 171. See also Irving H. Siegel, "Appropriate Government and Private Research Roles in a Mixed Economy," in Richard A. Tybout (ed.), *Economics of Research and Development* (Ohio State University, 1965), pp. 268–73.

be stunted and with it the technical advances which are fundamental to the continuing growth of economic well-being.[10] The public benefits from government-sponsored research and development spillovers have been very great,[11] but such benefits from recent programs have been disappointing (or at least delayed).[12] The fears expressed by industry arise not so much from the rising costs of research personnel for privately supported efforts as from their inability to recruit the desired share of superior talent.[13] The way in which the federal government manages the information generated by its programs is also a matter of concern.[14] It is suggested, for example, that "to the extent that the government takes away or independently generates technology, it will frequently if not always remove a potential base for expansion of private business enterprise."[15] The possibility does exist that a government objective is pursued at the expense of less clearly defined but nevertheless important objectives that affect the growth of technology directed to private values.[16] Some of the criticism is directed to alleged wastefulness in some defense programs. It is directed also to objec-

[10] Richard J. Barber, *The Politics of Research* (Public Affairs Press, 1966), p. 28.

[11] On the adoption by the civilian economy of military sponsored research and development, see papers by General C. W. Clark, Lieutenant General Howell M. Estes, and Vice Admiral W. F. Raborn, in National Security Industry Association, *The Impact of Government Research and Development Expenditures on Industrial Growth* (Government Printing Office, 1963), pp. 37–66.

[12] See the articles by Richard S. Morse, Thomas P. Carney, and Robert L. Hershey in National Security Industry Association, *Motivation and Support of R&D To Achieve National Goals;* and Richard R. Nelson, "The Allocation of Research and Development Resources: Some Problems of Public Policy," in Tybout (ed.), *Economics of Research and Development,* pp. 288–306.

[13] See John H. Rubel, "Priority in Research and Development," *Idea: The Patent, Trademark, and Copyright Journal of Research and Education,* vol. 8 (Summer 1964), p. 72; Richard S. Rosenbloom, *Technology Transfer—Process and Policy, An Analysis of the Utilization of Technological By-Products of Military and Space R&D,* National Planning Association. Special Report No. 62 (1965); and David Allison, "The Civilian Technology Lag," *International Science and Technology,* December 1963.

[14] Robert A. Solo, in "Gearing Military R&D to Economic Growth," *Harvard Business Review,* November-December 1962, pp. 49–50, argues for a restructuring of the machinery whereby new knowledge is transmitted in order to make it more readily available.

[15] John H. Rubel, "Priority in Research and Development," p. 236.

[16] For example, Samuel Lenher, vice-president of DuPont, writes: "I find myself allied with a growing body of scientists and research administrators who are deeply concerned about the growing imbalance of research and development spending. The more I reflect upon the question, the more I become convinced that such a heavy weighting of expenditures from a single type of sponsor is neither the most effec-

tives—a current favorite is the relative value of the space objectives as compared with more mundane social and economic problems such as urban transportation and urban slum conditions. It is this type of concern that arouses interest in providing machinery that, in the determination of goals, will assure that consideration is given to all alternative uses of the relevant resources that reflect possible national interests.

In the late 1940's, some efforts were made to limit federal R&D budgets on the basis of the manpower believed to be available. Since that time considerations of urgency have dominated some areas, particularly in defense and health. The fact that transfer of scientific and technical personnel from other activities to government programs would be necessary and that some sacrifice might be involved was recognized.[17]

The availability of manpower is a factor when new programs are being considered, but lack of data prevents manpower questions from being a determining influence.[18] The question tends to

---

tive nor the most efficient approach. It is an approach based on the premise that all forms of research can be done as well under one sponsor as another, a premise which experience refutes. It assumes that we can skew science very markedly in one direction, without endangering it or ourselves. I do not think we can" (National Security Industry Association, *The Impact of Government Research and Development Expenditures* . . . , pp. 203–4.

Similarly, Donald W. Collier of the Borg-Warner Corporation states: "When this 'civilian' looks at government-sponsored research and development, he becomes alarmed by what he sees. No other equally vital factor in our national economy is so largely dominated by government, and yet the directions it seems to be taking appear contrary to the best interests of the country. I believe the time has come to re-appraise our total research and development effort, with a perspective that looks beyond the next missile system or putting a man on the moon. Without the foundation of a sound economy nothing else can long endure. Let us set our targets more realistically and more selectively. Let us slow down demands that have created this galloping inflation in research costs. Let us re-balance the resulting—sound—national research and development effort to permit greater relative emphasis on the continuing healthy growth of our economy. In short, gentlemen, let us regain control of this bull whose tail we grasp before it pulls us to our own destruction" (*ibid.*, p. 171). See also Barber, *Politics of Research*, p. 68.

[17] National Academy of Sciences, *Toward Better Utilization of Scientific and Engineering Talent* [the Killian report] (1964).

[18] See Elmer B. Staats, "Making the 1967 Science Budget," in Harold Orlans (ed.), *Science Policy and the University* (Brookings Institution, 1968). For a summary of economist's analyses of the problem, see Edwin Mansfield, "Technological Change: Measurement, Determinants, and Diffusion," in National Commission on Technology, Automation, and Economic Progress, *The Employment Impact of Technological Change* (Government Printing Office, 1966), Append. vol. 2, pp. 117–19.

be dealt with by requiring from potential contractors assurances that they have the key personnel necessary and that they can acquire other skilled workers. Predictions of a shortage of scientific and technical personnel have been met by a variety of programs directed to educational institutions and to students—programs designed to increase the supply of trained people as well as to promote the acceptance of strong upward movements in salaries. The President's Science Advisor, has testified that "What has uniformly emerged from manpower studies is that everyone thinks there is probably a manpower problem. There certainly are never enough good people to manage the things that matter. But, in fact, it has not been possible to show . . . that we have been inhibited at any time in what we wanted to do by a manpower problem. . . . There are many manpower tools. That is the first point. Secondly, they are very flexible. Thirdly, I would say at this point we have not found yet that our manpower is completely committed in the sense that there is an overt manpower budget problem."[19] The Elliott committee agreed, observing that it "found no persuasive evidence of a manpower crisis though there may be shortages in specified areas."[20] The large expenditures on federal programs have substantially increased the salaries of the scientific and technical people in the affected areas, drawn qualified people from related areas, upgraded the assignments given to others, drawn newcomers into these fields from other employment, and provided the more highly trained with the assistance of those less highly trained.[21]

[19] Donald Hornig, in *Federal Research and Development Programs,* Hearings, pp. 49–50. Dr. Hornig continues: "One asks why this is so. I do not pretend to be able to give a final answer, but what becomes clear is that manpower is extraordinarily flexible in the scientific areas. Men are not simply traded between one technical area and another. People move in and out of research and development and into production and business activities as well. They do not move necessarily from one research and development activity to another. . . . Moreover, the people who are available in one area cannot contribute to a very different area of research and development because they do not have the kind of talent and knowledge and background. . . ."

[20] House Select Committee on Government Research, *Impact of Federal Research and Development Programs,* H. Rept. 1938, 88 Cong. 2 sess. (1964), p. 73. See also the same committee's *Manpower for Research and Development,* Study Number 2, particularly p. 13, on the difficulties of measurement arising from changing activities of scientists and engineers.

[21] The forces that operate are briefly dealt with in a discussion of the question, "Is the Whole Budget Any More Than the Sum of Its Parts?" in Harold Orlans (ed.), *Science Policy and the University* (Brookings Institution, 1968), pp. 222 ff.

Increased salaries to stimulate job transfers as well as the recruitment of new personnel were no doubt necessary to implement the nation's R&D priorities. Once salaries have been established at levels sufficient to attract the present and near-future supply, society gains nothing from further competitive bidding for qualified personnel through increased salaries. The suggestion occasionally made that the federal government apply more stringent controls over contractor salaries than now exist is fraught with difficulties. The same end would be achieved by greater restraint in the funding of programs, and by requiring greater assurance than is now sought that the necessary manpower is available for new or expanding programs without drawing upon other ongoing programs of approximately equal priority.

The fact that the R&D expenditures of the Department of Defense and of NASA seem to have reached a plateau and the recent substitution of incentive for cost-plus-fixed-fee contracts suggest that the salaries of scientific and technical personnel in those large areas may well be subjected to less vigorous upward pressures than prevailed during most of the 1950's. However, it is clear that the continuing increases in the funding of health programs press heavily upon the supply of trained people, inflate the salary structure, and to some extent draw personnel from related employments. Similar pressures can be anticipated in such newly established or rapidly growing programs as oceanography and air and water pollution. Experience strongly suggests that in making funds available to specific programs there should be greater recognition given to the availability of qualified manpower than has been the practice in the past, avoiding the upward spiral of salaries that results from transfer of large numbers of technical personnel between programs.

Only a rough balancing of the factors that operate in the relationships of federal programs to the nation's civilian-oriented technical growth is possible at this time. No reasonable basis exists for speculating on the level of effort of private research that might have existed had federal programs been substantially smaller. It is also premature to appraise the contributions of defense and space-directed R&D to other objectives. A significant time lag is characteristic of even fairly direct applications of defense-related developments to civilian uses—as in the case of the computer or the aerosol can. Furthermore, many of the effects of government-financed R&D will be indirect and correspondingly difficult to identify. Several observations can, however, be made:

1. The effect of federal research programs upon private research efforts oriented to the private markets involves complex interrelationships. Research and development expenditures by business firms out of their own funds have increased markedly in dollars, although relatively little in real terms. The allocation of such expenditures—as between government and private objectives—cannot be precisely identified. Some part of private industry expenditures is no doubt related to government programs. Some increases in expenditures have occurred in industries that receive little government R&D money. It does seem clear that continued increases in federal expenditures of R&D at the rates of the past decade would claim more than current additions to manpower and would have unfavorable effects upon the level of private programs.[22]

2. As a result of the very large increase in support for basic and applied research, new knowledge and techniques are accumulating at unprecedented rates. Participation in these advances and awareness of the desirability of applying the new knowledge are widespread. There are no doubt frictions and gaps in communication and hence lags in application that must be reduced. There are also serious problems of relevance not convincingly dealt with by existing procedures.

3. The contractual procedure has left the new knowledge and skills acquired from R&D with private institutions. The pressures of the government's requirements continue to absorb the attention of development firms and exploration of possible civilian applications of knowledge gained has had a low priority. Nevertheless the system does permit the usual private incentives to operate in discovering new applications for the results of research and development.[23] The problems that exist in the patent area are discussed below.

[22] See Augustus B. Kinzel, "Government's Impact on Civilian Research and Development Manpower: An Industrial View," in *Toward Better Utilization of Scientific and Engineering Talent,* pp. 135–36.

[23] The effect of federal programs upon the growth of the nation's civilian technology is a matter of controversy. But some European observers see the contractual relationships between the government and private industry as a source of great strength to the United States. P. M. S. Blackett in an address to the Parliamentary and Scientific Committee of the British House of Commons observed that "I have

4. The contractual procedure also permits the government to undertake programs with objectives which contribute to civilian technology and private effort but which cannot be attained quickly and effectively solely through the private market mechanism. A striking example is the rapid and continuing development of aircraft. The rapidly increasing commitment directed to environmental problems is another. The private nuclear energy industry, which has received substantial assistance from the Atomic Energy Commission, is a further case in point.[24]

5. The contract has permitted the mobilization of skills to achieve extremely complex objectives. Much pertinent administrative experience has been gained by private firms. Indeed, it may well be that one of the most significant achievements of the past decade is a greatly enhanced capacity of both public and private

---

slowly come to the conclusion that Britain after the war inadvertently took a wrong turning when it continued to rely so much for Defence and Atomic Energy R&D on its own Government Stations, rather than on industry. I believe that in the U.S.A. a bigger fraction of Government funds for defence and atomic energy went to industry and less to Government Stations. Few would now doubt that the U.S.A. has gained greatly from the resulting strengthening and building up of very strong firms, and that Britain has lost relatively" (cited in John Walsh, "Their Decision-Making Process Bothers Some of the British," *Science*, vol. 155 [March 31, 1967], p. 1655).

A similar view was expressed by H. W. Julius, Director of the Central Organization for Applied Scientific Research of the Netherlands: ". . . It has not remained unobserved that especially the United States have a system that could almost be called the diametrical opposite of the Dutch pattern. Government-sponsored research in your country is frequently, or so to speak even preferably, entrusted to the big and biggest companies. . . . This has led to enormous expansion of the research capacities of many companies; the bigger ones among them even have transformed their research groups into independent research corporations, receiving astronomic amounts out of the Federal research contracts. This has created the unprecedented scientific leadership of your nation" (House Committee on Science and Astronautics, *Government, Science, and International Policy*, 90 Cong. 1 sess. [1967], p. 40). In Norway the National Research Council for Scientific and Industrial Research has recommended that "the technical agencies of the government, in their purchasing procedure, should use research and development contracts to Norwegian industrial firms to strengthen their competitiveness in fields where national production should be encouraged. . . ." Robert Major, the Director, observed that "the Research Council, which so far has spent its money mainly through research institutes, should also be allowed to give research contracts to industrial companies or groups of companies to build up national technical competence in important fields" (*ibid.*, p. 56).

[24] Through fiscal year 1967, the Atomic Energy Commission expended $1.9 billion in direct support of the development of civilian nuclear energy. Data are from the AEC (*The Energy Report* [Washington, D.C.], December 1967).

organizations to deal rapidly with very large and very complex problems.

6. Finally, it should be observed that the generation of new knowledge and the development of new devices and techniques in such fields as health and control of air and water pollution are qualitative contributions which are not accurately appraised by conventional market measures. The importance of such objectives is clear. It is possible though unlikely that the shift of R&D talent from concern with consumer products and gadgets to the objectives cited above will have little effect on real per capita income. The measures of well-being now in use provide only partial and capricious evaluations of the gains in welfare provided by better health, the existence of a new source of energy, or the discovery of ways to counteract such adverse effects of industrialism as polluted air and water.

These observations are not meant to imply that the current or near future allocation of research funds should be accepted without continuing concern for private market-oriented research. The ease with which the government can establish large programs and the facility with which contracts can be used may lead to less than optimal use of the nation's resources. The government's responsible officials in the executive agencies and in the Congress must exercise restraint in utilizing the nation's limited supply of qualified manpower. There is need for greater public consideration of the distribution of manpower among the many objectives and of the possible sacrifices inherent in the process. There is also need to maintain strong private institutions adequately motivated to undertake to accomplish objectives that remain the responsibility of private enterprise. It has been suggested that more inclusive national goals be sought and that a broader congressional concern with science and technology may be needed.[25] Formal committee assignment of such responsibilities would provide a valuable way

[25] S. C. Gilfillan wrote in 1937 that "the fundamental problem of the working of our social institutions for eliciting, paying for, and securing early and widespread use of desirable inventions has never been completely examined. It is a problem calling for a national policy" ("Social Effects of Inventions," in National Resources Committee, *Technological Trends and National Policy* [Government Printing Office, 1937], p. 26). A recent brief survey of existing knowledge of technological change observes that "policy making in this field has suffered from an inability to delineate the proper role of private and public financing and institutions, and from the lack of agreement on criteria for determining when government programs are justified." The study recommends five types of policies to be undertaken by the federal gov-

for responsible consideration of broad issues not now adequately dealt with.

The Integrity of the System

The advantages of the contractual system to the nation are attainable in full measure only as the government is effective in identifying the public interest in the selection of its objectives. That public interest is broadly defined by Congress, more specifically by the individual agency in its program, in further detail when the agency invites the submission of proposals and selects from among them, and still further when the agency's operations are reviewed. When uncertainty exists in the work assigned to a contractor further delegation of the function of defining the public interest occurs.

The possible advantages of the contractual system exist only insofar as the contractor identifies with the objectives of the contracting agency and hence with the public interest which the agency is charged to pursue. In preparing specifications intended to accomplish an objective, the contractor undertakes responsibilities traditionally attached to employment with the government. In accepting a proposal and entering into a contract, the agency must assume that it will receive value commensurate with payments to be made.

The contracting system rests upon authority to negotiate contracts (or grants) with private institutions as provided in the Armed Services Procurement Act of 1947 and in similar legislation. In providing authority to select contractors on the basis of the quality of their proposals, and to negotiate both the work to be done and the price to be paid, the Congress broke dramatically with its historic position. For more than a century, the procurement procedures of the agencies had been rigidly circumscribed. Such controls had evolved as reactions to scandals involving abuses by both contractors and government officials. Successive Congresses had sought controls which permitted a minimum of administrative discretion and which were as impersonal and automatic as could be devised.

ernment, assuming that private institutions would be responsive. See Richard R. Nelson, Merton J. Peck, and Edward D. Kalachek, *Technology, Economic Growth, and Public Policy*, A RAND Corporation and Brookings Institution Study (1967), pp. 3, 171 ff.

It was this history which President Truman presumably had in mind when, upon signing the Armed Services Procurement Act into law in February 1948, he issued a warning regarding its use. The President wrote the Secretary of Defense,

This bill grants unprecedented freedom from specific procurement restrictions during peacetime. That freedom is given to permit the flexibility and latitude needed in present day national defense activities. The basic need, however, remains to assure favorable price and adequate service to the Government. To the degree that restrictions have been diminished, therefore, responsibility upon the Defense establishment has been increased. There is danger that the natural desire for flexibility and speed in procurement will lead to excessive placement of contracts by negotiation and undue reliance upon large concerns, and this must not occur.[26]

The President urged that detailed standards be established to guide procurement officers since "otherwise, differences in interpretation and policies may result in imprudent contracts and give rise to doubts about the wisdom of this new procurement system."

The Department of Defense and other agencies operating under similar contract authority have sought to establish such controls. A high degree of uniformity of treatment of proposals from private institutions has been instituted. It is true, however, that whatever legal form a research and development contract may take, it rests upon some form of negotiation between the government and possible performers. It is further true that the objectivity and the almost mechanical nature of contractor selection characteristic of procurement based upon price has been displaced by subjective selection resting on judgments of the quality of the scientific and technical content of proposals within a framework of responsiveness to an agency's objectives. In the case of development contracts, the objective of maximizing the technical gains leads in the large majority of cases to the cost-plus contract in which the government continues to exercise judgment.

While a contract seeks to define objectives and procedures in the degree of specificity necessary to the maintenance of control, to do so in excessive detail imperils the purchaser's interest in gaining

[26] *Report Pursuant to Section 4, Public Law 86–89*, H. Rept. 1959, 86 Cong. 2 sess. (1960), p. 11.

from the performer his best judgment in dealing with the uncertainties inherent in every project. The purchaser must make assumptions about the actions of the supplier. The agency must assume that accomplishing the government's objective will be the ultimate consideration in the frequent judgments that the contractor must make regarding detailed technical steps. The government agency necessarily delegates some degree of discretion to the contractor in spending of funds, in furnishing the government with the results of the work, and in advising the agency when some changes from original plans are desirable.

The actions of the contractor are also controlled by the fact that the funds provided under a contract are public funds and that the stated objectives sought are of such importance as to have been established as public objectives. A government R&D contract, therefore, involves not only the sponsor and the contractor but also the government as a whole, the interested and technically qualified community, and the general public. Contractors then operate under the restraints that apply to the spending of public funds not only as stated in the language of the contract but also as they may be expressed by authoritative spokesmen for the public.

Since only a fraction of all proposals are accepted, it is remarkable that the technical judgment of the government's decision-makers is so rarely seriously challenged in public. No formal administrative machinery for appeal exists nor is there any demand that such machinery be created. Appeal by the political route up to and including the Congress is available but is used in very few cases. More typically the rejected proposer, if confident of the merits of his proposal, has sought to continue his work on his own initiative and to vindicate his judgment by greater and more convincing efforts. Offering further opportunity to such a person or group is a highly important role of the private and independent institutions in the system.

On his part the contractor recognizes that a reputation for acting in the interest of his client is of critical importance to him. In the R&D area, at least, there is a large element of truth in the frequent observation that a partnership exists. While there are limits and restraints upon that partnership, there nevertheless must be a mutuality of interests if there is to be an effective relationship.

On its part the government must recognize that the proliferation of regulations and restraints is not only a costly procedure but inconsistent with the maintenance of an effective relationship.

In the larger perspective, President Truman's hopes that the "wisdom" of the system would be defended and protected have been realized. However, a different if no less important issue has emerged—that of government's capacity to control the system it has created. President Eisenhower posed the problem in his farewell address of January 18, 1961. Pointing out that the nation had been compelled to create a "permanent armaments industry of vast proportions" and to maintain large military forces, he observed, "This conjunction of an immense military establishment and a large arms industry is new in the American experience . . . [and] we must not fail to comprehend its grave implications." The President continued:

In the councils of government, we must guard against the acquisition of unwarranted influence, whether sought or unsought, by the military-industrial complex. The potential for the disastrous rise of misplaced power exists and will persist.

We must never let the weight of this combination endanger our liberties or democratic processes. We should take nothing for granted. Only an alert and knowledgeable citizenry can compel the proper meshing of the huge industrial and military machinery of defense with our peaceful methods and goals, so that security and liberty may prosper together.[27]

The President also noted that the "free university . . . has experienced a revolution in the conduct of research." He saw two opposite problems: "The prospect of domination of the nation's scholars by Federal employment, project allocations, and the power of money is ever present—and is gravely to be regarded." On the other hand, he said, "in holding scientific research and discovery in respect, as we should, we must also be alert to the equal and opposite danger that public policy could itself become the captive of a scientific-technological elite." The President concluded, "It is the task of statesmanship to mould, to balance, and to integrate

[27] Public Papers of the Presidents of the United States, *Dwight D. Eisenhower, 1960–61* (Government Printing Office, 1961), p. 1038. With regard to the comment on science, G. B. Kistiakowsky later indicated that the President intended to convey the thought that "the part of science which is engaged in for armaments purposes must never be allowed to dominate all of science or curtail basic research" (*Science*, vol. 133 [Feb. 10, 1961], p. 355).

these and other forces, new and old, within the principles of our democratic system—ever aiming toward the supreme goals of our free society."

There are those who hold that the nation has failed in the statesmanship that President Eisenhower prescribed, that the nation has become captive of vested interests, specifically now identified as its advisers on scientific and technical affairs, and that it has lost the freedom to choose its objectives and decide how they will be met.[28] Many such critiques should be recognized as disagreements with the nation's policies in certain areas, particularly defense, but also in space, high energy physics, and on down to state and local policies on the fluoridation of water. It is a common tactic to attempt to support an attack on an established policy with an attack on the process by which the policy was formulated. Since almost any area of policy affects and is affected by a group which holds a special interest, it is possible to discredit a policy if it can be shown that the special interest exercised an influence overshadowing that of the public.

The intimacy of the relationships between public and private agencies at many levels of the contractual system invites criticism of this type. Yet it is a clear duty of an agency charged with a mission responsibility to pursue whatever technological possibilities hold promise of contributing to its ability to meet the obligations imposed upon it. An agency must operate as advocate for efforts it deems essential to effective operations. There exists some feeling that on occasion the coincidence of interest[29] of an agency and those private institutions that contribute to it and are more or less identified with it result in an input to the policy-making process of such weight as to place the public and its elected representatives at a grave disadvantage. If such disadvantages exist, then the remedy is surely not to weaken the responsible agency and its sources of support but rather to strengthen the critical capacities of the review-

[28] See, for example, C. Wright Mills, *The Power Elite* (Oxford University Press, 1956), chap. 8; Fred J. Cook, *The Warfare State* (Macmillan, 1962); Victor Perlo, *Militarism and Industry: Arms Profiteering in the Missile Age* (International Publishers, 1963). The most detailed examination of the conspiracy complex thesis in the contemporary situation is Julius Duscha, *Arms, Money, & Politics* (Ives Washburn, Inc., 1964).

[29] The phrase is Adam Yarmolinsky's, from "How the Pentagon Works," *Atlantic*, March 1967, p. 61.

ing, policy-making and goal-setting machinery. There is at times vigorous and sometimes bitter debate over committing resources to a technological objective. Debate of this kind does test the democratic process but reflects the strength rather than any weaknesses of the system whereby science and technology are applied to the nation's problems.[30] The relationships between public and private institutions become diffuse and attenuated as a proposal moves through the elaborate structure which administers, reviews, and provides legislative foundations for the system. Furthermore, the system permits, and in large measure invites, public discussion at numerous points. In the expensive and critical area of development the structure is one in which the private expert proposes and may seek to persuade but in which government experts evaluate and recommend and the nonspecialists at the policy level of the agencies, the Executive Office of the President, and the Congress decide in terms of the broader range of values with which they are concerned. These differences of functions, contributions, and responsibilities may be baffling to critics who, unwilling to accept the decisions that emerge, frequently take refuge in finding a devil or a conspiracy in operation. It is difficult also for the public to appraise the contacts between private R&D organizations and the government as these may range from purely informational exchanges to what appear to be undesirable pressures.[31] Public discussion,

---

[30] The fact that a technological objective is possible cannot mean that it must, by that fact, be achieved at whatever cost. In the private sector, the market provides the evaluation machinery which in government must be provided through the responsible decision-making process. For an analysis of recent experience in the military area, see "Anti-Missile Missile: Next Entry in the Arms Race," *Science,* vol. 154 (1966), pp. 985–87.

[31] Secretary McNamara, after pointing out that "most of the big projects are really joint efforts of industry and the Department," was asked by Senator Saltonstall: "But they are kept in control of the military?" Secretary McNamara replied: "The Department controls them, and if the money is poorly spent, I don't think it is proper to say that it is because of industry pressure. It is our job to offset that pressure, and I think we can." *Military Procurement Authorization, Fiscal Year 1965,* Hearings, p. 180. Roswell Gilpatrick, as Deputy Secretary of Defense, stated: "I have seen no tangible evidence of the military-industry alliance former President Eisenhower was concerned about, but the very fact that people are concerned makes it something we must deal with. The issue comes up frequently" (*Armed Forces Management,* November 1962, p. 28). For industry comment on the conspiracy thesis, see Robert E. Beach, "What Military-Industrial Complex?" (unpublished speech at NSIA meeting, April 23, 1964, Wright-Patterson Air Force Base, Ohio. A general critique is by Daniel S. Greenberg, "Who Runs America?" *Science,* vol. 138 (1962), pp. 797 f.

high competence in positions of responsibility, and an avoidance of or at least a clear awareness of conflicts of interest are the public's protection in the determination of goals and methods.[32] In science or technology as in other areas, there is a continuing, broadly shared public responsibility that the integrity of the decision-making process be maintained.

At the same time, the uncertainties which inhere in any development program may obscure a lack of wisdom which has gone into its establishment and administration. It is frequently difficult to distinguish between failures that should have been foreseen and failures that followed from circumstances not easily anticipated. More and better analysis of our experience with the R&D process and the ways by which we have sought to manage it should contribute to better performance. Periodic appraisals, not only of the progress made on a program but also of its objectives and its prospects, from diverse sources are the public's best protection.

The nation has provided machinery whereby scientific and technical experts can contribute their knowledge on a broad spectrum of problems and opportunities. It has done so in the expectation that they will contribute to the solution of recognized problems and, more vaguely, identify opportunities to solve problems not yet recognized. In the past the nation has profited immensely from the work of such experts. The present situation differs in that the support of men who may change our scientific knowledge and the technology by which we live is deliberately sought on a large scale. A large element of faith is unquestionably required here as in any situation where the public must deal with experts. The public protection lies in the integrity of the expert, in an adequate number of experts as alternate sources of advice, an ability to distinguish between advice based on expertise and advice that is opinion resting upon no special knowledge,[33] and in public officials able to

---

[32] The conflict of interest problem is a perennially difficult one. Older laws, unduly restrictive, were revised by P.L. 87–489, followed by a presidential memorandum. See Roswell B. Perkins, "The New Federal Conflict-of-Interest Law," *Harvard Law Review*, vol. 76 (1963), pp. 1113–69; and Harold C. Petrowitz, "Conflict of Interest in Federal Procurement," *Law and Contemporary Problems*, vol. 29 (Winter 1964), pp. 196–224.

[33] The various roles of the expert-as-expert, the expert-as-an-intelligent-and-articulate-citizen, and the expert-as-a-source-of-opinion-without-expert-foundation-though-sometimes-masquerading-as-such create confusion. It is possible to discern from the experience of the past two decades that government officials and the public have become increasingly able to identify the various roles that may be played.

understand and react to the advice received. Objectives that are established in consequence have been selected by the standard process—ultimately by Congress—after review at successive levels in the executive agencies, frequently with public discussion, and always subject to periodic appraisal. The problem of dealing with experts and advocates is not new. The executive and Congress have dealt with the problem of controlling special interest groups throughout the political history of the nation. As in other areas, the attainment of the public interest rests upon broadly based participation in the discussion of objectives, the appraisal of progress, and in critical reaction to the results.

Institutional Competition

The roles and problems of R&D institutions require consideration from a broader perspective than that possible in Chapters VI to IX. The four principal types play complementary roles in the process. They are also in competition and in conflict, a fact that was recognized in the report of the Bell task force but only insofar as the government's R&D organizations were concerned. Such competition may take many forms, frequently involving what is, or may be viewed by one type of institution as, an invasion of its responsibilities and prerogatives by another. Some professional educators, associated with universities and school systems may, for example, feel concern over the rapid growth of interest by business firms—stimulated by the Department of Defense—in educational technology.[34]

Albert Wohlstetter observes that "in the United States the problem of scientists and strategists is, I think, by and large not so much in being heard as in *saying* something, that is, saying something that is the result of thought and empirical study" ("Scientists, Seers and Strategy," *Foreign Affairs,* vol. 41 [1963], p. 476 [italics in original]).

[34] Luther J. Carter, "Technology in the Schools: Educators Are Uneasy," *Science,* vol. 153 (Sept. 30, 1966), pp. 1624–26. The rapid movement of business firms into the field of educational technology has led a congressional committee to warn of the need to guide the revolution in education and to assert that it is "imperative that educators maintain and safeguard their proper role as formulators of education policy" (Joint Economic Committee, *Automation and Technology in Education,* 89 Cong. 2 sess. [1966], pp. 10–11). For some widely differing appraisals of the possible roles of business firms in educational technology, see the brief discussions by Paul Goodman, Donald W. Oliver, Gerald Holton, C. Howard Goold, and Edward L. Katzenbach, in *Harvard Educational Review,* vol. 37 (Winter 1967), pp. 107–24.

Each institutional form possesses characteristics peculiar to itself, but there are also broad areas of overlapping functions. Development is the special function of business firms. The development process requires intimate relationships with research not always effectively supplied by separate organizations devoted to research and, as a result, business firms are doing an increasing amount within their own establishments. Similarly, while research classified as "pure" has been presumed to be the special province of the universities, the universities actually perform as much or more research classified as "applied." Each of the other institutional forms also carries on pure and applied research which, in the aggregate, equals or exceeds the efforts of the universities.

Where the performance of research, both pure and applied, arises from the need for new knowledge to pursue an established objective, the increasing amount of such research done within business firms is consistent with the high priorities attached to the objectives they pursue. Much the same is true of the independent nonprofit organizations. The effect of the increase of R&D work in these quarters, it must be noted, is to reduce the volume of research activities that the universities are called upon to do.

Historical precedents and the chance location of key people often determine the activities pursued by institutions and organizations within each institutional group. It may also happen that the preferences of research personnel for affiliation with one or another type of organization is the deciding factor. There are differences in the objectives pursued by different types of organizations as well as differences in the effectiveness with which they advocate their interests.

It is also reasonable to presume that differences exist in the research effectiveness of the various institutional forms of organization. Such differences are obscured and are difficult to evaluate because the government's research centers, the universities, and most business firms have multiple functions and objectives.

It is not within the purview of this study—if it could be done at all—to attempt any comparison of the scientific and technological contributions of these various types of organizations. There are important differences in the assignments made to them which complicates such comparisons. The general impression does emerge, however, that the contractual project approach permits more frequent, more thorough, and more public appraisal of effectiveness than is the case with most of the research centers, whether operated under contract or by the government. Such a comparison must recognize that the government-operated centers have suffered from salary differentials which have severely reduced their ability to compete for personnel with other types of institutions. The correction of salary differentials should in time permit a more accurate appraisal of the role of government organizations conducting R&D which might be done under contract. Further experience is necessary to determine whether the centers are, in fact, effective sources of managerial talent for the government or whether recruitment methods drawing upon outside sources should also be more intensively cultivated to insure that the government has the experienced personnel essential to the operation of the system as a whole.[35]

The existence of competition between these institutional forms should be recognized, not as requiring action to protect one or another, but as an important avenue by which the nation can seek greater effectiveness in the execution of its programs. Much has been accomplished in rationalizing the relationships between business firms and the government. The universities and the government-operated centers present somewhat more difficult problems to the degree that they also perform other interrelated functions. In both areas, the government's policies should encourage competition with other institutions while placing minimal restrictions upon the administrative freedom of private institutions.

Other Problems

This study has dealt with the contractual system as a method which the government uses to accomplish its objectives. It is a system that, as has been pointed out, continues to evolve as experience with the R&D process and as appraisals of administrative practices and institutional relationships suggest. Some of the prob-

[35] There is also the possibility that the government might make more effective use of its scientific and technical personnel by making the services of the laboratories available to a number of agencies instead of solely to the sponsoring agency. See Bernard I. Spinrad, "Why Not National Laboratories?" *Bulletin of the Atomic Scientists,* vol. 22 (April 1966), pp. 20–23.

lems and opportunities for more effective operations have been pointed out in the preceding pages.

A variety of difficult problems remains. It would be presumptuous to attempt to discuss all of these. Four broad types of problems are discussed briefly below.

The Ownership of Knowledge

Work directed to the expansion and diffusion of knowledge responds to a complex structure of incentives, among them the equity of the investigator in the knowledge he has developed. Such equities vary widely, depending upon the nature of the knowledge and its significance to other investigators and to the society. Some of it, though relatively little, can be claimed by patents. Many equities, typically those in pure science, are established by publication and honored by crediting a discovery to its discoverer. By and large, recognition that a contribution has been made is left to the normal process of the interested scientific and technical community and, in the case of more dramatic developments, through the communication media of the larger society. There exists also an elaborate structure providing more formal recognition such as election to the National Academy of Sciences, Nobel prizes, the medals offered by scientific societies, and such public awards as the AEC's Fermi medal or the President's Medal for Science.

Recognition of accomplishment is the culmination of a process in which equities in knowledge play an important role. New knowledge is normally disclosed only when it is in some way advantageous to the discoverer and withheld when it is advantageous to the holder to do so. The contractual system can operate effectively only as it recognizes the existence of such equities. Many proposals, whether related to basic research or to development, contain ideas which the proposer believes to be original and which are valued not only as recommendations for continuing work but also as possible assets for the future of a personal career or of a business firm. Dealing with this sort of material requires that it be held in confidence, if the government is to secure full participation in its programs. Agreements that information be held in confidence are legally recognized in some areas; in others, the problem is dealt with through the government's policy on conflict of interest. Charges of violated confidence have been made against some agencies but they have been relatively few. It is frequently difficult to substantiate such claims since it is a common experience in R&D that general awareness of a problem generates a number of more or less identical solutions. Problems may also arise, particularly in development, when an agency determines that its objectives would be furthered if the information contained in two or more proposals were to be consolidated. If the conceptions in the proposals were generated under pre-existing contracts, the government has borne the cost and has rights to their use. If the proposer has borne the costs, payment for the use of knowledge is occasionally necessary and proper.

The recognition of the proprietary element in new knowledge is most clearly formalized in the government's patent policy—the nation's oldest policy relating to R&D. The policy provides exclusive rights in knowledge in return for its disclosure, thereby encouraging the investments necessary to the effective application of the knowledge.

The growth of large-scale programmed institutional research has raised a variety of questions regarding the proper role of the patent system (and in less acute form, the copyright system).[36] The vast growth of R&D has produced severe difficulties in administering the patent system of application, examination, and issuance— difficulties that are being met but slowly. Fortunately for an overburdened Patent Office, however, the number of patent applications has grown more slowly than has the nation's R&D effort.

Of more immediate concern are some basic questions about the relationship of patents to federal contractual R&D programs. One question relates to the division of the equity in patent rights between the contractor and the government, with the problems of the rights and prerogatives of the inventor a corollary issue. The possibility exists that the problems associated with proprietary information, and particularly patents, discourage participation in government programs by firms possessing unique capabilities.[37]

---

[36] See, regarding the policy of the Office of Education that material produced as a result of its sponsorship shall be placed in the public domain, Julius J. Marke, *Copyright and Intellectual Property* (Fund for the Advancement of Education, 1967), chap. 1; and House Committee on Government Operations, *The Uses of Social Research in Federal Programs*, 90 Cong. 1 sess. (1967), pt. 4, pp. 486 ff.

[37] Helge Holst, "Government Patent Policy—Its Impact on Contractor Cooperation with the Government and Widespread Use of Government Sponsored Technology,"

Another set of questions concerns the nature of the arrangements for patent utilization which will result in greatest social benefit. The policy of relinquishing title is subject to the criticism that the government has "given away" property which it has paid for. On the other hand, retention of title by the government apparently results in low rates of utilization, at least in the case of DOD.[38] There are the further questions regarding government-held patents as to the greater effectiveness of free versus exclusive licenses, and there are uncertainties also as to the most desirable terms under which exclusive licenses may be granted. The effort by NASA to accelerate evaluation and application of knowledge emerging from its activities through its Technology Utilization Program is an important attempt to overcome whatever frictions may exist in the process of evaluation and transfer.[39]

The government agencies supporting R&D have pursued varying policies regarding the ownership of patent rights acquired as a result of research efforts which they have financed. The Department of Defense has long pursued a policy of permitting research people to take title to patents, retaining for itself a royalty-free license. Under this license policy, the DOD has access to firms that might refuse to undertake work for fear of jeopardizing a patent position. The firm has the incentive to accept work which might yield patents with commercial possibilities. It should be noted that despite its policy of waiving title, the Defense Department holds about 65 percent of all active government patents, having acquired many of them because contractors relinquished their rights.

Idea, vol. 9 (Summer 1965), pp. 273–96. The problem may be particularly serious with regard to small business firm participation in government programs. See Spencer M. Smith, Jr., and Michael B. Carter, *Performance and Potential of Small Business in Research and Development Industries in Maryland and Metropolitan Washington, D.C.* (University of Maryland, 1963), pp. 85–89.

[38] A series of studies finds that 50 to 60 percent of patents issued to corporations and individuals find commercial utilization. The utilization rate of patents held by the Department of Defense, on the other hand, was about 13 percent (Barker S. Sanders, "Patterns of Commercial Exploitation of Patented Inventions by Large and Small Corporations," *The Patent, Trademark, and Copyright Journal of Research and Education,* vol. 8 [1964], and Sanders, "What Should the Federal Government's Patent Policy Be?" *ibid.,* pp. 168–222).

[39] National Aeronautics and Space Administration, *NASA's Technology Utilization Program* (1966). The NASA program is examined in some detail in ten articles in *R/D Research Development,* vol. 17 (September 1966), pp. 18–46.

Other agencies such as NASA, AEC, and the Department of Agriculture, usually because of statutory requirements, take title to all patents resulting from research financed by them. The policies of other agencies vary with differences in statutory requirements or the circumstances of a given situation.

The variety of agency arrangements and the absence of a clear rationale for such policies led President Kennedy in 1963 to promulgate a government-wide policy which sought to recognize the interests of inventors, the needs of the government, the equities of contractors, and the public interest. The policy provided that the government should acquire title where

[1] a principal purpose of the contract is to create, develop, or improve products, processes, or methods which are intended for commercial use (or which are otherwise intended to be made available for use) by the general public at home or abroad, or which will be required for such use by governmental regulations;

[2] a principal purpose of the contract is for exploration into fields which directly concern the public health or welfare;

[3] the contract is in a field of science or technology in which there has been little significant experience outside of work funded by the government or where the government has been the principal developer of the field, and the acquisition of exclusive rights at the time of contracting might confer on the contractor a preferred or dominant position; or

[4] the services of the contractor are (i) for the operations of a government-owned research or production facility; or (ii) for coordinating and directing the work of others.

This title-policy was qualified, however, by the provision that "in exceptional instances the contractor may acquire greater rights than a non-exclusive license at the time of contracting where the head of the department or agency certifies that such action will best serve the public interest." Greater rights might also be acquired by the contractor "after the invention has been identified where the invention when made in the course of or under the contract is not a primary object of the contract provided the acquisition of such greater rights is consistent with the purposes" stated under point 1 above and "is a necessary incentive to call forth private risk capital and expense to bring the invention to the point of practical application."[40]

[40] *Federal Register*, vol. 28 (Oct. 12, 1963), pp. 10944–45.

The contractor's presumptive right to patent title (subject to the government's royalty-free license) was recognized in situations where "the purpose of the contractor is to build on the state of the art for use by the government" and where the contractor has an established proprietary position. If "the commercial interests of the contractor are not sufficiently established, . . . the determination of title will be made by the agency after the invention has been identified," in accordance with public interest considerations and with reference to the contractor's intentions regarding commercial application. Even "where the principal or exclusive rights in an invention remain with the contractor," however, the contractor or assignee was to take effective steps within three years to bring the invention to the point of practical application or to make it available on reasonable terms. In the event of failure to do so, the government would retain the right to require the granting of a license to an applicant on a nonexclusive royalty-free basis.

These policies resolve no basic issues and must be viewed as tentative and experimental.[41] Their effectiveness will depend upon the reactions of private institutions as well as upon the ability of administrators to deal with the substantial discretionary authority vested in them. President Johnson therefore charged the Federal Council for Science and Technology to evaluate the application and operation of the policy and appointed a Commission to review the patent system as a whole.[42] Ultimately, congressional action is also necessary since the President's policies are in conflict with, though subordinate to, statutes determining agency policy. The complexity of the issues involved has encouraged a cautious approach.

A patent is issued after knowledge has been acquired, in return

[41] A thoughtful critique is Robert A. Solo, "Patent Policy for Government-Sponsored Research and Development," *Idea,* vol. 10 (Summer 1966), pp. 143–206.

[42] The President's Commission on the Patent System reported its findings in *To Promote the Progress of Useful Arts in an Age of Exploding Technology* (Government Printing Office, 1966). The Commission held that "a patent system today is capable of continuing to provide an incentive to research and development and innovation" and that there was "no practical substitute for the unique service it renders" (p. 2). Though it made numerous recommendations for improving the effectiveness of the patent system, the Commission chose not to consider the question of patents with regard to inventions resulting from work financed in whole or in part by the government.

for disclosure of the knowledge, and in expectation that the patentee will be willing and able by his own action or that of others to
make the investments usually necessary to develop the knowledge
to the point where it will be of interest to the buying public. The
application of patent policy to knowledge acquired in whole or in
part from public expenditure is complicated by the equity issue
but is essentially a debate over the nature of the incentives which
the public accepts as necessary to further its interest in promoting
technology.

The Politics of Geographic Distribution

The bulk of the nation's scientific and technical manpower is employed by a few hundred government-owned organizations, a few
thousand business firms, approximately a hundred institutions of
higher education and a small number of independent nonprofit
corporations. Within each category a relatively small percentage of
the organizations employ a large proportion of the manpower and
perform a large proportion of the R&D credited to the category.

These institutions are also geographically concentrated. In the
1920's, most R&D organizations were located in the northeastern
states. World War II stimulated some dispersion but on balance
slightly increased geographic concentration. The problems presented by existing and potential concentration were recognized before 1945[43] and have since been extensively discussed. Since 1945
other areas of concentration have appeared, reflecting changes in
the technological areas of interest to the government. The bulk of
the nation's R&D is now carried on within five large metropolitan
areas and a dozen or so centers of intermediate size.[44]

The existing distribution of R&D activities is not the direct re-

[43] As in *The Government's Wartime Research and Development, 1940–44: Part II,
Findings and Recommendations*, Senate Subcommittee on War Mobilization, 79 Cong.
1 sess. (1945), pp. 21–22. See also such discussions as in *Hearings on Science Legisla-
tion*, 79 Cong. 1 sess. (1945), pp. 967–69; Clarence A. Mills, "Distribution of American
Research Funds," *Science*, vol. 107 (1948), pp. 127–30; and *Bulletin of the Atomic
Scientists*, vol. 4 (1948), p. 60.

[44] Data on geographic distribution of federal R&D funds are available in con-
siderable detail in House Committee on Science and Astronautics, *Obligations for
Research and Development, and R&D Plant, by Geographic Divisions and States, by
Selected Federal Agencies, Fiscal Years 1961–1964*, Prepared by the National Science
Foundation for the Subcommittee on Science, Research, and Development, 88 Cong.
2 sess. (1964).

sult of government policies. That distribution has followed from the decisions of private institutions to participate in the government's R&D programs through the competitive proposal procedure, from their success in applying certain policies such as those relating to personnel recruitment and personnel utilization, and to a much lesser degree, from differences in success in such participation.[45] Some government actions in locating facilities have resulted in dispersion, as in the case of the AEC and some of the NASA organizations. Others have contributed to intensified concentration, as in the Washington, D.C., Baltimore, and northern Virginia area.[46]

The geographic concentration of federal R&D funds constitutes a political problem because of the interest of local groups and institutions in increasing their participation in federal R&D programs. In part, this interest centers in strengthening local universities, but it follows also from a desire to secure the employment- and income-generating benefits characteristic of industries experiencing rapid technological growth. It is true that, in the absence of local R&D activities, some such benefits can be obtained by diffusing the relevant knowledge. However, if such diffusion is to serve as a source of employment, it requires people familiar with technical developments, able to visualize their application, and willing to make the necessary investments. Plant relocation by large firms provides a partial answer. Other than such relocation, with its limited benefits, what is needed in an area is a larger population oriented to R&D activities. It is widely believed that the route to fuller participation is a strong university oriented to science and technology.[47]

The existing distribution has followed from the application of

[45] The point is made frequently. See, for example, General William J. Ely who points out that there was a lot of planning and hard work on the part of the educational institutions, industrial organizations, and the communities in which they are located, which resulted in these centers of excellence (*Federal Research Contracts and Grants,* Hearings before the House Committee on Science and Astronautics, 88 Cong. 2 sess. [1964], pt. 1, pp. 4–5).

[46] The decision to locate NASA's new electronics research center in the Boston area obviously increased the concentration of R&D in that region. For the considerations leading to the decision, see Senate Committee on Aeronautics and Space Sciences, *NASA Electronics Research Center,* 88 Cong. 2 sess. (1964).

[47] See David Allison, "The University and Regional Prosperity," *International Science and Technology,* April 1965, pp. 22–31, and the bibliography on p. 88.

the principle of selecting proposals on the basis of their quality and responsiveness to the government's programs, a principle that stands at the heart of the contractual system. There is, however, political appeal in promising government contracts and political danger to R&D programs from disaffected constituents. Government administrators and congressmen can and do meet complaints from constituents by pointing out that few or no proposals have been submitted to government agencies by institutions in their districts. The implied solution is, however, difficult. The difficulties are compounded by the fact that existing R&D centers draw part of their talent from areas of low participation which means that the losing area becomes still less qualified for greater participation in the future. There exist also certain economies of scale which, if not well understood, nevertheless operate to require concentration of skilled manpower if the skills are to be effectively applied. There can then be only a limited number of outstanding scientific and technological centers. It is this latter fact that presumably leads one knowledgeable observer to comment that to speak of "equitable geographic distribution . . . is to complicate the problem beyond all hope of rational discussion."[48]

The possibilities of modifying the geographic and institutional concentration of government supported R&D are limited. Congress does not question the fact, particularly as regards the development programs of the mission-oriented agencies, that they "must purchase excellence wherever they can find it" and that "a more equitable geographical distribution cannot be achieved without some danger of degrading the results of the research desired, and more importantly, the applications and end items required."[49] The federal government can supplement local efforts to increase the number of universities of high quality, at the same time strengthening the nation's pool of highly trained manpower. This approach has been and is being followed in a number of federal programs.

[48] Leland J. Haworth, Director of the National Science Foundation, "Some Problem Areas in the Relationship between Government and Universities," *NAS-NRC News Report*, vol. 14 (November-December 1964), p. 93.

[49] House Committee on Science and Astronautics, *Inquiries, Legislation, Policy Studies Re: Science and Technology, Review and Forecast*, 89 Cong. 2 sess. (1966), p. 7.

Under pressure from Congress and a policy statement by President Johnson in 1965,[50] an increasing number of government programs are directed to strengthening the research capability of those universities which are not heavily involved in federally sponsored research, but which have a sufficient base from which to expand their research abilities. Such agencies as the National Science Foundation, the National Aeronautics and Space Administration, the Department of Health, Education and Welfare, and the Department of Defense maintain a variety of programs in support of the growth of educational institutions, some of them specifically directed to strengthening facilities in science and technology.

An increase in the number of high quality universities is desirable for its own sake. It should be recognized, however, that the assumed geographic relationship between universities and vigorous technology-based industries is open to serious doubt. There are regions that possess substantial research activities but that do not manifest the employment-generating effects obtained elsewhere. A marked tendency has existed on the part of spokesmen for such areas to seek a solution to the problem by seeking even more research activities. A change in the character of the research conducted in such an area may be desirable. Research, however, is only one element in a complex process that leads to more and better employment and higher income. The presence of businessmen alert to such application opportunities is a critical factor. Their absence is a problem that invites more attention than it has received. A recent study concludes tentatively that "graduate research capabilities and extensive university research programs do not play a substantial role in attracting defense R&D to an area" and that the large defense R&D company "does not depend upon 'its local environment for its supply of labor.' . . ." The study suggests also that although no one factor can be singled out as necessary and sufficient in itself, "two factors that are necessary, but not sufficient for the development of a defense R&D complex are: (1)

[50] The President's memorandum to agency heads stated that "research supported to further agency missions should be administered not only with a view to producing specific results, but also with a view to strengthening academic institutions and increasing the number of institutions capable of performing research of high quality" (*Weekly Compilation of Presidential Documents*, Sept. 20, 1965, p. 269).

the presence of R&D-oriented entrepreneurs in the community . . . and (2) the availability of local financial support for companies engaged in defense R&D.''[51]

It seems clear that the geographic location of contractual work now being done in advanced development technologies such as missiles and space is well established and will change principally with changes in the work required by the procuring agencies. Some of the new technologies now on the horizon, as, for example, those connected with oceanography, will, no doubt, be concentrated in relatively few areas, unpredictable in advance since the principal factor will be the quality of work proposed and done by private organizations. The nature of other technologies may well dictate the dispersion of work on their development as in the case of water resources, water pollution, and air pollution although it is also likely that these will have limited local employment impacts.

Summary

The nation's experience with the contracting system now covers a quarter century. The war experience was, of course, a point of departure followed by a period of slow experimental growth. The period of aggressive federal initiative in R&D, of large expenditures, and ramifying programs covers somewhat more than a decade. While appraisals of that experience are increasing, much remains to be learned, not merely about the contractual relationship but also about the research and development process which the contract implements and to which administrative procedures must be adapted.

Had the objectives assigned to and achieved by the contractual system been sought by traditional methods, a vast expansion of

---

[51] These observations are presented as "inferences, hypotheses and implications" (Albert Shapero, Richard P. Howell, James R. Tombaugh, *The Structure and Dynamics of the Defense R&D Industry: The Los Angeles and Boston Complexes,* R&D Studies Series [November 1965], pp. 96–97). A recent executive branch study of the problem emphasizes the "need for a favorable environment in which useful (growth promoting) R&D can be undertaken" and suggests "that Federal policies cannot usefully be altered until these environmental considerations are recognized" (U.S. Department of Commerce, Economic Development Administration, *Regional Effects of Government Procurement and Related Policies,* Report of the Independent Study Board [1967], pp. 36–37).

government employment in intramural facilities would have been required. Though there exist strong ideological objections to such increases in government employment, such expansion would surely have taken place in some way had it been necessary for defense. If historical precedents had operated, such a form of organization would have isolated in some large degree the government's operations from those of private institutions. The orderliness of conventional administrative arrangements would have been a poor substitute for the greater stimulus provided by an open, competitive system. Both private and public objectives would have suffered in consequence.

Congress not only approves of the contractual system but occasionally insists that it be used. The congressional attitude is not to be interpreted solely as reflecting a horror of an increasing federal bureaucracy. It must be understood as springing from a conviction —not always well articulated—that superior results could be achieved and wider objectives served by following the more difficult and more hazardous procedure of utilizing the resources of private institutions and their readiness to respond to incentives.

It must be kept in mind also that the contract system has developed in an environment of year-to-year increases in aggregate government expenditures for R&D. Such expansion, the underlying sense of urgency, and agreement on goals have unquestionably served to mute criticism of the system as efforts have been concentrated on building workable relationships. To a large degree the arrangements that now exist are the product of the peculiar problems and opportunities existing at the time of origin rather than of consciously predetermined policies. They are therefore experimental arrangements, subject to change as appraisals of experience suggest. As expenditures move to relative stability—such as a fixed percentage of GNP—and to meeting new, socially oriented goals, it may well be that the system will be subjected to stresses that have not been clearly evident in the past.

These pages have sought to identify the more important problems which confront the contractual system at this stage of its development. Many others have been dealt with in the preceding discussion. It is clear that the government's capacity to administer the system has grown with the expansion of its program. It will be necessary for that capacity to continue to grow if the country is to expand its technological environment and to achieve objectives in new areas. One problem scarcely needs reiteration: the continuing need for the highest quality of personnel within the government to provide the type of management that can consistently deal with novel problems in an environment of strong and articulate interest groups. The task of harnessing these interests and their capabilities to public objectives is one which calls for unusual skills. The effectiveness with which such tasks are executed may well determine the future of the contractual system—and with it the nation's security and leadership in world affairs, and the hope of increasing well-being for its citizens.

A second major problem is then that of providing more and better means of communication in determining the objectives to which the nation's scientific and technical resources should be directed. The contract is a powerful tool that can be applied for good or ill depending upon the care with which its application is determined. There is need for the Congress to provide a continuing forum for identifying alternative goals, appraising the values involved, and determining the feasibility of end and means. There are obvious difficulties and limitations, but the procedures now available are too limited in range and perspective to be considered adequate.

The experience of the past two decades has demonstrated that it is possible to identify and to attain important public objectives by methods that exploit the advantages of each of the institutional forms by which R&D capabilities are organized in the United States today. The capacities and the incentive characteristics of the business firm, the university, the independent institute and the government laboratory can be employed as appropriate. As has been noted, further efforts to apply incentives are necessary, but, at the same time, procedures must be avoided which jeopardize the ability of R&D institutions to meet society's other demands upon them.

In assuming responsibility for attaining difficult goals of great social importance and for directing a large part of the nation's R&D capabilities, the government chose to pursue a difficult course. Numerous problems have been successfully dealt with; those that remain relate primarily to the assignment of social priorities and the more efficient operation of a well articulated structure. Possibilities of abuse remain as a continuing hazard of this system, as of any other. But the fact remains that the United States has developed a tool for accomplishing public objectives that might have been beyond the reach of either private institutions or the government alone. The nation has clearly been the gainer.

Name Index

Abelson, Philip H., 194, 343
Allen, Ernest M., 302
Allison, David, 424, 447
Almond, Gabriel A., 72
Ames, Charles S., 241
Anderson, Clinton P., 205
Anderson, Oscar E., 57
Andrews, B. H., 155
Arnold, Christian K., 345, 348
Auerbach, Lewis E., 34

Baldwin, William L., 277
Ballhaus, William F., 229
Bannerman, Graeme C., 248, 253, 268
Barber, Richard J., 14, 424, 425
Barnard, Chester, 421
Barnes, John W., 369
Barzun, Jacques, 281
Baxter, James Phinney, III, 36, 284
Beach, Robert E., 218, 249, 436
Beaufré, André, 72
Beckler, David, 132
Bell, David E., 118, 119, 198, 276, 414
Benoit, Harry, Jr., 272
Bergen, W. B., 231, 240
Bernstein, Marver, 207
Bixler, H. Randall, 234
Bjorksten, Johan, 149, 257, 260
Black, Guy, 245
Blackett, P. M. S., 428–29
Blank, David M., 245
Blasingame, F. J. L., 367
Bledsoe, Edwin P., 51
Boehm, George A. W., 320
Borklund, C. W., 262
Bowen, Harold G., 22
Bowen, William G., 317
Boyd, William B., 22
Brackett, Ernest W., 260
Brademas, John, 216
Bricker, Herbert A., 269
Brodie, Bernard, 395
Brooks, Harvey, 187, 194

Broughton, Philip S., 343
Brown, Charles D., 231
Brown, Harold, 149, 152, 409, 415
Brown, Harrison, 343
Brubacher, John S., 281, 282
Brunner, E. D., 76
Bryan, Stanley E., 217
Bunnell, Kevin, 317
Burchard, John E., 284, 388
Burke, John G., 354
Burnham, James, 203
Bush, Vannevar, 10, 30, 34, 39, 42, 47, 55, 59–60, 61, 62, 63, 139, 140, 288, 342, 421

Cagle, Fred R., 315, 346
Campbell, Levin H., Jr., 30, 53
Carey, William D., 190, 191, 212
Carney, Thomas P., 424
Carpenter, C. Ray, 295
Carter, Luther J., 438
Carter, Michael B., 443
Case, Clifford P., 219
Cate, James Lea, 25, 28
Cater, Douglass, 203
Charpie, Robert A., 220
Church, Joseph, 248
Clapp, Charles L., 201
Clark, General Chester W., 30, 238, 424
Clark, Harold F., 337
Cliffe, Frank B., Jr., 415
Coddington, Dean C., 236, 242
Cole, W. Sterling, 44
Collier, Donald W., 243, 245, 425
Colman, William G., 233
Condon, Edward U., 55
Cook, Fred J., 435
Cordiner, Ralph J., 102, 394, 411
Craven, Wesley Frank, 25, 28
Crawford, Meredith P., 389
Creyke, Geoffrey, Jr., 234
Culhan, R. H., 259
Cummings, Milton C., Jr., 415

NOTE: Most entries in the Name Index refer to footnotes in the text.

455

Subject Index

Naval Research, Office of (ONR), 48, 49, 64, 69, 175, 179, 285, 287, 314, 323
Naval Research Laboratory, 48, 81
Naval Studies, Institute for, 388
Navy, Department of the: R&D in World War II and postwar growth, 36, 73; contracts with private institutions, 55, 68, 111, 322; new-material development programs, 154–55; systems commands, 155; use of incentive contracts, 165–66; basic research programs, 175; contracts with management institutions, 221–22, 285; laboratories for developing new technology, 404–5; Sidewinder project, 405. *See also specific Navy subdivisions*
Navy Biological Laboratory, 379
Navy Bureau of Aeronautics, 24, 56
Navy Bureaus of Ships and of Ordnance, 19, 403
Navy Fast Deployment Logistic (FDL) ship project, 229
Navy Operations Evaluation Group, 388
Navy Special Projects Office, 386
NBS. *See* National Bureau of Standards
NDRC. *See* National Defense Research Committee.
New Zealand, U.S. support of project research by, 371
NIH. *See* National Institutes of Health
Nike projects, 148, 205, 245, 383
Nonprofit organizations in R&D: functions performed by, 350–51; types of, 352–56; specialized competence of, 357–58; profit-making corporations' criticism of, 359; importance of, 359–60; use of, by contractual R&D centers, 384; effect of competition among, 438–40
North East Corridor rail transportation project, 171
North Star Research and Development Institute in Minnesota, 356
NRC. *See* National Research Council
NSF. *See* National Science Foundation

Oak Ridge Institute for Nuclear Studies, 84, 393n
Oak Ridge National Laboratory, 393n, 399
Oceanic Institute of Hawaii, 356
Oceanography programs, 210–11, 427, 450
OEO. *See* Economic Opportunity, Office of
Offices. *See other part of title*

ONR. *See* Naval Research, Office of
Organization for Economic Cooperation and Development, 3
OSRD. *See* Scientific Research and Development, Office of
OST. *See* Science and Technology, Office of
OSW. *See* Saline Water, Office of
OTS. *See* Technical Services, Office of
Overseas programs: technical and economic aid to underdeveloped countries, 89–90, 297–98, 368, 372; projects in physical and medical sciences, 368; expenditures for project research by foreign nationals, 368–69, 370–71; Air Force, Navy, and Army research offices in Europe, 369; agricultural grants, 369–70; limitations in prosperous countries, 371–72

Pacific Northwest Laboratories, 354n
Pan American Airways, 7, 221
Parkinson's law, 98n
Patent Office, R&D functions of, 136, 442
Patent rights in inventions made under federal contracts, 246n; agency policies, 443; title vs. license policies, 443; Kennedy policy, 444. *See also* Contractual R&D system
Peace Corps, 7, 90, 297–98
PERT. *See* Program evaluation and review technique
PHS. *See* Public Health Service
Planning and budgeting operations, 150–52; phased project concept of, 159
Planning-programming-budgeting system (PPBS), 169, 189n, 211
Polaris program, 151, 166n, 192, 386
Political pressures for participation in R&D programs: on agencies by private groups, 191, 227; on award-making, 217; of vested interests, 435; by local groups, 447–48
Pollution of air and water, programs to apply new technologies to, 169, 427, 430, 450
Polytechnic Institute of Brooklyn, 294
Post Office Department, 24, 90–91, 136, 169
Post-War Research, Committee on, joint action of War and Navy Secretaries, 45–46
Poverty program, 169
PPBS. *See* Planning-programming-budgeting system
President, the: authority of, under the